CYRUS THE GREAT
530 B.C.

SCYTHIANS

SCYTHIANS

MASSAGETAE

RIVER OF THE SANDS

Hyrcanian Sea

SARMATIANS
("DAHAE")

ISLAND
SEA

Cyra

SOGDIA

CHORASMIA

RIVER OF THE SEA

Maracanda

R. KUR

Bactria

BACTRIA

Zadracarta

HYRCANIA

PARTHIA

ARIA

Cabura

MEDIA

Rhagae

Agbatana

SALT

Shushan

NISAYAN
PASTURES

DRANGIANA

DESERT

LANDS

Parsagard

German

SAGARTIA

INDUS R.

PARSA

Harmuz

PERSIAN
GULF

ERYTHREAN SEA

BY HAROLD LAMB

Biographical Narratives

CYRUS THE GREAT
HANNIBAL: *One Man Against Rome*
CHARLEMAGNE: *The Legend and the Man*
THEODORA AND THE EMPEROR
SULEIMAN THE MAGNIFICENT
GENGHIS KHAN
NUR MAHAL
OMAR KHAYYAM
ALEXANDER OF MACEDON: *The Journey to World's End*

Novel

A GARDEN TO THE EASTWARD

Historical Narratives

CONSTANTINOPLE: *Birth of an Empire*
NEW FOUND WORLD: *How North America Was Discovered and Explored*
THE EARTH SHAKERS: *Tamerlane and the March of the Barbarians*
THE CRUSADES: *Iron Men and Saints and the Flame of Islam*
THE MARCH OF MUSCOVY: *Ivan the Terrible*
THE CITY AND THE TSAR: *Peter the Great*

For Older Children

DURANDAL
WHITE FALCON
KIRDY: THE ROAD OUT OF THE WORLD
GENGHIS KHAN AND THE MONGOL HORDE
CHIEF OF THE COSSACKS

CYRUS THE GREAT

CYRUS THE GREAT

By *Harold Lamb*

Garden City, New York

DOUBLEDAY & COMPANY, INC.

1960

Foreword

CYRUS is a very familiar name. In our grandfathers' day it was perhaps the most common proper name for men in America. Yet it came from an almost unknown king of the East who lived in the dawn of history. Even so, familiar sayings surround the name: the handwriting on the wall, the laws of the Medes and Persians, the Magi, who were wise men of the East. Other details of his time have become proverbial—the wealth of Croesus, the Delphic oracle, and the controversial Tower of Babel.

There is no great mystery about all this because our forefathers read much in the Old Testament, and the little-known Cyrus, called king of the Medes and Persians, received rather remarkable mention in those pages. One, in the beginning of the Book of Ezra, relates: "*Thus saith Cyrus king of Persia, The Lord God hath given me all the kingdoms of the earth; and he hath charged me to build him an house at Jerusalem which is in Judah.*" 'The kingdoms of the earth' sounds fantastic. However, in the beginning of another Book, that of Esther, they are described further: "*. . . in the days of Ahasuerus (this is Ahasuerus which reigned from India even unto Ethiopia, over an hundred and seven and twenty provinces;)*"

Now the prophets of the dawn age are telling the truth about a man known to them in the world, as they understood it to be, between the River Indus and the Upper Nile. Of the many mysteries of ancient history, this man, Cyrus, remains perhaps the most baffling mystery. The secret of the unknown Hittite people has

been at least uncovered; the lost Minoan civilization has taken
form as it existed on the Great Sea, the Mediterranean. What came
after Cyrus the Achaemenian has been detailed and written into
the records, but not the man himself. He emerges from nowhere,
yet leaves behind him the first ordered world state. He brings with
him a new idea—if not ideal—and somehow upsets the course of
history to make an end of the ancient world of Ur of the Chaldeans,
the Pharaohs, Assur, and Babylon. Why and how did he do this,
and for what purpose? What means did he possess, and who aided
him to utilize them? Above all, what kind of a man was he in
reality? We cannot answer these questions with historical evidence;
yet the answers must be there. We can find them in only one way.

We can search back into his lifetime, ignoring during the search
all that has happened since. We can look only for what existed
then, from the sleeping rugs to the small ivory chairs and the asphalt cement of the stone steps that led up to the limestone altars
for the fires, and to the keepers of the everlasting fires. We can go

out on the road from these fire altars to the breeding ground of
the chosen horses and on to the gate of the domain that was not
guarded by walls but by mountains. By so doing, we can imagine

ourselves afoot in the small domain of Cyrus and can search for the other persons who are there.

This will be in the beginning of the sixth century before Christ, when Necho was Pharaoh of Saitic Egypt—seven years after Necho's chariots had been hurled into rout at Carchemish by Nebuchadnezzar, King of the Lands, King of Babylon. In Judah Josiah had fallen before that same Pharaoh at Armageddon, and now the Judean king and his people were led as captives by Nebuchadnezzar back to Babylon.

To the east, in the mountains, reigned Cyaxares the Mede. The mountains were remote from the wars of the great plains that caused the rout of armed hosts and the march of captives from their homes.

In those remote mountains Cyrus the Achaemenian was born.

Contents

ONE

Settlement in the Mountains

THE BOYS AT THE GATES

THEY named him Cyrus after his grandfather. The name
meant Shepherd—Kurash, in their speech. This did not signify that the boy had anything to do with tending sheep. Hundreds
of flocks grazed the upland pastures, climbing where the snow
melted. The Old People watched over them with the mastiffs.
It was simply a legend that a Kurash, a royal Shepherd, watched
over his people, guiding them toward food and guarding them from
wild beasts, human raiders, or demons.

Since his mother died soon after he was born, the family consulted together and decided that the place of the child's birth was
ill-fated and, in consequence, the family should move on to other
grazing grounds. However, his father, Cambyses, after taking
thought, said: "This is not a choice to be made by the family alone;
the council of the Three Tribes must say either yes or no. And
now I say we will not move on again. This valley is good for horses,
good for men. Why, it is a true paradise." For Cambyses—
Kanbujiya—the small king of the Persians, had a stubborn mind.
This valley lay high toward the snowline, cold enough except in
midsummer. Yet heights to the northwest shielded it, and a tor-
rential stream threaded through it, bringing unfailing water and
the echoing voice of Anahita. When Cambyses commanded
twin fire altars to be raised on the opposite bank of the stream,
the flames of sacred Atar rose bright in the darkness. Yet Cambyses reasoned that in addition to the good auspices of water

and fire, this valley now occupied by the Persians offered natural defenses against enemies. Caravan traders began to call it Parsagard, the encampment of the Persians. It was hardly a town.

So the boy Cyrus came to know, first of all, the seclusion of this mountain valley. He grew up among highlanders who believed themselves superior to the inhabitants of the Plain beneath them. That was not the actual truth, but all mountain people shared the belief. Then, too, he became accustomed to horseback at the age of five or six, when lowland boys still made themselves toys of clay, dried by the canal banks. With his cousins, both boys and girls, he climbed to the bare back of a horse, the children holding on by the mane or gripping each other. They saw at once that only captives or the Old People walked afoot. This ceaseless riding about accustomed them to make quite long journeys and also to look down in every sense on those who walked through the dirt. Emba, the Hyrcanian who groomed Cyrus's horse, said that he rode like a small king, like Cambyses himself.

Cyrus shook his wrist under the eyes of the slave. From his silver bracelet dangled a crystal carved with the image of spreading wings above the shape of Azhi Dahaka, the three-headed demon, foremost of the evil ones. "Emba, by this sign I am son of a great king. Why do you speak of a small king?"

When the Hyrcanian wiped his hands on his leather trousers and examined the royal seal, he shook his head. "Because I have also seen the Median who rules lands afar, with many peoples speaking different tongues. Well, he is a great king. Now your father rules one land, one people, and one tongue. Well, is he not a small king?"

Impressed by the Hyrcanian's knowledge, the boy asked Cambyses to tell him the truth of the matter. Cambyses took thought, rubbing his short gray beard. Then he smiled. "The truth? Why within our tribes men think me a great king; outlanders think me a small one. It all depends."

"And what do you think?"

This time his father kept silence as long as Cyrus could hold his breath. "Say I, Cambyses, this land of Parsa which I hold, which has within it good horses, good men, the great gods granted me. By their aid, may I, Cambyses, keep it."

He said this as if to himself, and at the time Cyrus was satisfied. After some years he did not think so well of his father's answer, except that it was indeed the truth.

To speak the truth was the first thing of all in importance. So the boy, the Shepherd, had been taught. These boys younger than sword-bearing age listened to their teachers at the king's gate. At the first stroke of day, whether the red shaft of sunrise or the gray veil of rain, they gathered at the black stone steps. At either side of the wide steps Cambyses planned to erect the stone figures of spirits which would guard his portal. But he had put off doing that, saying it took much thought to choose the best pair of protectors for his gate. Not even lance-bearers or huntsmen kept watch at the steps. Only grooms like Emba squatted there to take the reins of the horses of the nobles who dismounted at the steps when they sought Cambyses. Visitors walked several hundred paces along the road of burned mud bricks that led through the paradise shaded by sycamore trees. Then, more often than not, they found the king shouting at his gardeners from the wide porch of his house. Elegant visitors from the Land of the Two Rivers smiled when they saw rounded tree trunks upholding the porch. Cambyses remarked irritably that his house was not a temple, to have polished stone columns. The truth was, however, that he had no wish to wait for polished stone to be hauled up to his new-built paradise of Parsagard.

Since the boys at the gate school knew nothing of written signs, they relied perforce on the spoken words of their teachers. If a lie crept into such spoken words, it would give them a wrong thought. In the same way, not being able to write either with a wedge stamp upon clay or black ink mark upon papyrus, they had to store away in their memories what they heard, like winnowed grain in a dry bin. They sat on bare benches to listen to the poets who intoned legends of their ancestral Iran, of their ancient homeland, *Aryan-vej*, far to the north and toward the sunrise. Cyrus was never allowed to forget that he was an *Aryan*, a rider of horses and a conqueror. He heard the hymns to the sun and to the seven stars that guarded the north sky; he heard the wisdom of healing by growing herbs and the wisdom of numbers; he had to do the problems of numbers in his mind and to answer the trickiest riddles. (What hides the mountaintops and vanishes to run into the valleys and vanishes again to help feed man and beast? Of course, the snow that melts into streams and nourishes growing grain!) The older, sword-bearing youths made light of all this listening and learning by the boys at the gate. "What really matters," they said, "is to ride well, shoot straight, and speak the truth."

Because he was the first-born of a mother who died young, Cyrus had no brothers, although he had a bevy of half brothers and cousins who turned their wits against him. The youths, the near-warriors, also looked at him askance, especially the sons of chieftains of other tribes who had no reason to cherish a Parsagardian of blood no better than their own.

After the noon meal the schoolboys went to the meadows for practice in riding, in swimming the torrent stream, or in using bow and arrow. Cyrus did not outdo the others except in swimming the rushing water, and he heard the taunts of the youths who watched him. One evening a band of the older youths consulted together and, to his delight, bade him come with them to a sword dance. At a fire they stripped to the belt and drank *haoma* brew before they sang together until flutes made music and drums sounded in cadence, and the youths leaped at each other with bright blades flying and shields clashing against shields. It was more combat than dance, and blood dripped when the sharp iron blades touched flesh. Yet no swordsman gave way to another. They showed no fear of wounds.

This sword dance was a ritual of the youths. It belonged to the older life when the Aryans had been nomads, wandering on horseback, dwelling in tents, meeting together around fires. The seven-year-old Cyrus hardly realized its history, but the dance to the drumbeat stirred his blood. At the end a tall youth, Mithradat, son of the Maspian chieftain, came over to him and asked, "Were you afraid?"

"No."

Mithradat had a way of tossing his yellow-maned head when he spoke to a boy. Taking Cyrus's wrist, he raised the royal bracelet to the light. "You carry the image of Azhi Dahaka. Have you ever set eyes on the three evil faces of the god? No? I have seen them in the darkness near at hand where Azhi Dahaka waits in hiding. Are you afraid to go forth alone to behold him?"

Cyrus considered the question as if it had been a riddle. Although he felt fear, he knew he must not refuse a test of his courage. Silently he shook his head.

"Well, then," said Mithradat, "we will show you the path to the lair. When you reach the end of the path, Cyrus, you must wait until darkness ends or you will not see the three faces of Azhi Dahaka nor the serpents coiling around them."

They took their horses as a matter of course, the Maspian riding ahead of the boy, another youth behind. Before bridling his pony, Cyrus ordered the dog-boy to hold back Gor, the mastiff who slept nightly at his door. They left the glow of the firelight and headed away from the stream, descending through thickets for a long time until Cyrus could make out his surroundings by the clear starlight. Presently, however, mist rose around them, and his companions whispered to him not to speak aloud. Cyrus smelled salt in the night air and knew they were approaching a stagnant lake bordered by reeds. Here Mithradat cast about until he reached two stones whitened by salt rime. Then he signaled Cyrus to dismount and took the pony's rein from the boy.

Leaning down to whisper, Mithradat told the boy to follow the path through the rushes until he reached a standing stone with three heads. At this stone he must kneel down, placing his hands before him and making no sound. If he did that without making a mistake, then he would hear the evil god coming into his lair, and he would hear the voice of Azhi Dahaka.

After the other two turned back with the horses, Cyrus pushed carefully through the thicket of rushes where a pathway seemed to open up. He could not tell in what direction he went, because the dark mist covered him. At times the salt crust around him gleamed with elusive light. When his cautious feet broke through the crust, he felt chill liquid suck at them; a stench filled his nose and he remembered that the breath of Azhi Dahaka was poisonous. He felt the cold of fear in his blood.

When his groping hands touched a dark stone higher than himself, he stifled a cry. The great stone appeared to have three heads bending over him. Cyrus dropped to his knees, and his outstretched hands sank into icy ooze. The thicket of rushes seemed gigantic around him, and he thought that if he lost his way he might sink into the stagnant depths where he could neither run nor swim.

So he waited, growing colder, until sound broke the silence. Something was coming after him along the path to the stone—something living, because it made a sound of panting and snuffling. With quivering fingers, the boy gripped the bracelet on his wrist. "I am Cyrus," he whispered, "son of the great king, the Achaemenian, of Aryan race." He often repeated that when he felt afraid.

The beast at his heels had more than two feet trampling the salt marsh. The beast snuffled loud and sniffed at his rump. Cyrus stifled a scream and laughed. The mastiff, Gor, came pushing against him. The powerful hunting dog had gotten away from the dog-boy and had trailed the horses and his master to the black stone in the swamp. Gor sighed and peered around, then lay down on a bed of broken rushes. Presently the hound was asleep. Cyrus ceased to be afraid because the dog would sense the coming of any evil deva. In fact almost at once Gor lifted his head. There was a sound in the rushes, behind the veil of mist. Cyrus listened attentively but watched the shape of the mastiff. Gor turned his head slowly, sniffed deep, and lowered his head to his paws. Whatever might be moving near them, Gor recognized or did not resent.

The movement ceased. A shrill voice cried out. "O man! What gift do you bring to the feet of Azhi Dahaka of the three heads, guardian of the darkness beneath the earth? Lay down your gift and pray that you may keep the life in you."

Listening, Cyrus watched Gor. The mastiff lay quiet. He had no gift of any kind in his hands, and he thought that the dog had saved him from much anxiety.

When the stroke of dawn lightened the mist, Cyrus retraced his way through the thicket. At the edge of the swamp, Mithradat waited with his fellow and the three bridled horses. The youths looked closely at the boy and the dog, while Mithradat asked whether Cyrus had beheld the three faces of the deva and heard its voice.

Cyrus considered the question before answering. "No. I saw a standing stone; I heard your voice."

"Mine?" Mithradat seemed surprised. "Why do you say such a thing?"

"Because, Mithradat, who else knew where to find me, where I waited until the stroke of day?"

Mithradat's head tossed angrily and he rode off alone without another word. Later on he warned his companion, "Watch out for Cyrus the Achaemenian when he begins to think!" Often thereafter the Maspian chief's son spoke against Cyrus, but he did not try to trick him again. The anger between them grew to a feud.

To escape the spite of the warrior youths, Cyrus sought a refuge of his own. By swimming the swift river he gained the far bank and climbed the rocks of the narrow gorge to a cave. Being near the summit of the gorge, the low cave overlooked the grove of Parsagard and even the bare summit of the twin fire altars. Hidden within it, Cyrus could observe what went on around his father's palace and what ceremonies took place at the lighting of Atar's altars. By lying still within the rock, Cyrus managed to hear the voice of Anahita calling to him.

The lovely goddess of the heights, he knew, dwelt at the well-springs of the mountain streams and seldom appeared to human eyes. At times in her sporting she leaped up in the foam of a water-fall and often scattered dazzling colors through the spray against the strong sunlight. He caught her voice in the whispering and laughing of water down in the gorge. The sound echoed musically within the cave and for this reason it was sacred to Anahita. Devout Aryans took care never to dirty flowing water. At ten years Cyrus vowed devotion to the lovely goddess. Perhaps he confused her with his own young mother of whom he had no memory except that she had been buried in a crypt near Anahita's cave. But he imagined that the hands of the goddess sustained him when he was bruised against boulders or swirled in rapids. He had no fear of rushing water.

"He is too much of a dreamer," Mithradat observed. "We all have our notions, but Cyrus tries to act out a dream."

AN ARROW ON THE TRAIL

Others also said that Cyrus believed too little and dreamed too much. About that time his exploit in tumbling on the leopard added to the talk. Being ten years old then, the Shepherd had the privilege of mounting the Nisayan steeds, which were dangerous for the younger children to ride.

These Nisayan horses came from the farthest pasturelands of the Persians. They were not as sure-footed as the shaggy ponies of the Old People; much heavier, with long barrels and great speed of leg, they served as mounts for the warriors, and in a battle the Nisayans tore at foes with their teeth and struck with their hoofs because they had no fear of men. In speeding across open ground, they kept an even pace by striding forward on the weapon-hand side and the rein-hand side in turn. Still, Cyrus did not find it easy to keep his seat on a Nisayan. One evening when he pursued a leopard with a band of youths, he had his worst fall. The leopard raced away through brush beneath a cliff, obviously seeking a lair in the rocks. Elusive in the thickets, he offered no mark for a thrown javelin, and Cyrus tried to ride him down. His Nisayan crashed through the thorn bush and came atop the speeding beast. Leaning out to stab with his javelin, Cyrus lost his knee grip on the saddlecloth and fell headlong.

For an instant, bruised and torn, he stared into the snarling muzzle of the beast. Then the leopard leaped away in fright. When his companions sprang from their horses to aid him, Cyrus was laughing at the glimpse of fright in the frantic animal. His flesh had been torn only by thorns in his fall. "Nay," he assured the staring huntsmen, "these leopards do no harm to my family. My ancestor Achaemenes wore a leopard's head and skin on his shoulders."

"The lion is guardian of my family," retorted another youth, "but that is no reason why I would tumble on one. Your beast got away."

Cyrus rose to glance along the limestone cliff above them. "I know where he went to his lair," he asserted.

When his companions refused to believe him, he led them up into the rocks, warning them to leave the horses behind. Turning into a chasm he climbed in the dim light to a turning where a smooth rock face almost closed the way. There was no sign of the leopard, but the rock itself bore a picture at eye level—a tracery of running animals and mounted warriors. The others peered at it closely, because the picture carved in the rock did not appear to be a hunt. The wild animals were running with the riders, not away from them. "What is this?" one asked.

"Hear me," intoned Cyrus in the manner of a poet. "In the time of our first ancestors, when men ceased to be beasts and learned the use of fire and the controlling of water, their king was Kaymars who gave them the laws. Then befell the invasion of the demons from the northern darkness, and these demons slew the son of Kaymars. When Kaymars girded on his arms and called all the warriors to him, they marched on the road to the north to avenge his son. It is said that along their road all the lions and panthers and leopards ran to join them. The well-disposed beasts went with them to the war and aided our first ancestors to overcome the demons and avenge the death of their king's son."

The listeners all knew this legend of the poets, but they were impressed by the disappearance of the hunted leopard and by the sight of the rock carving in the silent chasm. They did not know that Cyrus had it made by the skill of two stonecutters of Parsagard. It was an old custom of the wandering Aryans to leave tracings of their deeds or of their gods—especially the warrior god Mithra—in caverns or on cliffs where they would endure. When Mithradat the Maspian heard of the episode of the leopard, he said with anger, "If you follow after the Shepherd, he will lead you only to Kangdiz."

Since Kangdiz was a never-never land, a mythical castle of the spirits who dwell in high places, this remark meant that Cyrus would take his followers on a vain quest.

In that same moon month of the leopard hunt, Cyrus struck out at his mocker, Mithradat. It happened on the narrow path leading from the archery field, which also served for riding because the Persians always practiced with the bow on horseback—shooting at marks while they rode past at a gallop. So when Cyrus, wearied by a hard afternoon, walked from this field, he carried his powerful Scythian bow still strung. He heard the tread of a Nisayan fighting steed approaching and looked up to see Mithradat mounted, speeding along the path.

By now the Maspian prince had taken a warrior's vows, so that he wore a double-sword girdle and a round shield which was braced on his rein arm. When he recognized Cyrus, he called harshly: "Out of the way, boy!" When Cyrus stood still in the path, Mithradat raised his hunting javelin, kneeing the horse forward. The Nisayan charger would not turn aside for a man.

Anger inflamed Cyrus, tensing his muscles. Without thinking, he pulled an arrow from his belt and loosed it from the strung bow with his full strength. The shaft flicked home above the horse's shoulder and beneath Mithradat's shield. Cyrus jumped away from the plunging horse. The Maspian slid from the saddlecloth and lay where he fell, moaning.

A single movement and the bronze-tipped shaft had brought the head-tossing Maspian to the ground like a stricken boar. A fierce exultation swept the anger from Cyrus. Mithradat lay helpless, with the shaft deep inside his hip. There was no one else on the path to witness the wounding, except an Achaemenian girl balancing a water jar on her dark head. Cyrus knew her as Kassandan, who often lingered during her work to watch the warriors on the training field. He called to Kassandan to fetch slaves to carry Mithradat to shelter; then, dropping his bow, he caught the reins of the restive charger. He managed to jump to the horse's back.

"Cyrus," the girl implored, "go to your father's gate, quickly, quickly."

Cyrus, however, did something quite different. Galloping from the entrance gorge of Parsagard, he headed the horse across the plain toward the nearest village of the Maspians. His joy had gone from him, and he felt sharp anxiety that his arrow might bring about a blood feud between the tribes. Inevitably the tale of the wounding of Mithradat would reach all the Maspian warriors, and he determined that he would be the first to tell it. The young Shepherd had the failing of acting without conscious thought. Reaching the village in the evening hour of driving in the herds, he guided the swift Nisayan through the dust clouds raised by the animals to a stone house in a grove where noblemen resided. There on the porch he would accept neither water nor bread until he spoke his message.

"I come here," he told his hosts, "because an arrow from my hand struck down Mithradat, the son of your chieftain. I had no cause to wound him except that he tried to ride over me. But as to that you must be the judges."

Unarmed and dust-streaked, in his round felt cap and neck hood, his tunic girdled by a boy's belt, wearing leather trousers and soft high boots for horseback, Cyrus told the listeners about the encounter on the path, wording it carefully to make clear what had happened. Afterward, the Maspian nobles consulted together and responded that this was not a matter to be judged by them; it would be decided by the *kavis*, the leaders. Cyrus took care to sip some water and taste the bread the women offered before he departed.

Mithradat did not die of the arrow wound; it maimed his thigh so that he could not bestride a war horse or rejoin the *Asvaran*—the mounted warriors. Henceforth he carried a staff because it pained him to walk. The Maspian kavis asked no compensation from the family of Cambyses for his injury.

"You acted in anger," Cambyses summed it up to his son afterward. "You showed cunning only later, when you rode straight to Mithradat's kinsmen. Now Mithradat may watch for an opportunity to slay you. Yet I do not believe," Cambyses added thoughtfully, "he will do that. Your punishment will be a scar that you will soon bear."

"What is that?"

"Your memory."

Although Cyrus thought little of that at the time, he came to realize that his mild father had prophesied truly. His heedless temper brought misfortune as swiftly as thunder follows lightning. That autumn after the harvest festival his father had him make his warrior's vow, before the usual age. At the twin fire altars he was given the long sword of edged iron, the double belt, and iron cap— the ritual weapons of the Asvaran. When his hands were cleansed in river water by the attendants, he kept watch there alone except for the altar priests who merely tended the flames. The priests, silent in white robes, looked to the sky after full starlight for some sign that might be reported as favorable to the king's son. They watched for the coming of a comet or a glimpse of the Golden Bull among the star clusters. Meanwhile, Cyrus reflected that a sword was an ancient weapon of the Aryans, much less effective than a long lance or the new Scythian bows. Then he remembered how he had waited out the night in the salt swamp for the coming of Azhi Dahaka and heard only the voice of Mithradat.

It was a strange fate that removed the strong Mithradat from the company of the Asvaran, against his longing, while he—Cyrus the Achaemenian—became a warrior against his wishes. He looked wistfully across the ravine at the loom of the cliff where he had found refuge in Anahita's cavern. Did the unseen gods in reality decide the fate of human life? Cyrus did not believe so. His fate lay in his own mind and hands, and he did not hope for much from the iron sword which he could not use very well.

He was wearing the sword when he met the crippled Mithradat again on the path to the stables. The Maspian prince, limping, leaned on the shoulder of the girl Kassandan, but at sight of Cyrus he took his hand from the woman and attempted to walk alone. Cyrus stepped aside from the path. Mithradat's eyes gleamed with silent hatred and he said no word of greeting to the king's son. When they passed, Kassandan turned her shapely head to look quickly after Cyrus.

In Cyrus's fifteenth year his father was summoned to bring a gift of horses to the Median court and, before departing on this

journey, Cambyses announced to his Law-bearers and chieftains that the young Shepherd was his heir as well as his son by his first wife. Whereupon Cyrus knelt down to place his hands between the gnarled hands of his father and swear that by hand and heart he would serve the king's glory, keep the king's peace, and never turn his hand against Cambyses, King of Anshan. For so they called their grazing lands that stretched from Parsagard to the frontier stones of the all-powerful Medes. It was an ancient law of the Persians that if a king left his land he must first name his heir—so that if he was killed on the journey, the Persian nobles would not select an heir by fighting among themselves. The Law-bearers saw to that, saying that because of it peace had been kept within the Three Tribes from the time of Achaemenes to Cambyses. Yet Cyrus wondered if many of the chieftains really desired to wear the odd crown of ringed feathers with the crest of silver wings topped by a gold-rayed sun.

True, most of the chieftains rode in gleefully when signal fires were lighted on the peaks around Parsagard. That called all the Asvaran to arm themselves and journey north to the city of the Medes, to take their part in a war of the Medes. Those who commanded in such wars became the *khshatras*, commanding lords. And the others brought back spoil to ornament their women and their homes, after paying a third of the spoil into the king's treasury. Of course some did not come back; yet these dead had their deeds recited at all family gatherings and became known as heroes.

Cambyses, who chose not to be a leader in war, said dryly that it was more useful to be a live cultivator of fields than a dead hero.

Emba the Hyrcanian did not altogether agree. "This great king of the Medes," he pointed out, "he who is named Spear-thrower, has taken the spoil of rich lands; even his servants smell of sweet unguents, and the ceilings of his palace are plated with the best gold. *Ahi*—it is more pleasant and profitable to swat flies for the Spear-thrower than to hold horses at your gate."

No one swatted the flies away from the low table when Cyrus sat in the king's ivory chair to eat during the absence of his father. Swallows and blackbirds swooped down to peck at crumbs on the stone paving, because the tables were set in the inner courtyard

that should have been the audience hall, with a throne of carved marble at the sunrise end. These birds left their droppings where they perched; a law of the Persians protected them from harm. And burly Cambyses gadded about so much that he ordered the servants to carry the ivory stool around after him so that he might sit in judgment wherever he happened to be.

Before the servants brought food to the tables they waited for Cyrus to repeat a ritual of the Achaemenians. Raising his arms, he bent his head to the sky and said: "We greet the spirits of the beasts who are tamed, and of the wild herbs that heal; we greet our people, men and women both wherever they may be, who have right thought and no evil conscience." Then lifting a cup of blue turquoise—"We sacrifice to him who created all of us, giving us the light of fire and of the sun, making fountains flow, and highways fork to the river fords, and torrents flow from the mountains for the welfare of man." With these words he let water drip to the stone paving as if into the raw earth.

Usually when the meal ended with relishes of honey cakes, sugared fruits, and cheese, a flute would pipe up and an old poet would rise to stretch out his hand and bow his head, intoning: "Hear me, Cyrus, son of the Achaemenian king!"

Invariably these wandering poets would sing of the life and deeds of Achaemenes to flatter their hosts. Cyrus became heartily sick of the feats of his now-legendary ancestor. Achaemenes vanquished every enemy with the aid of his noble steed and his death-dealing sword. He even slashed off the three heads of Azhi Dahaka. Some poets maintained that he did this with a single blow; others said that he struck thrice. But Cyrus knew that Evil had not been slain; Evil waited, near at hand, breathing out poison in the hours of darkness. He thought about Achaemenes until he decided that this battle hero was no more than a memory of the time when the wandering Persians had come across the great Nisayan steeds as well as the long iron swords made by smiths in the northern mountains. So mounted and so armed, these ancestral Persians had begun to overthrow enemies in battle. The first Cyrus, grandsire of the Shepherd, had still claimed the fine orchard shores of the Salt Sea of the Hyrcanians in the north. That land, as Emba re-

marked instantly, was now the heart of the wide domain of the Medes.

"And I shall get it again," cried Cyrus, who spoke his mind to the horse-tender. "Was it not the land of my grandfather?"

"A dog may bark at a wild ox."

Since Cyrus had become the heir of Cambyses, he had less joy in his days. From his waking to his sleeping he was required to attend ceremonies. He became the shadow of Cambyses, with no more voice than a shadow. If a sheepherder appeared at the porch steps with a complaint against a sheep-killing mastiff of Parsagard, Cyrus heard his complaint, but the lawmen—the Law-bearers—decided the matter. If Cyrus wished to give a shekel of silver to a fruitgrower with a crop blighted by frost, the Keeper of the Treasure objected that he must have an order from Cambyses to pay out the shekel. Yet the Keeper merely packed away the silver ingots, with other gifts to the king's glory, in chests piled around the portico of the open-air dining hall. He locked these treasure chests only at night and kept his account of ingoing and outgoing silver in his head. Cyrus objected that silver stored in chests did no good. The Keeper retorted that it was kept in the treasury by the law of the Persians.

Cyrus had been obliged to memorize all the laws of the Persians and the Medes, which had never been written down. As far as he could discover, these laws had never been altered in the memory of the oldest grandsire. In fact they seemed to have become the property of the elders and to be used to restrain the youths. When a custom grew old enough, it was made into a law. Once in anger he called for some Law-bearer to change them. The Law-bearers put their fingers to their bearded lips, astonished. "Whoever," they cried out, "would change the laws of the Persians and the Medes?"

For generations those laws had been written down in wedge marks on clay tablets, but few except the Law-bearers could read them.

Very soon the girl Kassandan added to Cyrus's unrest. He seemed to stumble across her bringing gifts of fruit and the like to the crippled Mithradat. It did not occur to him that she contrived to be doing so in his sight. He merely thought it strange that the silent girl should be so attentive unless she belonged to the Maspian. Kassandan was of noble Achaemenian birth, in fact a second cousin, and her father possessed one of the largest cherry orchards upriver. By ancestral law, Achaemenian men took wives only from women of the clan, even at times more closely related than second cousins. By degrees he began to watch for the girl who had flowing dark hair. Cyrus's close-clipped hair was tawny as a lion's.

Once he climbed the far bank of the river to look at her homeland. It was a day of early summer warmth, a time of cherry picking, and Cyrus was pleased when he came upon a tumbling waterfall above a pool of swirling water—a place surely frequented by his protective goddess Anahita. The spray leaped up, almost hiding the opposite shore. While he stared into it expectantly he beheld a girl laughing on the other bank. Her white body tunic whipped about her in the wind gusts, and he recognized Kassandan holding up a basket of cherries, offering it to him as a gift. Her voice could not be heard over the roar of the river in spate. She was teasing him because the river kept him from taking the gift. Or so she seemed to think.

Cyrus dropped his spear, unclasped his cloak, and slid off his trousers and boots. He dived into the vortex of the pool and felt rocks bruise his body. He fought through the current and drew himself out between the boulders beneath the orchard. The girl put down her basket and fled. When he neared her, she darted to the side into wild tree growth. The sandals slipped from her small feet and she stumbled in the gloom of the trees. Cyrus caught her and pulled her to the ground.

Her long hair lay like a veil across her face. The anger in his veins yielded to a wild exultation. When his hands felt the warmth of her smooth body, Kassandan began to cry softly. Swiftly he mastered her, taking full joy from her body.

She lay still when he released her, and her eyes sought the sky beyond his face. She whispered, "I am afraid. There was someone else above you."

Before leaving him, Kassandan offered him a gift, the brooch that held the throat of her chiton. There was blood from her breast on the silver clasp. When he met her the next day in the orchard, Cyrus brought her the round clasp of his sword girdle, bearing the Achaemenian wings. It pleased Kassandan, and she said that now they had exchanged gifts, they were bound together. After that, for some reason, she ceased to be afraid.

When she came to the palace at festivals, with the other women, she wore Cyrus's clasp, brightly polished, on her breast. He felt a stinging of pride because this shapely and intelligent girl belonged to him. One evening before Cambyses poured the sacrifices at the dinner table, Cyrus caught her hand and led her forth from the women, calling upon all the Achaemenians to be witness that he took Kassandan, the daughter of Farnaspes, to be his wife. At once the girl went to kneel before the surprised Cambyses, who stroked her dark head for a moment of silence. Then the king of the Achaemenians kissed her forehead, acknowledging her to be his daughter-in-law and giving her a goblet from which she and Cyrus sipped. But that night he called Cyrus to his sleeping chamber. He rubbed his creased forehead and fingered his beard and said: "Well, she has true Achaemenian beauty—she will bear you handsome sons." He sighed. "So was your mother to me, Cyrus. By the Seven Stars, I still dream of the warmth of her thighs." Then he frowned. "But now that you have sown your wild oats, take thought and consult with me about a second bride. I myself have thought of a certain princess of the Medes."

Cyrus did not answer these pompous words. He wanted no other woman by his side, least of all an arrogant Mede.

So Kassandan bound up her lovely hair and wore the winged clasp in the matron's diadem on her forehead; she lowered her dark eyes modestly when other men glanced her way, and she did not speak again to Mithradat, who stared at her with the hatred he felt for her husband. Kassandan brought a wealth of embroidered cloths and silver ornaments in carved sandalwood chests when she came to Cyrus's chambers with two silent Caspian maids and her father's gift of a mile of orchard land along the river. Gracefully she knelt before the fire in the living room, to signify that this hearth was now her home. And she made herself desirable in every way.

"Now," she told Cyrus, "I have no fear of that other woman."

As husbands have done ever since the day of enlightenment from bestial ignorance, Cyrus made answer: "There *is* no other woman."

He merely dreamed at night, when the voice of the river quickened in the silence, of the goddess Anahita. Now that dream figure merged into Kassandan, breathing, very much alive at his side. Had he not beheld his bride at their first mating in the spray of the goddess's waterfall? Was not that a sign of good will on the part of Anahita?

Regarding that, Kassandan kept her thoughts to herself—unless they concerned Cyrus in practical matters. She remarked once that he rode about his lands alone, having no other chieftains for companions. That was quite true. Cyrus rode with the overseers, and Emba to attend to the horses, and the Scythian Volka for self-appointed bodyguard. Other chieftains had business of their own, which usually amounted to training the Asvaran and faring forth to the distant wars of the Medes.

"Yet, Cyrus," observed his bride, "there is no fellowship like that of the warriors. Among Persian nobles, that is. The other chieftains share it; yet you do not."

"They wish me well enough."

"Mithradat does not. The others indulge you because Cambyses does not bother them with taxes. Still, your father must die. When that day comes what will you do to hold the loyalty of the others? Remember that you have gained no fame as yet in the wars."

"Others? What others?"

Kassandan looked at him fondly and held up one finger. "First, of course, the Maspians and Maraphians, who make up the Three Tribes with ours. Then, second, as you know better than I, the seven others including the Germanians of the Salt Desert, the brigand Mardians who dare to name their town the City of the Persians—nay, I have heard Greek traders call it Persepolis—and the nomad folk, the Dayans. Have you bound all these ten to you by some hope?"

Cyrus had done no such thing, and his wife's anxiety amused him. He laughed at her, saying that he would empty the treasury of Parsagard into the hands of the chieftains. But Kassandan was not amused. "Silver is pleasing to every chieftain," she admitted thoughtfully, "although Persian chieftains always say they desire fame more than treasure. There is only one way to gain profit and fame as well, and that is by conquest of lands afar and distant peoples."

She seemed to be talking to the fire on the hearth. "From the time of our ancestors," she went on, "the royal glory has come from conquest."

It was the first time Kassandan had used the ancient phrase, royal glory. Poets intoned it in their song of Achaemenes. Cyrus ceased to be merry and felt anger at her insistence.

"I have no idea what I shall do when Cambyses dies," he said brusquely. "When that day comes, I will know."

Actually he could not manage to make plans and carry them out. When an emergency arose, he acted by instinct. He had not thought of marrying Kassandan until he had taken her hand. When she bore him a son, she ceased to worry about Cyrus's companions. The child seemed to take up all her planning. He was named Cambyses, after his royal grandfather.

WARNING OF THE MAGIAN

It happened because Cyrus explored the caves. He was tireless in following streams up to the bare mountain summits. In so doing he had stumbled into the caves hidden by pine growth at an elevation where wind stunted the trees and hunters did not venture, except after ibex. Here, close to the snow-fed streams, holes appeared in the cliffs behind boulders. The holes looked natural enough until Cyrus crawled into one and found himself in a cavern where the sides had been cut away by stone picks. The floor was blackened by charcoal of countless fires, and wisps of rushes still lay in the corners, like the wreckage of sleeping beds. In several of these hidden caves Cyrus picked up spear points of flint. At some age of the past, he decided, people had sheltered themselves in these caverns and had taken some pains to conceal the entrances. No one in Parsagard knew anything of the hidden caves. But he noticed that when he told his wife about finding them, her young Caspian maids listened intently until he had finished.

If the Caspians knew the secret of the caverns, they would certainly tell him nothing.

The Caspians were the dark and weak folk, the original inhabitants of the great plateau. As a boy, Cyrus had called them the Old People and sometimes the Earth People. They delved in the ground like marmots, planting seed, reaping crops, making pots out of wet clay with their hands, and even making their dwellings out of mud bricks dried in the hot sun. Cambyses tried to persuade them to burn the bricks over fires, because burned bricks would withstand flood water and rain as well, while the mud bricks melted away in a rush of water. He also forced them to build dams of withes and stones, to store up water against the dry season.

The Caspians spoke a language unlike any civilized tongue, and they seemed to have no heroic legends, being in this respect unlike their conquerors, the Aryans. They were better skilled at thieving than fighting with honorable weapons; if attacked they fled from their villages in the bottom lands and disappeared somewhere in the upland forests. So when Cyrus discovered the hidden caverns, he imagined he had come upon a refuge of the Caspians. Yet these caves had not been used by men for a long time.

Ordinarily the Persian masters had little communication with the natives, unless hunters or warriors chose to make sport with young peasant girls in the barley fields. A wide cleavage lay between noble Aryan birth and ignoble Caspian. The Iranians—as the Aryans of the Persian plateau came to be called—rode the Nisayan chargers; the aborigines had their shaggy ponies and carried loads on their own backs; their smiths wrought the precious metals, iron and bronze, into weapons or horse gear, while the Iranians fashioned clever things out of the softer metals, silver and shining copper. As for tamed animals, the conquerors kept noble milk-giving cows and oxen, while the submissive natives tended sheep and black goats, and their women wove weatherproof garments out of the long black wool. As for their gods, the Caspians kept them secret, going off into the forests to sacrifice. Although no Caspians entered Parsagard except as house slaves, Cyrus noticed that they seemed to be increasing in numbers within their mud villages. He told Cambyses, who merely said it was a good thing. Why, Cyrus asked, was it a good thing for a few Iranians to rule over so many Caspians?

Thereupon his father blinked in his oracular manner and uttered a riddle. "By what five things do we Iranians live?"

Cyrus could think of more than five things but he knew that his father expected an answer to his own thought, not to Cyrus's surmise. He remembered the answer of his school days. "By seed grain, by the tools that plant it, the water that gives growth, the tame animals that cultivate it, and the human labor that garners its harvest."

Cambyses nodded. "Now think: of all those five things we possess not a single one—unless the seed I have stored—while the Caspians possess them all. You know well enough that they live upon the earth and we live upon them, but do you consider what comes from that? They hate us and fear us. I cannot change their minds toward us, but if they spawn large families and have many hands for the labor, and full bellies, they will accordingly hate us less."

Cyrus recalled his father's oracular saying the morning he went with Volka to hunt the ibex. The Scythian had sighted one above the timber line and craved to bring it down with an arrow. Only a Scythian would attempt it, but only a Scythian might succeed. They were riding village ponies, screening themselves in the tree growth while watching the rock wall overhead. In such a place, devas might echo their voices with mocking cries and on that account Parsagardians seldom ventured so near the sacred summits. Volka, being born on the steppes, had no fear of the mountain gods. Suddenly the mastiffs accompanying them surged beyond the ponies and raced away on a scent.

Mastiffs would follow a panther's track while they would hardly pursue an ibex. Gripping his spear, Cyrus reined his pony into a gallop after the dogs and discovered that an old Caspian man clad in hides ran from them. He came up barely in time to beat the great dogs back with his spear haft as they tore at the legs of the peasant, who had a patriarch's white hair under his headband. He also had a cloth-wrapped bundle in his arms. Cyrus made him open the bundle to see if he had stolen anything. But it held only fresh baked barley cakes, pomegranates, and white cheese. It seemed strange that a village patriarch would carry a whole day's food to a bare mountain peak to eat it. Glancing up, Cyrus beheld the mouth of a cave and another man, not a Caspian, standing in it watching him.

"Now I am glad that the dogs did not eat my friend," called out the stranger. "Will you share my supper?"

He was as young as Cyrus, unarmed, with a weather-browned face. A hair cord girdled his gray robe and he wore sandals instead of laced riding boots. He spoke with the soft dialect of the eastern parts. No shining ornaments revealed his rank or dignity. Dismounting, Cyrus carried the bundle up to him and noticed that the mastiffs, after sniffing at the stranger, took no further heed of him. Curiously, the Achaemenian asked his family name, his tribe, and where he journeyed. A sign seemed to pass between the old Caspian and the youth, who answered that he no longer had a family or tribe and sought rest upon his journey.

"Tell the truth," exclaimed Cyrus. "You are a fugitive from an eastern land, sheltering in a refuge of the village folk who feed you in secret."

Quick anger shone in the stranger's gray eyes. Then he smiled ruefully. "It happens that the truth is harder to believe than useful lies. Young huntsman, the truth is that a Magian has no longer a family or tribe." Thoughtfully, he spread the cloth on the ground and divided the food upon it into two parts. A clay jar of water stood by the cave entrance, with a bowl. The Magian, as he called himself, could not have fled far because his thin hands and feet were clean. "I suppose I am a fugitive from death. I came to this refuge because the villagers in the valley told me that here I might find what I sought."

He spoke somewhat like a poet; yet poets always sought the gate of a king's palace. "What?" Cyrus demanded.

"The peace of the Achaemenians," explained the Magian, pouring clear water into the bowl.

Obviously the stranger did not realize that he was talking with the king's son. "Do you expect me to believe that the villagers know anything about my f—about Achaemenians, whether in strife or peace?"

"They seem to. They have quite a saga to relate. It goes this way——"

And the Magian repeated casually that through all the Caspian lands Aryan hordes had invaded with sword and fire and passed on. In the land of the Achaemenian king, however, the invaders had settled down in a peace of the king, protecting life. "You who wear the Achaemenian wings," he challenged, "do you know nothing of the refugees who journey hither from the Blue Mountains, or from the death of the earth in Shushan?"

Then he apologized—almost as if he had the manners of a noble —for his rude question and begged Cyrus to sit and share his supper, even if they could not share their thoughts. Cyrus felt like accepting; then he refused, being unwilling to bind himself to a fugitive by the breaking of bread. He sensed a hidden pride in the self-styled Magian who wore no sword girdle. With a gesture of farewell he went to follow Volka who had gone on tracking his ibex. He glanced back to find the stranger and the village patriarch eating supper together. Above them the gray summit stood like a rampart beneath the moving clouds.

It crossed Cyrus's mind that this Magian, for all his poetic story, had avoided the gate of Parsagard.

THE CITY OF DEATH

Another refugee did not avoid the gate but came in to Cyrus's door. The bearers behind him laid down packs of goods fetched from a donkey caravan, and he said he was a Habiru, or Hebrew, and a refugee only in the sense that his king was captive by the waters of Babylon, which were actually canals and quite different from the clear running river of Parsagard. This bearded Hebrew merchant wore a silver ring in his ear as a token of semi-captivity and he made Kassandan a gift of a leaf wrapping of sweet myrrh before he opened a bolt of splendid purple wool, saying that it was royal purple drawn from the depths of the Great Sea and most suitable for a royal Achaemenian lady. Kassandan instantly desired the rare cloth, although it cost two shekels a cubit, but Cyrus disliked it and chose for her instead a pair of matched bracelets of soft gold, bearing tiny winged griffins. These, he said, were really ornaments and not a costume that anyone might put on.

When their business was ended, and the Hebrew, as was customary with merchants, had related the news of the outlands, he walked around the limits of Parsagard as if seeking something he did not find. "There are no walls!" he exclaimed to the Achaemenians at the evening meal.

Until that day, he said, he had never beheld a city without walls —even deserted Nineveh, or mighty Babylon where the ramparts of Imgur Bel and Nimitti Bel had been built by Nebuchadnezzar into the city itself. The Hebrew added in the tone of a prayer, "May Yahweh be a shield to those who dwell here."

Cyrus knew of no god having the name of Yahweh; still the Hebrew, being a stranger, might be expected to have an unknown deity.

"Even in Shushan upon the road hither," the Hebrew added thoughtfully, "they are rebuilding the citadel wall with strong burned brick."

Cyrus recalled what the other wayfarer, the Magian, had said of Shushan, that it lay in the throes of the death of the earth. He himself had seen that long before when he turned aside with boy companions from the trail to the Nisayan pastures to explore the ruins of that once glorious citadel of Elam between the mountains and the Plain. He had seen how weeds choked the tilled fields, and the forests were hewn to dead wood, while floods from broken dams scoured the hot bare earth. Foxes ran from the burned shells of buildings. Thieves of the road sheltered themselves in the halls of the great kings of Elam. And the reason for this death of the inhabited earth had been inscribed on a stone tablet set over the empty gateway. A wandering scribe read the message of the tablet, which Cyrus fixed in his memory:

"I Assur-bani-pal, great king of all lands, took the carved furniture from these chambers; I took the horses and mules with gold-adorned bits from the stables. I burned with fire the bronze pinnacles of the temple; I carried off to Assyria the god of Elam with all his riches. I carried off the statues of thirty-two kings, together with the mighty stone bulls that guarded the gates. Thus have I entirely laid waste this land and slain those who dwelt in it. I have laid their tombs open to the sun and have carried off the bones of those who did not venerate Assur and Ishtar, my lords—leaving the ghosts of these dead forever without repose, without offerings of food and water."

By the evidence of this writing, the Assyrians had marched over Elam. It could not have been more than three generations ago. Yet Nineveh, the city of Assur-bani-pal himself, now lay deserted and open to the heat of the sun.

"So you see," Cyrus ended his tale, "that these great cities have become great deserts inhabited by ghosts."

The Hebrew shook his oiled head and threw up his hands. "How great is the wisdom of the illustrious son of Cambyses! Verily is his memory like a written scroll! Yet these ghosts of Shushan bought seed-sowing plows from me, paying with an order for silver from the House of Egibi in Babylon."

At the end of the evening Kassandan spoke her mind about this as soon as she entered the sleeping chamber. If unknown people were actually rebuilding the ruins of Shushan, and if they had sufficient wealth to deal with bankers, they should pay tribute to Parsagard.

"Tribute for what, loveliest of wives?" asked Cyrus idly, wondering what kind of a plow could sow seeds.

"For protection, of course. Do not pretend, wisest of husbands, that a new city does not require protection against brigands and foreign conquerors. Is not Susa—this Shushan of the merchant—well within the limits of Anshan? And is there any protection equal to that of the Persian horse-bowmen?"

Cyrus smiled at her woman's argument. "And if I demand tribute as you suggest, what am I, a brigand or a foreign conqueror? What would my father Cambyses think?"

He was not willing to let his wife always have the last word.

"You might think, instead, Cyrus," she said, "of Cambyses your son."

The end of this was that the Shepherd rode to Shushan himself. He had a habit of looking into a doubtful matter with his own eyes. Among the several hundred Asvaran who served as his escort, he took some Germanian noble heroes who were tired of hanging their swords over their hearths while waiting for the Medes to begin another war. The long road wound through the mountains and dropped through a "gate," or gorge leading to the western Plain. In this natural gateway a tribe of robbers came rushing down like wolves, but when the tribesmen sighted the Persian bows they fled like startled goats. The Germanians would not waste an arrow on them. When the Asvaran rode from the hills into hot dust clouds, they pulled their neckcloths over their mouths and swore. Mountain men never ventured willingly into lowland heat.

Soon the trail ran by the cascades of the Shushan River, and Cyrus noticed the green of cultivated fields in the brown waste below. Where Shushan rose at the bend in the river, the broken bridge had been rebuilt of stone. The ghosts had been at some useful work. At sight of the oncoming riders, herders sprang up to drive their sheep and cattle to hiding. Cyrus led his warriors to the bridge, and only the Germanians used their swords on fugitive men to inspire respect. Not many were killed before the Persians drew rein beneath the citadel on its height. As the Hebrew had told them, new brick walls stood around the ruins left by the Assyrians. Men with shields and spears appeared on the wall summit and in the entrance where no gates had been set in place as yet. The Germanian heroes pointed out that the shields of the Shushans were of hide instead of gleaming metal; if Cyrus would cover them, they suggested, with the arrows of his warriors, they could rush the gate and secure a safe entry for him. By doing so, of course, the veterans would have first chance at any spoil or captives inside the citadel.

Cyrus was examining a plow abandoned in a watered field

whence the plowman had fled with his oxen—judging by the tracks. This plow had a box atop its vertical shaft, and the box held seed grain. A hollow in the shaft allowed the seed to trickle down into the upturned earth. Thus the one man using it could sow his grain as he ran a furrow. It was quite a new kind of plow. When Cyrus had finished examining it, he warned his horsemen that they should circle the citadel wall and judge the strength of its defenders before rushing in the gate.

Before they could do so, a solitary figure emerged from the great gate, afoot and without guards. He wore the long fringed robe of a dignitary, yet without crown or staff or gold tokens of rank except for the medal on his chest, which turned out to be the image of Shushinak, the supreme god of the Elamites, a sun deity with some attribute of justice. He walked down with a soldier's stride, holding his head high as he touched the rein of Cyrus's Nisayan in respect. "A truce, son of Cambyses," he requested in good Persian. "The next time, send a galloper ahead with your name, and I will greet you at the bridge. For I am Gubaru, lord of Shushan and the Sealands and the Bitter Waters."

Oddly, this Gubaru did not give his title as governor for a monarch or as king himself. He invited the Achaemenian to dismount and sit down with his warriors to a poor feast within the half-finished palace. When the Persians exchanged doubtful glances at the invitation, Gubaru said quickly that if his guests preferred to eat outside, his servants would fetch out the feast to them. Cyrus decided that this lord of a ruined city had a nimble mind and might prove to be a dangerous host. So he suggested that Gubaru send out all his armed servants instead; after that the Persians could go in to inspect the citadel. "I am curious," Cyrus assured him, "to see your handiwork here, because when I came the last time only foxes dwelt in your walls."

Gubaru hesitated an instant before bowing his handsome head and declaring that the wish of his glorious guest was law to him. Apparently he gave order in Elamite speech for his palace to be vacated. The armed guards marched out to the river bank. Cyrus left half his warriors with the troublesome Germanians to hold the gate and the horses as well. The other Persians thronged in behind him, watchful of a trap. In the entrance hall of blue tiling still damp with cement, they were surprised to find a fountain casting forth spray and beside it a tall girl waiting, half-veiled in royal linen, with her eyebrows made into dark bows and sweet scent coming from her slim body as she bent her knees before Cyrus and rose to offer him a tray bearing cakes and a bowl of the juice of grapes. Her half-seen face reminded him of Kassandan laughing through the spray of Anahita's fall, and he felt it to be a favorable omen. Gubaru explained that this was his daughter who had forsaken the delights of Babylon for the wilderness of their ancestral Elam, which she had never seen.

It was true that they must have little wealth because the wall pillars were merely palm trunks set in heavy asphalt. While Cyrus sipped from the bowl before handing it over to his chieftains, he praised the miracle of the flowing fountain and the beauty of the Elamite princess; he decided that Gubaru was speaking the truth and they need fear no harm as long as they kept the girl within reach of their swords. Gubaru explained that he had learned about waterworks while serving as an engineer in Nebuchadnezzar's army.

He explained as well the mystery of the life restored to the ruins of Shushan. After the scorching of their earth by the Assyrians, some survivors of Elam had escaped to the Achaemenian rule in the eastern mountains, and a few, including Gubaru's family, had fled west to the mighty walls of Babylon. After the fall of Nineveh, the anger of the Assyrian conquerors had become as dust before the wind and their enmity had vanished. Thereupon, Gubaru had forsaken his post with the splendid Nebuchadnezzar to migrate back to his scorched homeland. He was trying to make the earth yield food again. "In like case," he asked Cyrus, "if your magnificent Parsagard lay in broken ruins, would you not return to the tombs of your ancestors?"

Cyrus thought that there was little enough to demolish in the Parsa homestead and no ancestors had left their tombs by his river as yet; still, he understood what the Elamite felt. "Yes," he agreed.

Surprisingly, the lovely girl Amytis broke the silence of decorum to whisper: "O son of a great king, have mercy toward us! You have seen our poverty."

When evening fell, the chieftains gathered about Cyrus to discuss their most advantageous camping place. During daylight, mounted on their chargers, they held the Shushans at their mercy. Asleep in darkness, they could be murdered by the knives of the Elamites. Cyrus bade them pitch the tents from the wagon train around the open gate of the citadel. Then if attacked from the outside, they could withdraw within the wall; if attacked from the palace, they could mount the horses and ride forth. He bade the horse guards take mastiffs with them on their rounds. To Gubaru he explained courteously that his rude warriors were too numerous to intrude upon the palace chambers. The lord of Shushan said he was grateful for the kindness of the royal Achaemenian, and he bade the kitchen servants carry out the feast hastily prepared from roasted lambs seasoned with cloves and mounds of white rice sweetened with stewed fruit. He knew that Persians had never learned to drink wine. At a polite interval after the meal, he came with his elders and nobles to learn the reason for Cyrus's visit.

The young Aryan thought that these Elamites resembled the Hebrew merchant; they hid their thoughts behind courtesy. Being unaccustomed to diplomatic speech, he spoke his mind frankly, praising their good work in restoring fertility to Elam, which was, after all, a dependency of Anshan; he offered them the protection of Cambyses, against the payment of an annual tribute.

These Elamites were really more like Law-bearers than chieftains. Unexpectedly, Gubaru asked if Cyrus would not fetch him a drove of the splendid Nisayan horses each year. Cyrus explained that a law of the Persians prevented him from giving horses of that breed to others. At this, Gubaru smiled in his beard. "Yet every spring Cambyses himself drives brood mares as well as stallions to the court of the king of the Medes. That is tribute."

"My royal father rules Anshan in his own right," Cyrus retorted. "The gift of white horses is merely a token of his friendship toward Astyages—the Spear-thrower."

He sensed that Gubaru implied that Elam should pay tribute to the ruling Medes, not to the Persians.

"And we shall offer tokens of our friendship toward the honorable and victorious Achaemenians," replied Gubaru. He drew a small black stone from his girdle pocket, and his finger traced the wedge marks of writing on it. "'I am Nebuchadnezzar the Chaldean,'" he repeated the words. "'My justice extends as far as the sun's light; let all who are weak and oppressed appeal to my justice, say I.'" And he explained gently that his revived state of Elam had the protection of Nebuchadnezzar in mighty Babylon.

After that, Cyrus found there was nothing more he could argue. He could, of course, lead forth his Asvaran the next day to loot the dwellings in Shushan. However, he remembered the pleading whisper of the girl and decided to be merciful. All at once he laughed, with an uplift of heart. "Well, let us be friends, Lord Gubaru! Give me only one of your new seed plows for a token."

For the first time, shrewd Gubaru appeared surprised. "By the Sun of Shushinak! The word of an Achaemenian is more binding than a law graven on stone. Cyrus, I have heard your pledge of friendship."

The next dawn when the Persian riders packed their wagons, Gubaru had a plow ready for Cyrus, with some sacks of delectable rice and spices. As a memento for Cambyses, he explained. Then he led Cyrus away from his men to the bridge, where the rush of water muted their words. For a space the lord of Shushan appeared to commune with the flowing water and the lines softened in his taut face. "Shepherd," he said so quietly that Cyrus had to strain to hear, "I am neither a prophet of the Hebrews nor a reader of fate in the stars, a Chaldean. My soul is held within Elam. I served faithfully that mighty builder and planner, Nebuchadnezzar—may the gods grant him long years of life! Yet seven devils of sickness plague him. When you hear that Nebuchadnezzar is dead"—his voice sank to a whisper—"mount a swift horse and come to me, and we will talk together of greater things." He smiled at the water. "You can come alone safely."

So Gubaru the Elamite extended the tie of understanding to the Achaemenian.

The Persian horsemen were glad to leave the heat and dust of Shushan; they were weary of swatting flies and scratching out ants. When Cyrus returned to Parsagard, he related the truth of all that had passed in the city reviving from the throes of death, except for the last private word of Gubaru. Whereupon Kassandan shed tears and cried that the Elamites had pulled wool over his eyes. He had no tribute to show. Cambyses was delighted with the new plow, although he said it would be difficult to teach one Caspian peasant to do the work that had always been done by two.

When he thought his journey over, Cyrus determined to go with his father to the ruling court of the Medes at the next ripening of grass. He longed to observe for himself what it meant to be tributary to the Medes. He did not trouble to make a clear plan in his mind. If he had thought twice about it, he might have avoided the danger.

SONG OF THE SACK OF NINEVEH

Agbatana, city of the king who ruled many kings, lay far toward the northern cold. Its ramparts of new gray stone rose above the dark pine growth beneath a solitary snow peak. Its name signified the Gathering Place, because the Medes said their first distinguished ancestor had gathered all the wandering Medic tribes together for the first time here beneath this sacred mount of Alwand. Otherwise, Agbatana (Hamadan) merely stood on a junction of the great east-west caravan trail from the Hyrcanian Sea to the "gate" leading down to Nineveh on the Plain.

The Medes themselves were Iranians and blood kin (gen, they said) to the Persians, still divided into tribes. Medes and Persians spoke the same language but did not look at things the same way because the royal Medes had conquered lands for three generations, while the Persian horse archers had conquered nothing for themselves, not even half-ruined Shushan. The Medes, that is, had been victorious since the time of Cyaxares—Uvakhshatra, the Warrior—who had formed the first regular army on the Assyrian model, with the notable exception of using Persian cavalry. Accordingly, the Medes called Cyaxares the founder of their empire although they had no clear understanding as yet what an empire might be. It was a much easier task to conquer the Assyrian army than to copy the Assyrian dominion.

Astyages, the Spear-thrower, the somewhat elderly son of Cyaxares, had a silver plate made and inscribed with the deeds of his three famous ancestors; this plate was carried through his dining hall to be displayed to all his dinner guests, whether they could read it or not. Astyages could recite the family history because he knew it by heart; it no longer occurred to him that Cyaxares, his father, had spent his lifetime on horseback, and that he—Astyages—passed most of his time between the feast tables and the women's quarters where dwelt several princesses from neighboring courts, including the dedicated Mandane, daughter of the notable Nebuchadnezzar. Under these conditions, Astyages believed his royal glory to be equal to that of Nebuchadnezzar, and that the peace between them rested on mutual respect resulting from a balance of their powers. The Mede possessed an invincible armed host, while the Chaldean in his turn was master of impregnable fortifications. The truth was that the newly ennobled Astyages had an inferiority complex which required adulation to satisfy it, while Nebuchadnezzar labored like one possessed of a demon at building protecting roadblocks and even river blocks in the form of dams.

The far-wandering Hebrew merchant who had sold the seed plows to Gubaru prostrated himself before Astyages's slippered feet; he had no trouble in disposing of his royal purple cloth at the Agbatana palace. Noble Medes never bargained because they did not understand trading. Yet, if angered, they might seize a merchant's stock in trade and throw the man to their hunting dogs. In giving them the news of the road, the Hebrew was careful to describe the rude Achaemenian city as merely a garden paradise. Being quick at languages, he had picked up the Iranian word for a garden watered by a flowing stream and shaded by trees—*firudis* —which he pronounced paradise. The words *firudis-i-adam* signified a man's secluded garden. Inevitably it happened that Hebrew merchants who told about their travels in Babylon related that Yahweh had created a garden to the eastward, a paradise for Adam. It became a saying of their prophets. But that was after the great change and the ending of the death of the earth.

Reckoning by the still later calendar of the Christians, Cambyses and Cyrus set out for Agbatana in the year 563 before the birth of Christ. That was the year before the death of Nebuchadnezzar and two years before the release from jail of King Jehoiakim of the Hebrews, which did not, however, end their captivity.

Never had the valley of Parsagard been more fair. When they entered the gorge that was the gate of the north, Cyrus turned the rein of his horse to look back at the fresh green of the spring grass shot with blue and the fire of poppies. "It is like the ache of a wound," he said, "to leave the valley."

"If you feel that way, my son," put in Cambyses quickly, "why do you leave it? It must be your guardian spirit speaking now, not to mention that the law forbids you to journey from the frontier with me. Last night—I recall it now—I dreamed that the poisonous breath of Azhi Dahaka touched you and made you ill on the journey."

Cambyses had a way of remembering dreams when he wished to have a convenient omen. Cyrus wanted very much to turn back, but he would not yield to talk about an omen. "And I dreamed," he said, laughing, "that when I reined my horse into the gate of Agbatana a multitude bent down to the earth."

"You will strike fire from your body before you see that. Unless you give better heed to your guardian spirit," added his father morosely, "one of the three demons who shadow you will make an end of your life."

"Three? What three?" Cyrus still contemplated his valley.

Cambyses gripped his son's shoulder to arrest his thoughts. "Anger. An unknown woman. A blind courage."

When Cyrus made no answer, his father added thoughtfully, "And of these three the last is the worst. A wise warrior looks to his weapons and considers his enemy's before he fights. A fool dies swiftly."

Whereupon Cyrus kneed his horse forward. It is true that the evil in his fate prevailed at that moment. When they broke their journey at the pastures of the Nisayan steeds, they selected two white stallions and twenty brood mares to take as tribute to Astyages. However, the Median assessors who awaited them with scribes took their pick of the herds now that the foals had been dropped. Cyrus discovered that the few Nisayans they drove north were no more than a token of the draft of horses claimed by the Medes from the Persians. More bitter knowledge came to him in the splendor of the palace of Agbatana where he and his father became lost in the throng hastening to see the great king. It exasperated him to watch his anxious father hurrying to put on the ungainly feathered crown of ceremony and clasp the spotless white linen cloak under his straggling beard. Cyrus made no effort to change from his pointed riding boots and tasseled cap. Even Volka, his Scythian bodyguard, had adorned his arms with gold bracelets to display the spoil he had taken before they were led to the hall of Astyages.

At the entrance, guards in brass helmets and fish-scale silvered armor did not draw back their crossed spears until a chamberlain with a lion-head staff hastened up to greet the royal Achaemenians. Even then the guards made Volka remove his bow and quiver of battle arrows, which he did unwillingly before following Cyrus to the feast.

The great hall resounded like a kennel of mastiffs at feeding time. The feasters, whether standing or crouched on benches, whether chewing flesh or sucking sweets, all clamored at each other in strange tongues. Incense and the smoke from cooking fires veiled a mass of purple robes, gleaming with silver, shining with jewels. Over this pandemonium, Astyages presided, high on his white marble throne, his broad face pale between his clipped, pointed beard and his blue and gold tiara. Alone he sat on his dais before a circle of standing Medes, their ornaments revealing their rank and office. As Cyrus surveyed him, amazed, the guiding chamberlain jogged his elbow, warning him, "Don't stare!" And he whispered, nodding his tall cap upward, "The imperial ladies!"

Above and behind the throne stretched a gallery screened by fretted ivory. Cyrus could see no signs of women, but evidently they were hidden in the gallery, watching the feasting. At the king's feet a poet shouted over the uproar. At sight of Cambyses's bobbing feather crown, Astyages roared for silence and rose to cry a greeting.

"Behold my cousin who is King of Anshan!" His quick glance sought out Cyrus. "Behold his royal son."

To Cyrus's surprise, that ended the greeting. The chamberlain waved his staff to open a way through the feasters to a small table near the poet, just beneath the throne of Astyages upon the dais. There he seated Cambyses. Cyrus was led to a bench five spear lengths from the dais. By prodding with his staff, the chamberlain made a place for him between an Amorite chieftain who smelled of camels and a silent Chaldean who wore a curled false beard over a neck chain of gold talismans to enhance his dignity. The voice of the tireless poet resounded again:

". . . the blood in the streets of Nineveh rose over the fetlocks of the horses of the victorious Median host . . . sixty thousand and uncounted hundreds were yoked as captives before the eyes of the triumphant monarch of the Medes. Who could count the toll of chariots adorned with gold, of mules, of cattle, of donkeys? The sound of weeping was like to music of flutes in the ears of the mighty King of the Medes, the king over many lands——"

The noise of feasting drowned the words. This song of the sack of Nineveh seemed to Cyrus very much like the victory tablet placed by the Ninevite monarch, Assur-bani-pal, over the ruins of Shushan. Because the ignoble treatment of his father provoked him, Cyrus tried to remain quiet and show courtesy to his new table mates. "Is this stone woman also spoil from the Assyrians?" he asked.

Across from Astyages a flat purplish stone stood against the wall, bearing upon it the figure of a robed and crowned woman poised on a roaring lion, with stars about her head and a spear in her hand. The shaggy Amorite glanced over his shoulder and spat out his cud of meat politely before answering. "She? Nay, that must be a goddess of power if she can ride a lion."

"Ishtar," corrected the Chaldean through his beard, "in truth possesses both protective and destructive powers. More, she is the guardian of our queen, Mandane, who brought hither with her this great Lady of Babylon."

"I have heard her called the great whore of Babylon," remarked the Amorite, digging his beringed fingers into a dish of figs.

The Chaldean whinnied like a startled horse. "Think twice before you speak ill of Ishtar whose star is Venus, whose love is sought by many gods. Once the Elamites dared to carry off her statue as a trophy and death followed upon their footsteps. She has many names because she is present in all lands. Women keep her secrets, and perhaps she does protect them, while she may destroy men." His dark eyes turned to Cyrus, and he lowered his voice. "Eat something quickly, prince of Anshan. King Astyages has looked your way twice."

In his excitement Cyrus had no wish to taste the food piled before him, although Volka breathed hungrily in his ear. Quickly he picked up a bustard's leg and handed it over his shoulder to Volka. Then he heard the king's voice.

"Is our food so distasteful to you, Cyrus—or do you fear poison in it?"

Silence fell, while Astyages stared at him, frowning. Cambyses stood up anxiously. It was more than rude to refuse to eat at the table; it made Cyrus appear unwilling to become the guest of Astyages. Yet at that moment he could not force himself to eat. To say that he was ill would be a lie. While he tried to think of some excuse, a hand clamped upon his forearm, thrusting it toward the dishes. One of the armed guards had left the wall to persuade him in this manner.

It happened in the space of a breath. Hot with anger, Cyrus threw off the man's arm. Volka immediately grasped the guard and threw him heavily, the brass shield clanging on the stone floor. Two soldiers ran from the wall, plunging their spears into the back of the unarmed Scythian who leaped up convulsively. Springing from his bench, Cyrus pulled his sword free and slashed at Volka's slayers over their shields. They fell and blood flowed upon the stones. A group of Median guards hastened up, making a wall of their long shields, hemming in Cyrus and pushing him to the wall with their weight. In his rage he had shed blood and broken the king's peace. Hurriedly he struck at the lifted spears of his antagonists. In silence Astyages watched.

A woman's voice echoed musically in the hall.

"Say I, Mandane, this is now my son. Lower your spears; do no harm to the Achaemenian youth, my son."

The speaker remained invisible behind the screen of the gallery. Yet she was obeyed as if Astyages himself had given the command. Cyrus took no conscious thought of his fate except that it came from using the sword. Dropping the weapon, he signaled the Medes to carry out Volka. Before they passed the door, the Scythian was dead. Cyrus looked at him and went on blindly through the corridors, seeking a way out. He heard soft footsteps following him and turned quickly to find a robed eunuch panting after him on slippered feet. "Lord Cyrus," the stout eunuch whispered, "great evil have you accomplished. Yet is the heart of the queen, your mother, inclined toward you—ay, she bids you remain hidden until the closing of the gates after dark. Come, to a secure place!"

Whereupon this servant of Mandane slipped ahead and beckoned Cyrus to follow.

MERCY OF THE GREAT GODDESS

Here in the corridors of the Median palace the Shepherd sensed the presence of his guiding spirit; this *fravashi* accompanied him unseen on his right hand, and now it warned him without audible words. Danger waited before and behind him.

Until then, Cyrus had been sheltered like a child in the womb within his mountain fastness. Riding where he willed, he had still been unharmed. Now his flesh tingled as if raw to the air, and his fravashi bade him hasten to the stables to ride back with Emba to the protection of the paradise of Parsagard. Instead, he ran after the panting eunuch, knowing that only his own wits could protect him in this ambush of strange enemies. In thus becoming a fugitive, he left his boyhood behind him forever.

The eunuch led him through a door into a garden shaded by an arbor of grape vines. At its end rose a palisade with a gate of stone topped by a carving showing King Astyages, mounted, spearing a lion. The significance of the carving did not strike Cyrus at first. Glancing around him, the eunuch trotted to the gate in the wall of stakes. It was barred, but the creature pulled the linchpin from a narrow grating and motioned to Cyrus to slip through. "No one will look for you here." He pointed back to the gray wall of the palace beyond the garden and to a terrace at its summit, shaded by a tentlike awning. "The chambers of Mandane," he lisped, "are guarded by sharp weapons. She bids you seek her after the hour of full starlight. If you have courage to reach Mandane you will be safe."

When Cyrus stepped into the palisade, the queen's eunuch closed the grating after him, putting back the pin hastily. He glanced at the young Achaemenian, amusement in his dark eyes, and disappeared among the grapevines. Cyrus noticed first the hoof marks in the earth and then the wild growth within the palisade; when he sought cover in juniper bushes, a pair of antelope darted away. A wild ass flung up its head and followed them. Cyrus, familiar with the behavior of animals on the mountains, knew that this enclosure was no garden but a hunting park. Astyages chose to hunt captive beasts in his palace grounds. No sooner had Cyrus stretched out under the screen of the junipers than a full-grown lion appeared, pacing up to the gate and sniffing under it.

Although Cyrus no longer had a weapon in his belt, he did not worry about the lion pacing around the gate. A wild ox or boar might attack a man, but these could not be here because they could not be captured alive. The lion, of course, might turn on him if hurt, but this king of beasts—as city dwellers called him—was more intent on the door than on the human being penned up with him. After a while the lion circled away to stretch out on the ground, with its head toward the grating. And Cyrus lay still, waiting for the sun to go down behind the snow ridge. When guards appeared in the outer garden, walking in pairs, spears on their shoulders, they paused to stare into the hunting park, and he heard their laughter. It suddenly occurred to him that these Medes knew where he lay in hiding. And, if so, the eunuch must have revealed his hiding place. No doubt the people in the palace relished the jest of it. At the same time, it would be extremely difficult to pass through sentries who were watching for his coming, even in darkness.

While all this went through Cyrus's mind, he grieved for the death of Volka, his bodyguard. He knew that, instead of following after the dying man, he should have kept his sword in its sheath and challenged the weapon men of Astyages for their murder of his servant. He had acted without taking thought, but now that he meditated in quiet he realized that the seemingly benevolent eunuch had made it all but impossible for him to return to the palace. Cyrus did not wonder what kind of a woman Mandane might be, or why she had suddenly befriended him, because he had no least notion of a royal lady of Babylon.

He began to plan, instead, how he could slip through the watchers in the garden. And the best way seemed to be to have them looking for something else. When the last glow faded from the sky and all the clustered stars shone, Cyrus waited until the pair of guards came close to peer at the gate. Then Cyrus also walked to it and drew the linchpin of the grating. He stepped aside quickly. The lion slipped through the opening.

When it roared at the armed men in its path, they shouted and ran. Judging by the tumult that followed, the lion must have raced around the garden seeking a way out. Cyrus walked—it was senseless to run over strange ground in the dark—to the wall of the palace. Feeling the roughness of the lower courses of stone, ill-laid in cement, he gripped with his fingers, thrusting his feet into crannies and climbing swiftly. Below him torches waved and a lion hunt began through the garden. Above him, women's heads appeared over the terrace railing. Since they were unveiled, he knew them to be slaves. When he pulled himself up to their railing, they cried out and fled.

Cyrus followed swiftly to keep them in sight. The girls darted through swaying curtains. Suddenly the white light of a chamber dazzled him. It came from the flames of many lamps shining against white silk wall curtains, and it shone upon the erect woman motionless on an alabaster throne seat, her feet resting on the snarling heads of two marble lions. At first glimpse she appeared to be the statue of a goddess. Her eyes beneath the arch of her brows might have been tawny opals but they were alive.

The slave girls crouched about her, not touching her. From the outer darkness rumbled the angry roar of the lion, and Cyrus knew that it had been wounded and would presently be slain in the garden. The woman's eyes widened a little and he heard her low voice: "Iron pierces my servant that did no harm to men." The angry eyes turned to Cyrus. "Cleanse thyself!"

At once two of the maid slaves rose to take Cyrus by the arms and lead him gently to an alcove of the chamber where linen cloths hung by a tilted basin of water. This water did not flow but lay stagnant in the gold bowl. Quickly the girls drew off his mantle, and after washing the dirt and blood from his bare arms and legs beneath his kilt, they rubbed his flesh with sweet-smelling handfuls of powdered cedar and frankincense. Then they combed the juniper needles from his hair. They moved gracefully, their slim soft hands caressing his flesh. They smiled at him pleasantly, and the tension in him relaxed. Evidently Mandane had trained her slaves well. Although the woman on the throne had spoken of the slaughtered lion as her servant, and the lion was in truth the animal of the great goddess Ishtar, her voice was the voice of Mandane the queen.

When he returned to the white chamber, his feet making no sound in the soft carpet, the lamps were extinguished and a faint radiance from the curtain touched moving wreaths of incense. The scent struck his nostrils. Mandane sat veiled as before, the veil being a fringed scarf drawn above her head and mouth and falling from her shoulders down her body. Fringed leggings covered her knees. Cyrus was conscious of beauty in the woman but could not conjecture her age nor her will toward him. Mandane fitted into her stage setting well.

His amazed silence seemed to amuse her. "Cyrus, my son," she exclaimed, "I do not know why I shielded you in the hall of the feast except that you were defenseless in your stupid courage. And I have no other son. Yet now a sign has come between us, and in the death of the lion at your coming I see that the sign is from your divine Mother, the Great Goddess." Mandane fell silent in thought; she made no attempt now to pose as a goddess. "I wish I could be certain of the meaning of the sign. Surely the divine one is present to watch over our relationship, and it may be that in protecting you, unwitting, a power has come to both of us."

This simply astonished Cyrus who wondered why Mandane said nothing of the enmity of her lord husband, Astyages. Being a political bride from the court of Babylon, of course, she might have a mind bent upon other things. It was difficult, in the dim light, to watch her eyes, and the incense clogged his throat. Mandane acted more like a woman worshiper musing over an omen in the sacrifice of a victim. He remembered that he had not thanked her.

"Since my birth I have had no living mother," he assured her. "So I give reverence to you, with my heart, for the good will of the most glorious Queen of the Medes."

He thought she laughed a little. In truth, he had made a boorish remark. Mandane tilted her head, and the scarf slipped from the whiteness of her face. "Achaemenian youth, have you ever before ventured from your mountains and your droves of battle horses? Only to Shushan? That is a poor place. I think you will journey far to the great cities; beyond that I have no idea of your fate except that by all indications it will be no ordinary one. Still it rejoices me to have you for a son." She bent toward him and her fingers felt his wrist. "You wear only this talisman of wings over Evil? Nay, let me examine it. A child's trinket, say I. What power ever came down from the sky upon wings and what power can overmaster Evil, rooted deep in the earth?"

The bracelet was indeed no more than a family token, and Anahita, protecting goddess of his valley, revealed herself only in the cold waters of the streams. Mandane's curling hair brushed against his face. It was very dark. "Lady," he said unsteadily, "I have seen much of the Evil, of drought and deserted soil, of pestilence and hunger."

"No more than that, Cyrus, my son?" Again Mandane, although very near him, seemed to go far away in her thought. "There is only the one Lady, the Great Goddess known more to women than to men because only castrated men may serve her altar. You are hardly one of those. Often *she* takes the blood of other men as sacrifice, and often she draws their seed from them to give birth to others. It is evident indeed that fertility rests at her disposal because when

Ishtar—so they name her in Babylon—goes down to *arallu*—to the nether world of vastness ruled by Nergal, the source of Evil, why then the earth above is burned by the sun, and crops wither and water fails and the surface of the earth dies as you have seen it dying."

Now the woman Mandane seemed possessed by her thought, and her soft voice flowed on, telling him that the lovely Ishtar alone dared to go down through the seven gates of hell to the throne of Nergal who waits through the uncounted ages of time for the death of the earth and the triumph of hell. At each of the seven doors of hell the keeper opposed her entrance, and the lovely Lady bribed each keeper and passed on.

"Then she had courage," Cyrus muttered.

"Nay, she had wit. To the first fierce keeper she handed her jeweled crown; to the second she gave her earrings; to the third she handed her necklace of pearls——"

Cyrus felt his blood quicken because Mandane, in telling her story, began to act it out. Her dark hair fell across her bared white throat, and the scarf slipped away as she dropped her strings of pearls to the carpet.

"In the presence of the fourth keeper, she undid her breastband, heavy with gold; to the fifth guardian she gave the bracelets from her wrists and ankles"—Mandane bent down lithely to her feet. "To the sixth she offered her belt of stones of childbirth. Then to the seventh she gave the cloth from her thighs."

The scarf fell away from her body, and she rose to her toes to press the warmth of her body against Cyrus. When his arms gripped her, it surprised him to discover how small she was.

It was late in the night before Mandane drew her scarf about her shoulders and put on her garments, without summoning her maids.

Darkness covered the terrace when she led him out by the hand. Cyrus was hardly conscious of moving except when Mandane moved. When he ventured to speak upon the terrace, he managed to ask only a stupid question. "What befell the—the Lady when at last she reached Nergal on his throne?"

Mandane sighed, holding his hand. "Cyrus, my son, you have

so much to learn—even in holding a woman in your arms. Why, if you must know, when Ishtar at last stood naked before Nergal, his queen at his side screamed with jealousy and unleashed upon Ishtar, like a pack of hounds, blights and diseases in spells from her magic. So was the Lady made captive in hell until the gods above beheld drought coming over the earth, with pestilence. They sent down below a jar of charmed water to pour over the Lady, and they chose a man among mortals to sacrifice, to gain her freedom to return to the earth and restore its greenness and fertility."

At that moment Cyrus could not judge whether the woman at his side invented the story. Later on he realized that the queen from Babylon had told him the truth, as it was taught her. She believed that a life must be sacrificed to Ishtar, and perhaps at that moment she knew whose life it must be.

The drowsiness left her voice when she dismissed him. "Cyrus, because my mind has become clearer, I understand at last the meaning of the omen of the hunted lion. You will journey far and suffer much until royal glory descends upon you. Then you will return to me upon this terrace."

His father had a way of invoking omens to favor what he wished to be done. But Mandane believed her omen. And it seemed to be a joyful thing, to return to this palace to Mandane alone, if his father and Astyages were out of the way.

"Yes," he said, "I will come back."

Mandane nodded as if she also believed it. "What you have to do at the moment," she confided, "is to get out with your life, unlike the lion you loosed." "Achaemenian," she cried sharply, "rouse yourself from dreaming. Take this in your hand."

From somewhere in the darkness Mandane drew a sheathed dagger; its hilt was a woman's head upon the body of a lioness, wrought in gold as he could tell by the softness of the metal. Mandane bade him wear this, her token, in his girdle because it signified the loving protection of the Queen of the Medes, although otherwise it was not very useful as a weapon. "Now go, my son, to the one man who can lead you forth unchallenged. For he, Harpaig, is Kavi-khshatra, commanding all the armed forces, and his command is obeyed by all beneath the scepter of the king. Don't try to trick

Harpaig. It would be easier and much simpler to twist the tail of a wild ox."

When Cyrus made no answer, she pressed her head against his throat, sighing. "Go, and dream of returning victorious, and I shall be foolish enough to do the same."

CYRUS PASSES THE TOWER

When Mandane pushed him away into the darkness, Cyrus went in a daze, his body exulting and his mind confused. A maid took his hand, drawing him down narrow steps that led to the smoldering flame of a lamp. Above it a eunuch drowsed; from behind it stepped a thickset man who scanned Cyrus beneath shaggy brows. He wore a rough leather tunic and a necklet of heavy gold, and his broad pale face was gnarled by fatigue. In silence he motioned to the eunuch who caught up the lamp and hurried into the garden, whereupon the officer fitted a helmet on his head and drew an embroidered cloak over his square shoulders; he pulled Cyrus's neckcloth up over his chin. Walking ahead, the impassive officer, who must have been Harpaig, kept Cyrus in his shadow until they entered a courtyard where white mules drowsed at the shaft of a chariot. The driver jerked out of sleep on his perch and gathered up the reins. By the stars overhead, Cyrus judged that it was then the hour before the stroke of dawn. The cold air cleared his brain and he stopped in his tracks. In his mountains they made no use of clumsy chariots, nor mules either. "And where," he asked, "will this wheeled thing take me?"

The officer's nose seemed to curl down over his twisted beard, and he spat out words with anger. "Where *she* wills you to go." His ringed thumb touched the gold hilt of the dagger in Cyrus's hand, whereupon the Achaemenian thrust it out of sight in his girdle and voiced his anger as a sword strikes against a shield.

"Lord Harpaig, I shall go upon the way I choose, unless you call up more weapon men to hold me captive. Since my father and I entered the gate of your king, we have been treated like hunting dogs, to be fed at the king's command. Am I a prisoner?"

"No." For the first time Harpaig looked full into the eyes of the youth. "Cyrus, prince of Anshan, you can go to where your father chews his beard in anxiety, and he will hurry you home. Or you can go before Astyages at the hour of his first rising to apologize for spilling blood in his hall and breaking your way into his women's chambers. Yes, you can go upon either of those two ways. Astyages, of course, will pat your bowed shoulder and cry out his forgiveness —to the heir of the horses of Anshan. Then, Cyrus, he will take care to make your soul sick within you, because you have committed a crime greater than murder or adultery; you have stupidly injured his dignity, in the majesty of the great court of Agbatana."

The temper that Cyrus held in check burst out. "The majesty of Agbatana is a word in the mouth of fools, it is froth blown from a beer bowl, it is nothing. Can dignity cover up fear as your fine cloak covers your dirt? Do men hide behind mighty stone walls unless they fear attack? These guards at your gates are foreign folk hired with silver. Astyages cannot make my soul sick because it is fouled already with loathing."

For an instant Harpaig took thought, the lines creasing over his half-shut eyes. "Your rhetoric is honest enough," he said grudgingly.

"Then give me a thousand Persian Asvaran, and I will ride over your regiments of spearmen; I will pen your royal court within its walls."

A smile twitched at Harpaig's beard. "I am taking you to a thousand Persian horse bowmen."

Amazed, Cyrus waited for him to explain, and Harpaig did so bluntly. Mandane the Queen had decided that Cyrus would seek neither the aid of his father nor the mercy of the Medes. He would take neither of those two paths to safety but would find a third way of his own. But what way? "To my mind," Harpaig added, "you will be entirely safe among your countrymen, who will certainly greet you joyfully in the manner to which you are accustomed, and they will also dispose of any enemy who approaches you. So far, so good. Yet obviously, Lord Cyrus, you cannot sit in camp at the gates of Agbatana as you did"—his dark eyes glinted— "at Shushan. Therefore, this particular regiment will take the field. In fact, it loads its equipment this morning."

"To go whither?"

Harpaig nodded toward the north. "That way. Through the gate of the snow mountains. There beyond the light of our civilization and the Salt Sea rove innumerable barbaric tribes. You can gain much glory by attacking them because no one will ever know exactly what happened in that limbo—and it will add to the dignity of Astyages, King of the Medes, to have his frontiers extended by another conquest. At least it will be written down as a conquest. And then, after a year or so of that, your behavior in the king's hall and hunting park and harem will be forgotten, or at least obscured by other events. Do you agree?"

Cyrus was conscious of the voice of warning of his fravashi, heard at his right hand. There was something familiar in Harpaig's offer; the queen herself had spoken of his returning victorious. Had the two of them talked together of his fate? Surely, then, they had done so before that nightfall.

"If you doubt my faith," put in Harpaig quickly, "I myself will take you to the encampment of the Persians and my son will join you at the pass through the mountains."

Cyrus did not stop to consider why he had said that. It tired his mind to think of such complicated plans. The mention of far mountains stirred his longing. He could not draw back from fear.

"Well, then, commander of the Medes," he replied, "I will go."

Cyrus sprang into the chariot, and the driver jerked at the reins. They sped down the slope from the palace as gray light came into the sky on the right hand. On the left hand, the side of Evil, a shaft of the sun struck the snow summit of lofty Alwand, turning it blood red. Cyrus did not heed this ominous sign because he still felt the warmth of the arms of Mandane. Nor did he think twice of the omen of the watchtower.

This tower rose into sight at the north gate. In Agbatana only the Medes were allowed to dwell within the outer wall; other peoples had their towns and camps and caravanserais outside. The tower itself was being built to the glory of Astyages, son of Cyaxares, although it was actually copied from the great ziggurat of Babylon that reached toward the sky, being known to many as the Tower of Babel, which meant the gate of the gods. So its first story of dark asphalt made a firm foundation; its second story gleamed white, in purity; its third tapering story was red as the blood of mankind, rising to the fourth story of scarlet, and—against the sky —the fifth of deepest purple and the sixth of pure silver. The final summit of gold had not been built as yet on Astyages's tower.

At that hour no workmen appeared on the scaffolding. Only one living figure stood apart, apparently a pilgrim praying to the sunrise.

Beside this silent man Harpaig caused the chariot to stop, and he scanned him attentively while guards at the wall beyond hastened to throw open the gate for their commander. Cyrus did not know what to think of the many-hued structure spiraling up to the sky on his left hand. "It is a long way to climb up this watch-tower," he said.

"Yet it reminds everyone who comes here," Harpaig explained absently, "of the glory of the King of the Medes. When the crowning summit of gold is in place, the empire of the Medes will be established."

At this the pilgrim in the gray robe turned on them with his arms still upraised.

"When the summit is crowned with gold," he cried, "the kingdom of the Medes will be broken apart and cease to be!"

"You say that?"

"So said Zarathustra."

Then Cyrus recognized him—the young Magian who sought refuge in the cave over Parsagard. At once Harpaig called to the soldiers at the gate and they came running, trying to lower their heads and spears at the same time in fear of their commander in chief. At once Harpaig bade them strip the Magian, bind his arms to an ox yoke upon his shoulders, and scourge him until his white body turned red. "This Zarathustra was a prophet of the rabble," he assured Cyrus and glanced at him fleetingly. "A rebel, and stubborn."

Reflecting that the Magian, being a fugitive, had not shared the hospitality of the Achaemenian homestead, Cyrus restrained his impulse to speak for him. When the soldiers handled the youth savagely to please their officer, Cyrus observed: "If I were Astyages

I would summon this wanderer before me to ask what thing made him wish to rebel against my rule."

When they thrust the heavy yoke upon his neck, the Magian's dark eyes sought Cyrus. But he did not speak.

"You are not Astyages," said Harpaig and waved their chariot on through the gate.

Cyrus should have taken warning from this happening. Yet he still felt the false security of his life as king's son in the mountains above the cities. He sensed that the Medes of Astyages made use of lies at will, and that Mandane, for some woman's reason, had tried to bind him to her will, while Harpaig had hidden much from him. He did not add together the circumstances that Volka, his bodyguard, had been disposed of nor that he was being led from his father's sight, out of the city of Agbatana, to journey into strange heights and on to the prairies of the nomads "where no one will ever know what happened."

From that limbo Cyrus the Achaemenian was not meant to return. The malevolence of aged and politic Astyages had decreed his death as an unsuitable heir to the mild Cambyses. Astyages preferred to have a helpless grandchild succeed Cambyses.

When Cyrus whirled into the encampment of the horse archers, all misgivings left him. The uproar over the baggage beasts, the neighing of the proud Nisayan steeds exhilarated him like a breath of mountain air. The Persian warriors ran to his chariot, shouting: "Now praise to all the gods, the Shepherd is here!"

First of all, Emba, keeper of his horses, raced to the chariot's side and knelt to seize Cyrus's foot. Men already mounted tossed up their pennoned lances, and it was a meeting of friendship and good will.

"Now will you believe in my good faith?" cried Harpaig. "In the north my son awaits you with guides. May Ishtar and Shamash guard you both." With that, being a shrewd judge of the proper moment, he drove off in the chariot.

So it happened that Cyrus, with all good will, girded on a sword again and departed upon the journey which was also a war of the Medes, although a very small one. He continued to wear the dagger of Mandane because many warriors admired it.

Almost at once he had good tidings on the road. A courier from Agbatana overtook the regiment, bringing the congratulations of King Astyages and a message that a second son had been born to Cyrus, after the thirtieth year of his life, at Parsagard. His wife had named the boy Bardiya, which meant Fruitful. Cyrus did not relish that name but he could do nothing to change it.

When winter storms closed the passes behind the marching warriors, Cyrus no longer had news of the cities. He became as one blind, following an unknown road. He did not hear of the death of Nebuchadnezzar nor of the freeing from prison of Jehoiakim, King of the Hebrews, in Babylon. The message that Gubaru sent from Shushan to warn Cyrus, as he had promised, reached only Cambyses pottering in his gardens. Because, by the death of the great king of Babylon, Astyages the Mede waxed in strength and power, Gubaru, after delaying a little, sent earth and water as tokens of submission to Agbatana.

In Babylon itself there was strife between the priests of Marduk and the descendants of former kings. A prophet of the Hebrews, a certain Isaiah, the second of that name, beheld this burden upon Babylon. Isaiah lifted up his voice: "*Howl ye all, for the day of the Lord is at hand. Every man shall turn to his own people, and flee, everyone, to his own land. And Babylon, the glory of kingdoms, the beauty of the Chaldees' excellence, shall be as when God overthrew Sodom and Gomorrah.*"

Few stopped to listen to Isaiah in the alleys of Babylon. For he spoke to them as if the words came from Yahweh, the Lord. "*I will stir up the Medes against them. Their bows also shall slay the young men, and they shall have no pity.*" Isaiah called upon the listeners to look to the north and to harken to the mountains. "*The noise of a multitude in the mountains, of kingdoms of nations gathered together. The Lord of hosts mustereth the host of the battle.*"

In truth the strength of Astyages grew in the mountains and spread over Ararat, the Urartaeans, and Manneans, and Scythians.

Then Cambyses died of a sickness in Parsagard, with only unwitting grandchildren to stand by his couch.

TWO

The Oath of Cyrus

THE mountains served as a refuge for peoples. Cyrus had come to believe that. In the far north among the great Blue Mountains he found that to be as true as within the highlands around peaceful Parsagard. Wars and epidemics, as well as migrations, seemed to take their course like the larger rivers along the wide plains, especially those that led to the seas. So, for that matter, did civilization with its walled cities and frequented roads. When peoples wanted to escape for various reasons from the conflict of the lowlands, they sought the isolation of the heights and fared well enough as long as they managed to keep alive there.

At the Blue Mountains Cyrus had left the pale of civilization. These ranges rose to such heights that when seen from afar they appeared to be blue ramparts. Yet in this wilderness without roads he came with his army upon a sign of the Great Goddess. While following a ravine to the north, the riders passed beneath a rock face whereon other figures carved in the white stone marched with them. Some of them seemed to be gods of the heights because they stood on crouched figures that represented mountains. Most of the attendants were women with covered heads and long skirts. They followed after a crowned goddess poised on a lion. Cyrus recognized Ishtar of Babylon in this different guise, somewhat overgrown with lichens. Vartan, at his side, said he knew nothing about these gods because they belonged to the Old People who had disappeared from the country, leaving only their name of Hatti, or

Hittites—their name and the ruins of mighty stone citadels. Vartan did not think much of gods who allowed their worshipers to be scattered like dust in the wind. But possibly, he admitted, these Hittite deities had been displeased. He understood that the Great Goddess was hard to please, and her power extended to every land. "Even Lord Cyrus the Achaemenian," he said obliquely, "wears her sign upon his dagger."

Vartan was Harpaig's son, who had joined the Persian horsemen in the foothills. He proved to be an Armenian—which meant that his father, an Armenian, commanded the armed forces of the Medes. Like his father, he masked his thoughts and appeared too grieved ever to laugh from joy. His brow furrowed as he explained the omnipresence of Ishtar the Mother. "Women, and not men, know her mysteries. And women have no proper nation or fealty to a single king. If a land is conquered, the males are slain or driven off to slave labor, but the females survive and merely fetch their cooking pots and children to the hearth homes of their conquerors and breed new infants. Perhaps they may lay spells against their new husbands or poison them; still they do not die themselves. I am never surprised to find a Samaritan wench drawing water in Ur of the Chaldeans, especially if she is good-looking. Perhaps the Great Goddess has something to do with this matter. I have heard that beyond the White Mountains, out in the steppes, a whole tribe of women survive to ride around the tombs of their husbands. As to that, I do not know the facts but I suspect the Great Goddess will have little mercy on a man who offends her."

Evidently Vartan had little fear of the goddess. The Armenians had invaded the Blue Mountains only a few generations before and they were still building stone towers for dwellings in their farmlands; surly and brave, they marched swiftly on foot, wearing some good metal armor but carrying no bows. Several regiments followed Vartan willingly enough through the plateau where the Old People worshiped a solitary white mountain called Urartu, or Ararat. From the snow summit of Ararat, smoke rose like a beacon fire into the clouds, although no human beings could have kindled such a fire. But the Armenians did not desire to march against the tribes beyond Ararat, saying that these Kurds were barbarians without wealth in their villages and in consequence no spoil **worth** the effort of taking it.

Cyrus had been ordered by Harpaig to punish all robber bands along the roads, while he carried the victorious standards of the Medes and the Persians through to the Sea of Grass in the far north. Vartan, however, saw no sense in carrying a king's standards to new lands unless wealth could be gained at the end of the journey. By wealth he meant precious iron or gold or jewels valuable in trade with barbarians who coveted such ornaments. Unless they enriched themselves by the long journey, he argued, his warriors would be better occupied in planting winter grain on their farms. It seemed to Cyrus that these Armenians served Astyages more with their lips than their hearts; they admitted his authority without exerting themselves to strengthen it. He began to wonder why Harpaig, their chieftain, served Astyages.

"Your father," he replied, "gave me an order, and I shall carry it out as best I can."

His own warriors pressed on willingly to the north because at the end of that first summer the hunting was good, the deer fat, and Cyrus saw to it that they followed good grazing within the high valleys. He soon realized that the carrying out of a conquest was more a task of keeping the horses in condition and planning food for his followers than of brandishing weapons with war shouts. At any prospect of fighting, his experienced commanders took charge of the horsemen, aware that the young Shepherd lacked battle cunning. While this was true enough, Cyrus understood that he could not allow it; he must lead them in every situation or not at all.

The clash that he anticipated with his officers and Vartan came at the crossing of the river in the Hollow Land.

The expedition had passed the watershed of the Blue Mountains, and the streams flowed to the north. And there below the pines stretched the Hollow Land—a deep valley threaded by a single river, golden with ripe grain, speckled gray with sheep herds between the villages. Beyond this sunken valley reared loftier mountains with snow summits.

When the invaders followed a trail down to the river, it led them to a ford. And here on the far bank the inhabitants stood guard, weapons in hand. They were heavy barbarians, wearing animal pelts and armed with hunting spears, without shields. Cyrus noticed women pressing behind them, clutching knives. That meant the valley folk would offer a desperate resistance at the river, which was probably their only line of defense. Its swift gray current swirled around boulders in the ford. Vartan said these were Iberian herders, too stupid to be afraid; they named their river The Shepherd because it nourished their flocks.

The Persian commanders rode up to survey the river barrier and to consult with the Armenian captains as to the best way to force it. When they came to an agreement, they explained to Vartan that his Armenian warriors would make a show of charging across the ford. Meanwhile, the Mardians and Dayans of the horse archers would detach themselves and detour swiftly to another ford up the river, to cross unobserved. Then showing themselves unexpectedly on the other bank, the Persians would scourge the Iberians with their arrows, under cover of which the Armenian foot could rush the ford behind their iron shields. The barbarians, caught between two attacks, would mill around, an easy prey to the soldiers.

Cyrus judged this plan to be effective but too bloody. He needed to act instantly to prevent it because the trained soldiers were already in motion, girding themselves for battle. "An omen!" he shouted, and when the others stared at him, "This river bears my name and it summons me. Stand where you are!"

They fidgeted restlessly. One, the Mardian commander, proud of his valor, reined away impatiently and his horse changed pace, stumbling. It caught Cyrus's attention. Gripping its rein, he bent to raise the Nisayan's near hoof and saw, as he expected, a crack in the rim of the horn caused by some sharp stone. He ordered the rider: "You who whip on a lame horse—dismount."

The man laughed. "Nay, Cyrus—am I to fight afoot?"

Cyrus seized on his words. "Yes, as I do. Behold!" To the others, staring in surprise, he repeated: "Stand where you are. So say I, Cyrus the Achaemenian."

Going down to the water, he slipped off his sword belt and dropped the mantle from his shoulders. This was no time to argue, it was a time to act alone. Visibly unarmed, with empty hands outstretched, he ran into the flood, and the water sucked at his knees and waist. He felt assured of what he was doing, as if his fravashi urged him forward. Another man splashed at his elbow and he saw Vartan struggling to follow him. They strained to keep their feet in the flood and Cyrus came out first on the far bank where the shaggy Iberians clustered, gripping their spears. Evidently the barbarians saw nothing dangerous in two unarmed men coming among them, and when Cyrus sat down on a boulder, their bearded heads bent to peer at him closely. "Hear me," he urged them, "and let there be peace between us, while I discuss the quartering of the troops of King Astyages among you."

Because they did not understand his speech, the Iberians made no answer until Vartan, standing beside Cyrus, spoke to them. Then the people of the Hollow Land gathered about to hear. On the other bank, Persian and Armenian warriors perforce kept silent and motionless. Thus, in due time, by Vartan's aid a compact was arrived at for a truce and the provisioning of Cyrus's armed force, with grazing for his horses.

"It was wrong," observed Cyrus, pleased, "to attack these people without first talking it over." Then he laughed impulsively. "By the Seven Stars that guard us, we were lucky."

Vartan shook his dark head moodily. "You were!" He touched the shining hilt of Mandane's dagger, in Cyrus's girdle cloth. "Lift it up, and you will see."

Startled, the Achaemenian raised the gold-figured hilt. A sigh went through the thronged barbarians and their eyes fastened on it. "They obey the sign of the Great Goddess," said Vartan, and smiled.

Angered, Cyrus started to throw the dagger into the river that was his namesake. He had no desire to be obeyed because he carried the queen's token. Then he reflected that it had aided him in getting his followers safely across the embattled ford, and he replaced it in his girdle.

When the Asvaran commanders reached his side, they protested instantly because he had run ahead of them across the river. Cyrus agreed that in future he would consult with them before acting. From that hour he held the rein of decision in his hand, on the battlefield as well as in camp, and never let it go.

THE HOLLOW LAND

Cyrus made gifts to the expectant Iberian chieftains from the baggage wagons—bright alabaster bowls for drinking the wine of grapes they offered him and silver lamps to light the feast of that evening. The barbarians made music on flutes, and their young men danced clumsily, leaping while swinging great shields on their arms. Being so barbaric, they passed without thought from attempting to slay the invaders to urging hospitality upon them. Cyrus was careful to warn all the heroes among the Persian warriors that they were now guests of these dwellers in the Hollow Land and must accordingly keep their weapons sheathed. To compensate the pride of the Mardian he had accused of laming a horse, he gave the man authority to enforce this good conduct upon all the Persians.

It was not hard to do. The land was heavy with ripe crops, with boar and elk to offer sport to hunters in the uplands. Moreover, the Iberian women had fresh faces and the grace of animals in their lithe bodies. During the welcoming feast they surged around the warriors to finger the embroidery on their linen shirts. In spite of the language difficulty, the forthright Iberian women invited the warrior guests to a welcome within their houses. In entering a house, the women hung the bow case of a guest on the door. They meant no harm by this act of disarming a warrior because their husbands stayed away obligingly as long as a bow case hung on the door. However, very soon Cyrus noticed that the best-looking Iberian women appeared with the soldiers' bracelets on their wrists.

On the other hand, the Armenians were not so content. They

had no yearning to hunt wild boar or elk; but they longed for their own homes instead of the stone huts set in the Iberian hillsides. Vartan meditated in silence over the smoldering brazier of the house that had been given him. "Cyrus," he observed, after one spell of brooding, "I am told that Persians speak only the truth, although it must be inconvenient to do so, and you are not only a Persian but an Achaemenian, the proudest of their clans; not only an Achaemenian but a king's son."

Cyrus assented and waited. He had learned that Armenians never spoke outright of what preyed on their minds.

"Now if you return to Agbatana and say that you have conquered the Iberian land for Astyages, it will be a lie, for you have not managed to do that."

"No, I have not done that."

"You have contrived to win over these Iberians to friendship with Cyrus, not with the King of the Medes."

"Yes."

"Is it permitted"—the lines deepened in Vartan's sallow face—"to ask why?"

Cyrus took no heed of the other's sarcasm. "The laws of the Medes run only to their frontiers, and it seems clear to me that those frontiers remain very vague. Yet we passed them at sacred Mount Ararat. Now outside the frontiers there is a different law, and it is known as the king's law. If your Astyages should ever ride out—oh, into this Sea of Grass beyond us, he would give judgment from his throne seat by virtue of this king's law alone. Now I am here alone, but as son of Cambyses I must judge all matters that come before me. So I shall make my own decisions in these barbaric lands, and what I shall tell of them at Agbatana will be the truth." Cyrus touched the Armenian's hand. "What is troubling your mind?"

Winter, Vartan said, would confine them all in the Hollow Land when snow closed the mountain passes. His followers saw no use in hibernating like bears among the Iberian savages until the spring thaw. Cyrus understood very well that the Armenians resented his order against pillaging the valley people. They also made too great a number for the Iberians to feed all the winter. "Then take them back to their villages and their families," he decided.

If Vartan had any thought of claiming the desirable valley for his own, Cyrus believed, he would not agree. Vartan merely relapsed into silence again, nursing Cyrus's hunting spear across his knees—for they had exchanged spears at their first meeting as a pledge of good faith. "Cyrus," he said at length, "you are either a fool following a path through a dream, or you are one of the shrewdest of men. If you are the fool I believe you to be, I shall take care to have your body fittingly embalmed and sent back with honor to Parsagard to an Achaemenian tomb and forgetfulness."

Cyrus laughed. "And if I am wise?"

Vartan communed with the embers in the brazier. "Then I will be much surprised," he admitted.

The following morning he mustered his war bands, with their equipment packed, and started them back across the ford. With their faces turned homeward, they went at a swift pace. When they had passed, the son of Harpaig did not follow. Beside him there remained only his body servant and horse-tender and the half-dozen Scythian archers who had kept to themselves during the journey. "I will stay at your side," he informed the Shepherd. "Did we not exchange spears in pledge of friendship?"

"And these Scythians?" Cyrus had wondered at their presence on the march.

They were the guides, Vartan explained, sent by Astyages to lead them into the steppes. "Like you, Cyrus," he said thoughtfully, "I obey orders, but in a way of my own."

Cyrus did not know what to make of that. The Scythians chosen by Astyages as guides seemed to be like all other Scythian nomads; they spent their time grooming their swift-paced horses or shining up the ornaments of their saddlecloths. At intervals they disappeared for days, probably to hunt in the uplands, but always found their way back to the encampment of the Persians. His servant Emba the Hyrcanian said that they counted the days until they sighted their native Sea of Grass. Volka could have told Cyrus more about these hunters but Volka had been slain in Astyages's hall.

Cyrus did not hibernate like a bear that winter because he found much to discover in the pleasant Hollow Land. He did not believe that the river bore his name by any coincidence. Some passing Aryan had named the river The Shepherd. As he suspected, the Iberians assured him that the Aryans had migrated through the valley in a remote time, and it had taken a generation to recover from their passing.

He explored the valley to learn the reason for its well-being. It had no slaves to plow the earth, which, in fact, hardly needed plowing to grow a harvest. It seemed to have no sickness. Cyrus found this very different from the Elamite land, also warm and fertile, which still bore the scars of the passing of the Assyrian army. Here the earth was not dying. These Iberians made merry with the wine of their vines. Cyrus understood how their mountains protected them, and he dreamed fleetingly of making them allies with other mountain folk under the rule, presumably, of the Medes and the Persians. Yet even in his dreaming he did not wish to alter the well-being of the Iberians who enjoyed all the benefits of the creator of the earth. Cyrus counted off those benefits—warmth of the sun, clear water, the labor of tamed animals upon a very fertile soil.

Vartan complained that these people gave up the ground floor of their dwellings to their animals and slept themselves in the loft, and he could not sleep with swine rooting beneath him; furthermore, he pointed out that the Iberians had few valuables to trade—only hides and some copper they did not know how to work; they had built no highway for traffic, or city or temple. As for the eager women, Vartan said they had little more intelligence than water buffalo.

Vartan would not believe that these women served the Great Goddess. No men seemed to be missing, carried off as a sacrifice. Perhaps the women stared at Cyrus's dagger merely because it had the sheen of pure gold. When Vartan questioned them as to where such gold might be found, they simply pointed west and said, "There!"

VARTAN'S GOLDEN FLEECE

So it happened that after the spring thaw Cyrus led his expeditionary force to the west, partly to satisfy Vartan but also to explore on his own account the source of his river.

They found a giant land. They climbed beneath snow peaks until the land fell away to the west and to the shore of a still blue sea. The shore bore the name of Colchis, and the inhabitants fled like goats before the armed riders. The horsemen could not pursue over the crags. It was strange to behold the fire of the sunset upon motionless water.

They came upon two stranger things. In the shallows of the racing streams sheepskins had been pegged down, like carpets to ride over. These always had the fleece side up, for no apparent reason. Then, too, the Persian Asvaran sighted their first ships, tiny transports of wood moving lazily in the shifting air, with tent cloths hung to their poles. Later at the shore, when the soldiers had persuaded the shy goat folk to bring them offerings of fruit and grain, they discovered that the ships belonged to traders who spoke an unknown tongue.

Cyrus called these shipmen the Vase Painters because they exchanged their carefully-painted jars for the gold of the Colchians. The Vase Painters had curled beards beneath their swarthy, alert faces; they smelled of oil of sesame, and they carried their weapons to the trading, watching for a chance to overpower the Colchian tradesmen and carry them off as slaves to the oared vessels. When the wind did not blow, the Vase Painters could move their ships by oars. They were both fierce and argumentative and seemed to be Aryans of a kind, because they named themselves as Achaeans, from the cities of Miletus and Sparta. The Spartans, it seemed, were more warriors than traders. When Cyrus learned that the Spartans did not ride horses to battle, he had no further interest in them. These western traders disgusted him because they exerted themselves to set up a market place where they did nothing but argue fiercely about payment for their vases and trinkets. After that

INDIAN

BABYLONIAN

ARABIAN

LYDIAN

Heads of varied peoples, subjects of Achaemenian Empire (559-330 B.C.). Detail from the Procession of the Tribute Bearers, Persepolis. *Courtesy Oriental Institute, Chicago.*

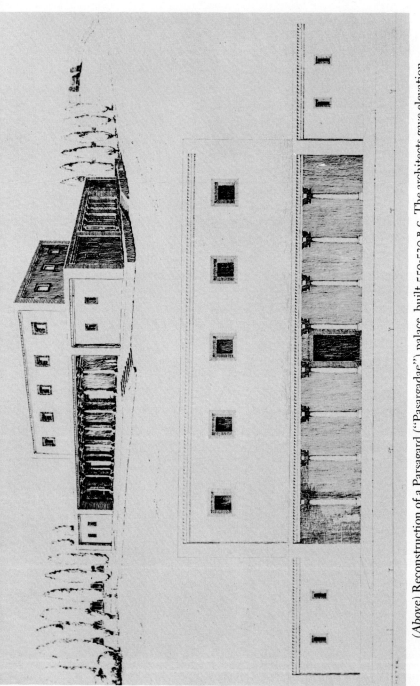

(Above) Reconstruction of a Parsagard ("Pasargadae") palace, built 559-520 B.C. The architects gave elevation and lofty lighting to the central hall. (Below) Reconstruction of palace façade. Except for the bulls'-head capitals of the entry columns and the varied stonework, there is no ornamentation. By F. Krefter; from Herzfeld–Iran in the Ancient East.

they amused themselves by drinking wine and arguing among themselves about unknown goddesses and the beauties of their native cities. However, they let fall one remark that Vartan seized upon.

These wandering tradesmen spoke of the "golden fleece." When Vartan asked to see a golden fleece, they merely pointed out some Colchians at a safe distance, shaking dry sheepskins over a great bronze caldron. After watching this done, Vartan remembered the wet sheepskins fastened in the rushing streams, and he reasoned that the Colchians secured their gold, or much of it, by collecting the heavy flakes, washed down by water, in the coarse wool of the skins. After this discovery, he was eager to return to the upper slopes to gather up the golden fleece of the Colchian streams.

Emba also begged Cyrus to march east instead of west. The big Hyrcanian had been born at the edge of a sea which he called the Hyrcanian Sea. Emba tasted the water off the Colchian shore and declared this was not the water of his sea. He swore to Cyrus that on his own shore strange gods had emerged from the depths of the earth to sear the land with fire, and that their fires still burned with everlasting flame.

Cyrus then led them to the east, hoping to explore the mouth of his river. On the way, Vartan stripped the sheepskins from the streams they crossed. But when he melted down the particles of gold combed from the dried skins, he had only a small ingot, easily carried in one hand.

"What will you do with it?" Cyrus asked, amused at so much labor bestowed on so little precious metal.

"Pay others to get more gold," said Vartan.

For the rest of that summer the expedition fought its way through barbarians fiercer than the Iberians and wilder than the Colchians, and Cyrus needed all his craft in getting food for his men and grazing for the Nisayan horses as they pressed toward the rising sun, until human beings ceased to appear around them and wild life dwindled. Great winds tore at them as they descended toward the Hyrcanian Sea; storms of dust strangled them, and the earth turned to yellow powder, smelling of sulphur, and black lava upon which the horses slipped and fell. Far ahead the wind whirled up smoke and beneath the smoke gleamed the red of fires that burned without ceasing. The Asvaran went forward unwillingly because they considered this shore to be an entrance to the nether world where even fire was accursed. Evidently they were drawing near the lair of Azhi Dahaka. Emba had told them the truth.

When the grass of the earth withered and vanished, Cyrus gave command to turn back to keep the cherished horses alive.

"There is nothing of good omen here," he said. "Take me instead to this Sea of Grass, and may it offer a good end to our journey!"

Whereupon Vartan called in the Scythian guides. Silently, at his order, they turned into a gorge leading north. After many days they began to climb upon heights rising into the clouds. The earth became moist again, with snow shining above them through the cloud veil; the horses cropped lichens and moss. When the clouds parted to the north, the Scythians reined in and pointed. Ahead of them and far below stretched a level green line that was not sea but earth.

(It is evident that Cyrus's expedition crossed the southern range of the Caucasus to winter in the low-lying valley of modern Tiflis, where the river still bears the name of the Kura. In his western march Cyrus reached the shore of the Black Sea where Ionian Greeks had trading settlements. The eastern march of the Persians took them unmistakably to the bare, oil-saturated shore near modern Baku on the sea known then as the Hyrcanian, today the Caspian. Surface oil burned here for many centuries. Then, heading north, Cyrus crossed the higher range of the Caucasus and came out on the steppes that are now Russian.)

THE SCYTHIAN TOMB

In the first moon of their riding across the great plain, the Persians realized that all human inhabitants were fleeing before them. They came upon ashes of long-burning fires in campsites leveled by the hoofs of horses and cattle and scarred by the wheels of carts. No natives remained to greet them or attack them.

At one encampment the embers still smoked, amid a confusion of leather thongs and clay bowls and bright red haircloth of tents. Cyrus picked up a whetstone with a gold-inlaid hilt, and he decided that the vanished occupants of the place were Scythian nomads who had fled in haste only a few hours before. His captive Scythian guides said nothing, as usual. At least, they told him as always that after a few marches he would come to a king's settlement with roofed dwellings.

Cyrus began to meditate about that. After leaving the last river of the mountains, he had not seen a single house. Apparently the dwellers in the Sea of Grass were all nomads who defended themselves by riding off with their property. The Asvaran were in high spirits because they had never before come upon such grazing; the grass rose to the knees of the riders, and clover burst through the gray mesh of tamarisks. Under the wind the immensity of grass rippled like the waters of a calm river and stirred with leaping antelopes. There was meat in plenty and the Nisayans waxed sleek and restless. The Asvaran made a jest of riding through this new kind of paradise without visible end.

When he heard them laughing about this one evening, Cyrus identified the cause of his own uneasiness. He no longer knew exactly where he was. In his mountain homeland he had never lacked for familiar landmarks. For the last days even the snow summits of the White Mountains had disappeared into the plain behind him. By studying the pattern of the seven guardian stars every evening when they first appeared, Cyrus was fairly certain of his direction, a little west of north. Tradition related that the ancestral homeland of the Aryans lay far to the east of north. How far? The guides, of course, could not say. Cyrus's instinct beckoned him toward the east, which was also the side of good omen on his right hand. Why were the Scythians drawing him toward the sunset? They seemed to go on willingly, because they might, if they so desired, disappear any night into the Sea of Grass. And if they left him, whither would Cyrus lead his men?

"Why worry?" Vartan asked when Cyrus spoke of their route. "You can't very well miss the White Mountains if you turn back. Or if you do, we'll tumble into one of the inland seas. Now that you speak of it, I see no gain whatever in riding further. We can certainly assure Astyages that we have ridden through all the Scythians of the great plains, and he will be happy to add the Sea of Grass to his conquests."

Something in the words heightened Cyrus's anxiety. It was not like Vartan to be indifferent; but perhaps the Armenian was simply weary of the monotony of their marches, while he—Cyrus—felt a leader's responsibility for his men. By now he realized that as long as he commanded an army, he would not be free from anxiety.

Soon after, they rode into the ambush.

At the hour of sunset the Asvaran were unloading the wagons by a wellspring in a hollow, and Cyrus dismounted to lead his charger on to look for a sheltered place to picket the Nisayans for the night. Emba and others followed idly. Arrows hissed through the air around them. A shaft tore through Cyrus's leather cape, painfully searing the skin under his arm.

The missiles seemed to come from an oak-grown knoll in front of the Persians, who shouted in surprise. Cyrus picked up the arrow that had drawn his blood and realized as he did so that it had fallen a pace ahead of him. Mounting hastily, he glanced back at Emba and a Scythian and a few Germanians who were preparing to ride out against the wood where hostile bowmen must be concealed. Yet the arrow that grazed him appeared to come from his back.

Cyrus restrained his followers from riding into the failing light. That night the invaluable horses were picketed within the line of the sentinels.

No mist arose on the windy plains. The rising sun drove the shadows from the ground instantly. In the moment of this clear light, Cyrus sent out two companies of his warriors, as if to hunt, to right and left. The bows were strung in the cases at their hips; Cyrus took the lead of one party, and when the Persians came up to the wooded knoll, they fanned out swiftly and closed in upon it, drawing their bows, as if to start wild beasts from a lair.

Instead of beasts, three slim riders broke from cover to race away. The experienced Nisayans, however, swerved like hawks in the air and overran the shaggy ponies of the steppe dwellers. One rider from the ambush was transfixed by an arrow; the others were knocked from their mounts by the charging Nisayans and were caught by noosed ropes as they tried to run. They fought savagely with knives and teeth until they were bound. They seemed to be fair of face and undersized; dark wool garments clung close to their limbs and their long hair streamed from silver headbands. They had the soft hair of Aryans.

When a warrior pulled the arrow from the slain Scythian, he found that the body had the breasts of a woman. The two captives also proved to be women, who uttered no word except to scream defiance. Cyrus examined the arrows left in their quivers and satisfied himself that these were ornamented in a different pattern than the one that had nearly slain him. The women had been foolish to keep watch during the night from their cover.

His warriors wondered what tribe sent out its wives to war for their husbands.

"It may well be," observed Vartan, "that these combative females have no husbands."

He had heard of a tribe in the Sea of Grass made up of women who attacked intruding men and slew their horses as well, possibly to make a sacrifice of blood to their Great Goddess. The guides insisted that the women archers belonged to an ancient tribe hostile to their own, the Royal Scythians.

After meditating on this happening, Cyrus called the captive girls before him and offered them food and drink, which they would not touch. Their eyes reminded him of trapped deer. He then asked, gesturing, in what direction he should go to reach the White Mountains—for he wished to depart from the great plain. They understood him because one pointed away from the sunrise. Thereupon, unexpectedly, his Scythian guides begged him to set free the captive girls with their horses.

Instead of doing so, Cyrus led out his Asvaran that morning straight toward the sunrise. He took the lead himself.

"Has your fravashi summoned you this way," Vartan wondered, "or does Lord Cyrus the Achaemenian seek more women warriors." Only in sarcasm did the Armenian address Cyrus in this way. "Neither your captives nor our guides are pleased."

"It never hurts," Cyrus answered absently, "to do the opposite of what your enemy wishes."

Yet it led them to a calamity. By midday they sighted an odd mound in the steppe. It was round as an inverted bowl and ringed about by dark objects from which wide-winged birds flew up. Presently the objects were seen to be mounted warriors posted as if on guardian duty. Cyrus circled the mound before approaching and then beheld the dismal truth that these sentinels were dead men on the backs of carcasses of horses propped up on stakes. Lances and shields hung on the dried-up bodies, and small bells chimed about them when the wind stirred.

They must have remained here at their post for years. Yet each warrior sat his charger with all his weapons tied in proper place. Cyrus wondered who had ministered to the dead guardians of the mound, and why. Then Vartan shouted with excitement and led him through the blind watchers up to the summit of the grassy dome. Looking down, they perceived that the grass on the dome differed from the wild growth of the plain and that other smaller mounds lay in a circle about the great dome of earth.

"A Scythian tomb!" cried the Armenian. "And by its size I judge that a rich and mighty chieftain was buried in the ground beneath us."

Looking farther, Cyrus beheld no human life out on the steppe. By experience, however, he knew that numbers of steppe dwellers might be moving about unseen in the gullies screened by sage and tamarisk. So he posted watchers on the summit of the burial mound before he rode down, to find Vartan at work with drivers and grooms clearing the tangle of brush from a single gray slab of granite. Vartan said that no such rock was to be found in this plain; therefore, it must have been fetched hither by the Scythians to block the entrance to the tomb. With ropes and poles the rock slab was overturned, and the workers started digging out the earth beneath. The Asvaran gathered to watch curiously. Being warriors born, none of them would touch a spade.

Soon the diggers came upon a door of logs of wood. Then the sentries above them cried a warning. Turning his horse, Cyrus saw women warriors emerging from the brush; several hundred of them paced their shaggy horses toward the mound, keeping their bows and spears in hand. It was strange to watch these long-haired riders coming out of nowhere, but Cyrus judged them to be no match for his veteran regiment.

One came forward to within half bowshot. Her hair gleamed with the gold of ripe wheat, her shield bore a device of a stag's head, and her slim body was sheathed in blue Chinese silk. She appeared to be no older than Cyrus. When she cried out, he could not understand her words and summoned a Scythian guide to explain them, which the man did after a fashion.

She asked for a truce between herself and the king of the invaders. She gave her name and rank: Tymiris, daughter of Gesir, the King of the Sarmatian Scythians. She—Tymiris—claimed that this was Sarmatian land and that her father waited in the tomb to return to life again.

"Agree to the truce," Cyrus told his Scythian. "What other thing does she want?"

Then Tymiris tossed back her hair and spoke swiftly as a rushing stream. The interpreter grunted that she was telling her life history, on behalf of her mother the queen who also waited in the mound. It seemed that her father, Gesir, had ruled with his Sarmatians from the White Mountains to the desert of Red Sands until the coming of the Royal Scythians on their heels. For a time the Sarmatians had held back the invaders. Then these Scythians from the east had called for a peace and a feast to celebrate it, and at the feast they had slain Gesir with all his lords and chieftains. Thus treachery had put an end to all the Sarmatian heroes. Whereupon the wives had embalmed the bodies and entombed them fittingly. The women left alive had kept watch over the tombs so that when the day of new life came, their husbands might return to earth and to them.

Cyrus reflected that this must be the truth of the tale that a solitary tribe of women made war on all intruders. It was a difficult task that they had set themselves, although an honorable one, and he did not think that the youthful Tymiris was capable of waging such a defensive war against savage nomads.

If he could have talked with the Sarmatian princess without

hindrance, the consequences might have been very different. After considering, he asked where the homeland of the Sarmatians lay.

Beyond the Red Sands, Tymiris cried, beyond the road of the Choara, beneath the rising of the sun.

"Then tell her," said Cyrus, "that she should lead her women thither. It is clear that they will not live long here without men to protect them."

Hearing that, the maiden warrior burst out again in melodious words. Never would she do that, unless the tombs were broken into and desecrated. For what would it avail to guard an empty house? And she rode close to Cyrus, her eyes aflame.

"Achaemenian," she cried at him, "it is true that you are strong and I am weak. I cannot oppose you here. If you break into my father's tomb, my hatred will follow you like the shadow of your handsome body. I will discover where you journey, and in my sleep I will devise great harm for you. I will be a friend to your enemies and an enemy to your friends. I will never come before your eyes again until the day when I will hold your body in my arms and watch the lifeblood flow out of it into the earth——"

Unexpectedly, Tymiris clasped her shining face in her hands and wept, bending her head to the mane of her horse to conceal her tears. Before Cyrus could answer, she turned her horse and raced away. The women warriors followed, disappearing into the wild growth. The two captives ran after them, unhindered by Cyrus.

It was like a woman, Cyrus thought, to threaten mischief and to break into tears when she could not have her way. Still, he had no doubt of the girl's courage.

At the excavation in the mound he found that Vartan and the diggers had cut through the door and were lighting torches to enter the burial chamber. "I don't like it," he said.

He remembered the tablet of Assur-bani-pal the Assyrian in the ruins of Shushan—the triumph of the Assyrian at tearing apart the graves of the Elamites to deprive their ghosts of peaceful rest and offerings.

"That is your Persian chivalry speaking." Vartan's teeth gleamed in the tangle of his beard. "But what is within this mound except some skeletons and a treasure hoard buried with them by superstitious barbarians? Or do you fear this Sarmatian girl so much that you will not enrich your men?"

"No," Cyrus admitted.

Thereupon some of the Asvaran crawled in eagerly after Vartan and the diggers.

Truly the great burial chamber, roofed over with timber, had been arranged carefully for a mighty chieftain to return to life. First the intruders came upon the carcasses of fine horses with costly trappings and dead grooms at their heads. Beyond these in the central chamber lay body servants with silver drinking horns in their hands. Upon the dais lay Gesir, almost lifelike with his yellow beard; he was crowned and clad in regalia of jeweled belt and armlets, and the gold-chased helmet by his head bore upon it a stag's head of gold with horn antlers. Beside him lay all necessary things, from hunting boots to gold-hilted whip, and all were enriched to be suitable to Gesir. In fact Cyrus judged that the Sarmatian's entire treasure had been buried with him. Certainly Tymiris, his daughter, had worn no such ornaments.

Because the stale air hindered their breathing, Vartan and the workmen stripped away the valuables hurriedly, piling them into a bronze caldron large enough to boil a whole sheep.

At the right hand of the Sarmatian lay a woman of about his age, still graceful in her satin and silk garments, with a silver lamp filled with oil and a hand mirror by her. Evidently she had killed herself, to be entombed with her husband. If so, she must have been the queen, and mother of Tymiris.

With an exclamation Cyrus picked up the bronze mirror. Its handle of gold bore the lioness and woman's head of the Great Goddess—so like his dagger hilt that they might have been shaped by the same hand.

After the stripping of the tomb, Vartan had trouble drawing the laden bronze caldron out through the entrance tunnel. Some of the Persians took this to be an ill omen. On his part, Vartan estimated that they were richer by a hundredweight of pure gold, not to mention the precious stones.

Cyrus still held Mandane's dagger in his hand. By a sudden impulse he tossed it upon the hoard of Scythian gold. All the objects, he noticed, were beautifully made by skilled artists.

Since the day was ending then, Vartan had the caldron carried into his own tent as soon as it was set up. Cyrus took care to double the guard beyond the horse lines after sunset. During the hours of darkness the steppe women might do harm enough even to trained warriors. Their princess seemed to be bent on mischief, if within a woman's power.

His sleep, however, was untroubled by an alarm. As usual, he rose from his sleeping robes in the chill of the first dawn. He stepped over Emba snoring in the entrance. Then he stumbled against a heavy mass outside the tent flap.

It was the bronze caldron. On top of it rested Vartan's head, the teeth shining through the beard. Beneath the head the treasure of gold had disappeared. The Armenian's naked body lay there, severed limb from limb and joint from joint, like animal meat prepared for the pot.

Before the fires were lighted, Cyrus summoned all the night guards to him to learn that they had seen nothing enter or leave their lines. Yet out by the tethered horses the Scythian guides had vanished to a man with their mounts.

It was clear what had happened. The women warriors had not ventured back after watching the despoiling of the burial mound. This, however, must have angered the silent Scythians—and Cyrus wished that he had understood all the words that passed between Tymiris and his interpreter. Then, too, the treasure of gold waited in the caldron; it could be carried off in the packs of a half-dozen horses. And the nomad hunters were capable of slipping through a cordon of soldiers.

So much Cyrus and his officers reasoned out. Long afterward he learned the secret of the Scythian guides—that they had been hired at high pay by the king of the Medes to contrive that he—Cyrus—be slain in the Sea of Grass. One must have tried to accomplish that with a single arrow before the capture of the women. Then, moved either by anger or greed, they had turned their weapons against Vartan. They had been better paid by that slaying than by the hand of Astyages.

It left Cyrus beside the pillaged tomb without a companion or guides. It left him with the duty of carrying back the severed body of Vartan to Harpaig, his father, for proper entombment.

Remembering that Vartan had promised he would do the same for him, Cyrus did not try to anticipate what might be the consequences of returning in this manner to the king and court of Agbatana. The tidings from the far south drove other anxieties from his mind.

(Already legends of the East were finding their way to the cities of the Greeks in the West, whence voyagers went out to find the golden fleece of Colchis. They brought back legends of the Sea of Grass where roamed nomads fixed to the backs of their horses; very soon the home-abiding citizens of Greece talked of tribes who had human bodies joined to the bodies of horses, in fact *centaurs*. By all odds the most popular legend told of a tribe of women who fought against men, true *Amazons*. Within a century the artists of Athens pictured the battle between heroes and Amazons in stone upon the pediments of their temples. But before then Tymiris and the women who had guarded the tombs of their husbands had departed to the East, to their homeland beyond the Hyrcanian Sea.)

CYRUS RIDES TO PARSAGARD

The tidings reached the Persian expedition as it journeyed swiftly south.

For Cyrus, as he had promised at the Iberian River, took counsel with his older commanders as to what they should do. All agreed that the Sea of Grass was a bitter land and they had no wish to linger in it. It crossed Cyrus's mind that evil had befallen them from the moment when he threw the dagger image of the Great Goddess into the Scythian gold. Thereupon he asked each commander what road he would take out of the steppe; as Cyrus expected, they all pointed south but in different directions. Each man had a different notion of where the river gate of the White Mountains might lie. Cyrus agreed to the route that he had already worked out in his mind by thinking back to the position of the stars he had observed each evening, by counting back the number of marches he had made, and by adding his estimate of the distance traveled in each one. He made this search of his memory several times, to be certain. He could not risk making a mistake.

So his horsemen were hastening to the east of south when they noticed dust rising swiftly along the track behind them. The earth was dry then, before the coming of winter. The Persians faced about and looked to their weapons until they saw that the riders galloping after them numbered less than ten, with as many spare mounts. And these wore the hooded caps and close-tied trousers of Persians who were traveling far and fast. The leader, a young Achaemenian, reined in with a glad shout. His eyes were slits, his skin dark with dust. "By the sun above and the fire of Atar," he greeted them, "you have left a trail like a snake to its hole." With pride he rose in the leather loops that held his feet. "Yet in two moons, I swear, we have overtaken you who rode for two years—from Parsagard I came."

Sighting Cyrus among the commanders, the young rider flung himself to the ground and ran to clasp his foot and bow his head to it. "Cyrus, son of Cambyses! I bow to the foot of Cyrus my lord, King of Anshan."

They made camp then to hear the tidings of the messenger—of how Cambyses lay in his tomb above the river, and of how word had come from Agbatana that Cyrus himself was slain in the wars. This was denied by Kassandan, the wife, who swore to the Law-bearers that in a dream she beheld Cyrus alive and journeying back to Parsagard. Mithradat the Lame added his word, that he recognized the son of Cambyses as the sole lawful king of Anshan. When the Achaemenians and Maspians stood together in this, the Marasphian chieftains joined them. So that the Three Tribes waited for the coming of Cyrus and the seven other Iranian tribes waited to learn his fate. Cyrus needed to cease wandering after royal glory, said the messenger, and must return swiftly to his own land.

Then Cyrus the Achaemenian gave his first decision as king. He would take the warriors of the Three Tribes with him to ride straight to Parsagard. The others of the army would escort the body of Vartan by way of the Hollow Land and Armenia to Agbatana. The severed body had been cleaned and embalmed, after a fashion, with pungent oils and packed in herbs. It was the best they could do.

Fast as Cyrus sped thence, winter came on more swiftly. He and his followers were forced to wait out the melting of the snow in the passes of the Blue Mountains. Anxious at the delay, Cyrus took Emba and ten chosen men with remounts and went ahead toward the winter sunrise.

He rode into his valley, as he had left it, at the ripening of grass. When he dismounted at the palace steps, he noticed that his father had failed to set up the guardian statues after all. At the porch of the stone palace he found Kassandan waiting with her two children, now grown to strong, small boys. She wore a new purple mantle clasped with the Achaemenian royal wings, and she bent her head before him.

"It was a happy dream you had," he told her, "at a most fortunate time."

When they were alone together at the hearth, she had her say. Tears ran from her fine eyes. "What have your enemies wrought upon my lord husband! How burned and thinned and weary you have become, in what tatters of garments!"

Cyrus assured his wife that he never felt better; it was simply that in winning some fame in the wars of the Medes, as she had desired, he had to undergo a few discomforts. Then after they were in bed together, he told Kassandan the full tale of his military service. Again she wept, although quietly. "What kind of fame have you won by this?" she lamented. "You have conquered no people, while you have made an enemy of Astyages the King and lost the Scythian treasure of gold. And you return with only ten men at your back!" She sighed and spoke her mind. "Now my lord husband you must act henceforth with the wise forethought of Cambyses, King of the Persians, or evil will befall your people."

The evil that befell Cyrus within the next years, however, arose from the single circumstance that he had failed to return to Agbatana—from that, and his own stubbornness.

AN ORDER FROM ASTYAGES

The Shepherd was thirty-eight when they consecrated him as King of Anshan, which in reality signified no more than the leadership of the Three Tribes around Parsagard. He chose to take the oath at the new shrine of Anahita. He felt then, and always, that flowing water aided him. Besides, the elusive Anahita was the only woman who did not somehow manage to worry him after embracing him. When all the priests and the chieftains of lofty name gathered at the white marble crypt, Cyrus partook of the foods they offered—figs, crushed terebinth, and a mess of sour milk. This, by ancient Aryan ritual, reminded him that he was not superior to his peasants who worked the soil. After that the Law-bearers administered the customary oath—that he would turn to the good in word and act, be a friend to his friends, judge the weak in equal measure with the strong, and always safeguard his people, not himself. Immediately he found these simple promises most difficult to carry out. And, like all new-crowned monarchs, he became absorbed by the tasks of ruling within his own domain and could take little thought of what happened elsewhere.

When he made rich gifts of silver to the chieftains attending the coronation, the silent Mithradat objected that he was emptying the treasure chests of his father. Cyrus considered, and appointed his old antagonist to be Keeper of the Treasure.

"Why me?" the lame Maspian prince demanded.

Cyrus did not say that it was because he had crippled Mithradat in a boy's anger, or that Mithradat could not perform a duty that required riding a horse. "Because you hate me," Cyrus told him, "yet you hold the Maspian people to loyalty to me. I know of no other man with your integrity."

And like other princes coming to rule, Cyrus longed to build a palace quite different from his father's homestead hall. He wanted distinguished visitors to enter a true Achaemenian audience hall, not a crow-ridden dining courtyard. When he explained his ideas to architects from Babylon and Memphis, those masters of techniques pointed out that he could not change a building without putting in new foundations, and to do that he must tear down the old structure. Cyrus agreed upon a new foundation of marble—with marble pillars on the porch—and a hall as large as that of Astyages at Agbatana, with pillars forty feet high, like trees, slender, to be spanned by a man's arm. Since—as the architects pointed out—such slender pillars could not support the weight of a flat roof, Cyrus declared it would be a peaked roof, in Aryan fashion, to shed the snow. The architects who came from sun-burned plains had not thought of snow.

Since Kassandan had to move out during the rebuilding, Cyrus ordered a homestead palace to be erected of burned brick for his family four hundred paces from the great hall. Since it soon proved more suitable to keep his family apart from his court sessions, Kassandan remained in her new palace home—somewhat like the queens in the citadel of the Medes. Besides, it seemed to the Persian mind that there should be a pair of precious things rather than a single one. So there were twin fire altars on the height that Cyrus beautified with a temple terrace. Somewhere back in Aryan thought had arisen this custom of always making two of a kind. Did not a man require a woman to give birth from his seed? Did not light require darkness to take effect? Did not the principle of good in life come from the conflict with evil? Cyrus remembered that Cambyses had planned for another wife for him of foreign and royal blood.

Now that he faced the task of riding the limits of his kingdom, he summoned to him the ten faithful warriors who had guarded his back from the Sea of Grass to their homeland; he bade each of the ten select ten more like him to escort him when he rode forth. (This nucleus of the noble-born hundred would grow to the Unchanging Thousand that the Greeks thereafter called the Immortals of the Persian King.)

With this splendid escort of the hundred sworn heroes, Cyrus made the first tour of his dominion. At every village of the Three

Tribes the nobles and Caspians alike came out to offer their gifts of fruit and delicacies, embroidered cloth and small treasures. In return he gave every Persian woman a gold coin of Croesus of Lydia. These were the only coins of stamped gold, rarely seen within the mountains.

Yet Cyrus rode beyond the Three Tribes to the outer peoples. They found him to be handsome and persuasive in talk; he made no demands except that they become "the king's friends." And he left them with a jest. "Even the tame animals, who graze at will in safety, herd together and follow a leader when danger appears. And will we not do the same if peril disturbs the peace of our lands? Then send for me to protect you when need arises."

Among all the outer Iranians the Germanians were the fiercest. They dwelt afar on the red highlands bordering the great Salt Desert. (These heights still bear the name of Kerman.) Tabal, their chieftain, made his own law. Tabal had not seen fit to come to the crowning of Cyrus—saying that he was no *khshatra* of the Achaemenian lord but a ruler in his own right. When Cyrus appeared in person beneath his city, which sprawled on a crag over the bend of a river, Tabal merely watched from the tower above his closed gate. Within the gate waited some thousands of Germanian swordsmen.

Before the Achaemenian paced standard-bearers and mounted flute players; behind him waited the hundred heroes, with their crests on their shields. After Cyrus surveyed the cliff, he reined his Nisayan steed, caparisoned for a festival, across the river ford and hailed the watching Tabal. "Why do you sit up there and refuse to come down?"

Tabal looked beyond him but perceived only servants and baggage beasts behind the small Achaemenian array. "Because I do not know what else to do," he bellowed back, with crafty frankness.

Then Cyrus explained he had heard that Tabal called himself not commander of warriors but king of a people.

"Well, it's true."

"Then come down and take your trial."

"My trial for what?"

"For your government of your people, the Germanians."

Tabal considered that. He was not in the least afraid but he did not find Cyrus easy to understand. "And who will try me?" he demanded.

"He who could sentence you without a trial."

"*Ahi!* And who might that be?"

"I, Cyrus the King."

Thereupon, Tabal found himself on the horns of a dilemma. As ruler, he could not refuse a hearing. After taking thought, he rode down the cliff path with no more than a hundred swordsmen, and all his Law-bearers and counselors. They set up the court on the river bank. Tabal, a veteran in the wars, needed to stand to make his argument before the persuasive Achaemenian seated on a rock. By the law of the Persians a man charged with guilt had the right to offer in evidence any of his good deeds. If the good overbalanced the evil, he would be acquitted of the charge. Tabal could cite many acts of courage and shrewd leadership in battle, as well as several lives saved.

"I have heard the testimony," Cyrus assured the listening court. "Tabal, as commander of Germanians, has done nothing evil. Yet," Cyrus went on, "Tabal, as ruler, has many counts against him."

The stalwart Germanian drew himself up. "What are they?"

Counting them off on his fingers, Cyrus said: "Your ill government of husbandmen, potters, fishers, weavers, smiths, traders, herders, and Caspians."

It happened that Tabal could cite little benefits he had bestowed on such people. The native Caspians had left his lands. Cyrus, well aware of this, listened to him patiently and gave the verdict as judge. "As commander of warriors, this man is without blame. As ruler of his people, he has been heedless of the good of those depending on him; he has been stupid in devising better ways for them, and they have suffered because of him."

The listening Law-bearers made no appeal against the judgment. Cyrus explained the measures that would aid the Germanian farmers. He was eloquent about the drainage not done upon the rivers. At the end of the hearing, Tabal changed his attitude and begged Cyrus to enter his gate and feast in his hall, to tell him personally what else the Achaemenian king might have in his mind. After this episode, the tribal folk began to call him the "people's king."

On the ride around his territories, Cyrus asked each chieftain why he should contribute a yearly quota of horses and "bows"—of mounted Persian archers—to the service of Astyages the King? Why should Persians continue to serve the Medes? They would fare better, Cyrus pointed out, in serving themselves.

And it was known from the Sealands to the Salt Desert that Cyrus himself refused to send any more Nisayan steeds or archers of the Three Tribes to Agbatana.

"One who rules," he said bitterly to Mithradat, "can never show himself as he truly is until he has accomplished his purpose."

"Your father was well aware of that. While he made pretense of pottering in gardens and fearing Astyages, he actually made himself a shield to safeguard his people against invasion. Is your purpose as wise as his?"

Cyrus thought that a cripple looked at matters with clearer eyes than strong men. He realized that Mithradat gave his loyalty to Persian tradition, not to Cyrus himself.

Every year of those early years the new king of Anshan refused to send either horses or men in tribute to the Medes. He did not reveal his purpose in doing so. It was really no more than a dream of his—to rouse the Iranian tribes to rebel against the yoke of Astyages. He sensed the strength of the separate nations under the yoke; they were like many strong horses held to a chariot by a flimsy rein. If that rein could be broken!

Then in one month of Nisan, the month of early grass, a herald of Astyages appeared at the gate of Parsagard where Cyrus had erected two limestone slabs on which to carve two guardian spirits. He found, as Cambyses had found, that it was difficult to decide what divine spirits protected his palace. The herald, Abradat, Chief of Council, came without gifts but with two bearded scribes to write down all spoken words. On his long staff gleamed an eagle of gold with outstretched wings. Young and forthright, he gave his message in a clear voice.

"In this first day of Nisan," he repeated, "the word of the Great

King, the King of the Lands, of all the Medic tribes, of Armenia, Hyrcania, the Manneans, Urartaeans, Elamites——"

Thus Abradat proceeded to number the peoples subject to Astyages. The message came at the end. "—the word is for Cyrus, King of Anshan, to come before the face of Astyages his lord by the last day of the month of Nisan."

After the scribes had written down the words, the young herald stepped close to the throne seat of Cyrus in the hall of audience that had not been roofed as yet. "Astyages has waited too long," he said quietly, "to welcome you."

At these twisted words a flash of anger went through Cyrus. "He will not welcome me when he does behold me!" he cried.

The herald hesitated. "Is that your answer?"

"Yes," said Cyrus.

He did not stir from his valley that month. In the warmth of midsummer appeared the Hebrew merchant who had been the first to offer Kassandan cloth of royal purple. This time he sought her in her separate palace and exclaimed at her new splendor—like the lilies in the fields! Over offerings of rare jewels at great price, he bent low to whisper some tidings of the northern road. "I passed an armed host of the Medes, whose tread was like the roaring of surf. Yea, it marched to the south, and Harpaig, lord of the Medic Host, rode with it."

That night Cyrus ordered the beacon fires to be lighted on the pinnacles above his valley. Thus he summoned his Persians to arm themselves for war, not in service to the Medes but against the Medes.

VENGEANCE OF HARPAIG, LORD OF THE HOST

Never had the Shepherd of the Persians felt such pride as at the stroke of dawn, upon the great north road, out on the prairies of the Nisayans. When the last stars vanished, sixty hundreds of his Asvaran stood by the bridles of their battle chargers, facing the place of the sun's rising. Helmets gleamed on their lifted heads, on the silver devices of their shields, and the metal plates sheathing their bodies. When they beheld the edge of the rising sun, they prayed in unison that they might be given strength to drive Evil from their land as the sun drove darkness from the earth. Flutes played a merry tune as they mounted their steeds, turning toward the dark mass of the enemy, motionless on the road between the river and a ridge of the mountains.

Cyrus kneed his white charger forward to lead the warriors of the Three Tribes against the host of the Medes. Because he wished to go ahead of the officers of the hundreds, he urged his horse on. With their bows sheathed in their cases, the warriors trotted after him. Cyrus could have shouted aloud for joy in this moment. The restless horses plunged into a gallop and the mass of them swept toward the brazen standards of the Medes and the ranks of foot soldiers waiting impassively behind a wall of great shields and serried lines of bristling spear points.

As the sun set, Cyrus swayed in his seat, gripping the saddle-cloth. Wounds burned his flesh as with fire. His horse, dark with sweat, stumbled even in the smoothness of the road. All around him the warriors pressed, aiding him to keep his seat, riding in silence with the setting sun on their right hands. Behind them they left the battlefield and its plunder to the Medes.

Cyrus had only fleeting memories of the day of battle, of the hissing of arrows passing him, and of blood streaming from battle-axes slashing at the heads of horses—of a wall of leather shields that stood before him like a wall of stone.

When the rim of the sun touched the earth, he made an effort to sit erect and to call out in a clear voice. "We will stand against them at the gates of Parsagard. We will drive them from our homeland as they drove us this day."

There was only a murmur in answer from the riders. The sun vanished and darkness covered the retreat of the Persians. Cyrus swayed in his weakness, and survivors of his Hundred of the guards gripped his arms. He forced his mind to plan a defense of his valley and city, where no walls stood except the hills themselves.

Another day came, when Cyrus and his officers waited in the hills, watching the column of the Medes climbing the slope like a sluggish serpent seeking a path.

Cyrus knew that this stand would necessarily be his last. He had less force here than in the northern prairies. Few riders had come in from the outlying peoples at his second summons. And the ranks of the Three Tribes had been thinned by the defeat.

His oldest commanders advised him to withdraw his people to the broad western plains, toward the nomad Dayans and the citadel of the Germanians. His Persians could move out swiftly with their herds. They would not leave much for the Medes to pillage and burn in Parsagard.

Cyrus would not do that. He remembered that Cambyses had always said their valley would be a secure refuge. If they migrated thence, they would become wanderers again, struggling for pasturage with the other tribes—or seeking some unknown land. Yet at the same time he realized that his people had no defense except his leadership. And already that had been proved futile against the skill of Harpaig.

Harpaig, the Armenian serving Astyages, knew the secret of leading trained troops to victory. As he pondered that, Cyrus perceived there was a way of halting the Medic army, somewhat desperate but not impossible. It would at least bring him without further delay to death or to victory.

While he turned the plan over in his mind, he did not confide it to his officers. They had no need to know it, and if it failed they would be free to act as they thought best. He kept the encampment of his Asvaran out of view of the enemy. Some mounted patrols stood watch around the ravine while the array of Medes drew nearer in its leisurely manner and set up its camp by a stream.

After the lamps had burned in his tent for three hours that night, Cyrus stepped out to the guards at his entrance. He bade them awaken their reliefs quietly, until they numbered a score in all, and then join him in the darkness beyond the lamps, leaving their shields and spears and taking only long knives and short hand axes.

When he joined the score of awakened warriors, he told them what he meant to do. He would lead them afoot down to the camp of the Medes. They would make their way through the sentries who would be watching chiefly for mounted riders. Under cover of darkness a score of men apparently unarmed might gain the pavilion of Harpaig where stood the standards of the army. Then, seizing the lord of the Medic Host, they must break a way out of the camp with their prisoner. Deprived of its commander, Cyrus did not believe the methodical army of the Medes could overcome the Persians a second time. Then he asked these twenty of his Hundred if they were willing to risk their lives in this venture.

At once they agreed to do so, insisting that Cyrus himself must not go. He remembered then to detach two of them to keep post at his tent entrance as if he himself were sleeping within it. Then he led the other eighteen in a wide circle past the Persian sentries. Cyrus had learned by now that sentries usually kept watch toward the enemy's lines. And he had made careful observation of the ground between them and the great pavilion of the Armenian general.

Like most plans of unexpected daring, this of Cyrus succeeded well at first. The small group of raiders kept touch with each other and they crawled past the sentries visible against the night sky. Although Cyrus's injuries had healed sufficiently for him to move easily, he grew weaker quickly, and this soon had an effect upon him. When they reached the hide tents of the soldiers, the raiders divided into groups of three or four and went forward casually. Those who carried axes held them close to the ground. In the still hour before dawn they reached the lighted pavilion of the enemy commander. A half-dozen spearmen sat or stood before it. The light came fitfully, as if from torches within, and Cyrus thought that torches might be useful to them.

He led the rush that overthrew the guards and burst into the curtains. Inside the huge pavilion, they discovered it to be divided into compartments. In one Harpaig stood, awake between two smoking torches. As they ran at him, swordsmen sprang from the curtains beside him. There was a clashing of weapons and a shouting of injured men as the raiders struggled with the sallying guards. Then came a splattering of flame, a stench of smoke, and near darkness. Harpaig had thrown the torches into the fighting mass. His voice rang out. "Stay your weapons—idiots!"

In astonishment or reaction to his sharp command, the struggling ceased and in that instant Cyrus realized that he had failed. By a trick, swift as the strike of a snake, the Armenian had taken control of the struggle. Surprisingly, then, Harpaig issued other orders, for all except Cyrus the Achaemenian to withdraw to the antechamber. When they gaped at him, he roared at them. "There is a truce! I will flay the skin off the one who breaks it."

No sooner had the warriors, Medic and Persian, withdrawn than Harpaig called for his body servants to bring lighted lamps and a bowl of Ionian wine. In another moment he was sucking at the wine bowl, a jeer twisting his sallow face. "Cyrus," he snarled, "remember after this that men coming out of darkness are blinded by light. Did you hope that I slept without an inner guard at call?"

Cyrus held a knife and he might have slain the Armenian who wore no armor. Because Harpaig had called for a truce, he could not. Weakness after the long effort seeped into his limbs. He was half-dazed by the bright lights. Harpaig did not allow him a moment for thought. The Armenian addressed him by no title of honor. "Did you believe that I would fail to avenge the murder of Vartan, my son, whose body was carved up for butcher's meat?" His dark eyes glared. "Cyrus, I ordered Vartan to go with you to cherish and guard you."

Stung, Cyrus threw down his knife and spoke, telling Harpaig the truth of Vartan's death in the steppes. The Armenian listened closely. A strange sense of familiarity came upon Cyrus, as if the two of them stood again over the lamp of the eunuch before that dawn in the courtyard of Agbatana. What had begun there seemed to be ending here, and Harpaig was aware of it. Curtly the general bade Cyrus seat himself, and he cast aside the empty silver bowl, while the furrows deepened in his face. "I do not believe you are lying," he said. "Tell me this. If a companion with broken head bones came to you for aid, would you take up a bag of surgeon's instruments and operate on him with your own hands?"

"No. Only a physician might do that."

Soundlessly the Armenian laughed. "Yet without experience in warfare you took command of six thousand warriors a fortnight ago. You cast these Asvaran, the finest of horse archers, against my set array of spears backed by missiles. Because of your folly, how many women mourn their dead in your city? I can tell you the count of the hands that were cut from the bodies and piled before my tent. Where were the bows of the Asvaran? Did you lack hours, or even days, to ride around my array and thin it down with arrows? Could we have hindered the ride around of your Nisayan chargers, the swiftest of horses? Could we have escaped from them?"

Cyrus understood that the Armenian would not be telling him this much if he expected that they would meet again as enemies on the battlefield. Yet Harpaig talked on savagely.

"No doubt Cyrus, King of Anshan, master of the Three Tribes, felt heroic pride when he galloped his charger across the grass to disaster. A hero is a weakling who can bethink him only of dying to achieve a little fame." Harpaig's sarcasm was like Vartan's. "I must use the simplest of words to penetrate your chivalric folly. A commander of men, leading them into danger, cannot afford the comfort of weakness. A commander must school himself in trickery to appear weak to his enemies when he is strong, and strong if he is really weak; he must spin a web of lies about his actions, plotting hidden treachery, stealing hostile secrets, plundering wealth, and showing no mercy until he has won everything he seeks."

Cyrus waited for the Armenian to come to the meaning behind his words.

"Well, you have a tongue. Which do you elect to be henceforth, a glorious Achaemenian or a wise leader of men?"

Cyrus still waited.

"My royal Achaemenian, did your intelligence grasp the fact that Astyages marches behind me at a week's interval? No? Astyages is doing that either to keep me under observation or to exult over your downfall. For you cast spittle on his dignity by refusing to come at his summons, thus proving yourself to be no faithful vassal king like your father. I do not know which he has in his mind— probably both. He was shrewd enough to keep the stronger array, with the Persian and dangerous Hyrcanian horse under his own banner." Harpaig scowled in thought. "I have reason to suspect that he believes I have become too powerful in the Medic armed forces, and he wishes a share in the triumph over you—or he would hardly have left his palace—which will set the last seal on the empire of the Medes."

A half-forgotten memory tugged at Cyrus. "Then the summit of gold has been completed upon the great tower of Agbatana."

Harpaig glanced up in surprise. "Yes. Ah, you think of the Magian seer at the gate. Yes. Of his prophecy that when the last story is upon the tower, the empire of the Medes will fall?"

"I have that in my mind."

Seating himself by his captive, Harpaig stared silently into the flame of the lamp. A subtle change came over him. "Lord Cyrus, you have one peculiarity—other than speaking the truth at all times. You do unexpected things. That bothers an enemy commander. I had an uncomfortable moment"—he glanced at the dripping water clock by his couch—"a half hour ago. Just possibly that Magian may be a sending of the god—unknown to me—who protects you, and never more than at this minute. You planned to defeat an army of the Medes and seize the rule from Astyages?"

"I still mean to do it."

Harpaig's beard parted in something like a smile. "Cyrus, by those words you have earned yourself chains, until you are set on a stake outside the gate of Agbatana to wriggle away your life like a fish. If Astyages were a Cyaxares, you would end that way."

If the Armenian was trying to instill fear into Cyrus's weakness, he failed. Cyrus still probed at the purpose behind his words.

"But Astyages is no more than a swine rooting in rich offal. He paid that band of captive Scythians to take your life on the steppes. Your god must have intervened, because they slew Vartan my son instead." Harpaig raised his heavy hands and let them fall. "My house is destroyed and my life has only one purpose now, to bring Astyages to his knees."

Rising suddenly, he called through the entrance curtain. "Dogs —cease to lick your wounds, and hasten to all commands to say that the truce in this tent holds for the army and the Persians as well. Cyrus bids me warn them."

He listened to the scurry of departure in the antechamber and went silently to peer through the side curtains. Then he returned to his seat and his scrutiny of the lamp.

"Give me a moment," he murmured, rubbing his beard, "to think how to put an end to the empire of the Medes."

"I will give you many minutes to do that."

"Yes. Now at this particular moment no one outside this curtain can be certain whether you are my captive or I am yours. I took some care to rid myself of witnesses. You might pick up your knife, Cyrus. Let us say that I am your prisoner." His shaggy brows knitted. "You will demand the surrender of my encampment. My Armenians will obey and the Medes must do so whether they like it or not. Let us see—let us suppose my forces are quartered behind yours, with weapons piled somewhere within reach. A week from today. The dawn of another day, Cyrus. Now let us think of Astyages coming on against us. Because he sent me ahead to do the dirty work, he has had no direct observation of our actions. Spies? They're all around me; yet it will do us no harm if they report what they have seen. Now Astyages has been fondling his women for too many years since he last commanded in battle. He will come straight on to crush you, his horsemen screening his advance."

"And if they see me ride out alone," put in Cyrus, "my Persians will gallop to greet me."

"True. And the Hyrcanians will follow after them to see what is happening. They'll all go over to you . . . then with the cavalry behind you . . . my Armenians armed . . . encircling this Great King and his Medic guardsmen . . . would they not wish they had a wittier leader? We can offer them one. Cyrus, King of the Medes and Persians."

Cyrus laughed. "Harpaig, did you not tell me that a wise leader weaves a web of lies around his actions? Are you not doing that now to deceive me?"

Without a sign of anger, the Armenian shook his grizzled head. "You learn a simple lesson very quickly, Cyrus. No doubt you wonder why, if I have decided to betray Astyages, I stood against you in bloody battle two weeks ago? It was necessary to deceive

Astyages. The fat son of Cyaxares may be slothful but he is no fool. He must have no scent of the trap we are setting in these hills." Striding to the curtain, Harpaig flung it back. No one waited outside except some wounded Persians. Satisfied, Harpaig said softly, "Son of Cambyses, you have a second lesson to learn. When we hold Astyages captive, it will seem very glorious to you. Yet we will hold no more than a figurehead, a robed actor after his play has ended. Victory will come to us only if we seize his city with its treasure and court of the Medes—before others can muster their strength in Agbatana." He lifted his scarred face to the faint daylight. "May your god aid you to become King of the Medes and Persians! Then, Cyrus, I think you will believe what I am telling you now."

Because Cyrus was weary and strained by listening, he could do no more than hope.

Ten days later the riders of the caravans and foreign spies as well took to the roads from Parsagard's mountains with astounding news. *The great army of the Medes revolted; its warriors laid down their weapons before the small king of Anshan. Astyages the Mede was captive to Cyrus the Persian. Cyrus did not slay Astyages; he did not burn out the eyes of his captive with hot iron. Instead, Cyrus held Astyages in his palace as a hostage.*

The messengers on the western road gave their news at Shushan and hurried on to Babylon where Nabu-naid reigned. Those on the northern road to Agbatana, however, were overtaken before they could give out their news.

THE OATH IN THE HALL OF THE MEDES

It happened because Cyrus could not sleep in the night after his bloodless victory at the hill gates of Parsagard.

The poets had finished their songs of praise, the officers had sought their quarters in the new encampment, and fires of rejoicing sparked the dark hills. One sight troubled Cyrus—Astyages's fat face wet with tears when the servants took off his armor of iron plates and he stood before them all in his soiled shirt and riding trousers. One memory nagged at Cyrus, persistent as a stinging fly. It was something that Harpaig, lord of the Host, had said to him that daybreak in his pavilion.

Everything had happened as the Armenian had foretold. There could be no doubt about that. Harpaig was asleep now in that same pavilion, while Cyrus meditated in the roofless audience hall, watched by curious guards. Cyrus was weary again, but in the silence he could search his memory for the elusive words that plagued him—lies spoken as truth. Truly Astyages had become no more than an actor stripped of his costume. After victory. Yet victory would come only when Cyrus and Harpaig seized Agbatana.

Cyrus brooded until the words made a refrain like the ripple of the river beneath. He listened to the water and relaxed. It spoke with a new voice, protecting him. And he felt his friendly fravashi drawing near to warn him.

A light came into the darkness of his thoughts. He laughed a little, throwing up his arms. Victory would come only when they seized Agbatana, *but to Harpaig,* not to Cyrus. For in that city of the Medes, Harpaig, the great commander, would proclaim the revolt of the Persians—ay, after he himself had thinned them down in the first battle—and the capture of Astyages. There in his citadel the lord of the Host would rally strength to him, perhaps—yes, surely—naming some brat of Astyages as puppet ruler and disowning Cyrus the Achaemenian as a foolish actor who, having played his part, expected to make it a reality. This purpose Harpaig had hidden behind a screen of half-truths, more deceptive than lies. He could be certain of carrying it out because Astyages was unpopular and Cyrus unknown in Agbatana, citadel of the Medes.

Whenever the son of Cambyses saw his way clear, he acted at once. The great encampment of Parsagard still slept, except for Mithradat and chieftains of the Three Tribes who walked beside him in urgent talk as he led a fresh horse toward the north ravine. Behind him followed the survivors of the Hundred, each one with a comrade roused to go on the mission, and all led an extra mount. They bore with them some captured standards of the Medes and the gold-inlaid armor of Astyages—who slumbered in Cyrus's residence palace—with its grotesque helmet bearing a griffin's head having shining jewels for eyes. Cyrus himself wore only a Persian riding hood and a plain cloak, and he kept within the group of his hundred and forty chosen horsemen.

The next day they overtook the foreign messengers on the north road and dismounted them, to follow behind on foot. Cyrus had learned that he could not easily be hindered in his course if no one knew he was coming.

A caravan took thirty days to make the stages from Parsagard to the ruling city of the Medes. On the fifth morning of their ride Cyrus and his followers appeared at the gate beneath the granite peak of Alwand. They entered unchallenged at that early hour because they appeared to be no more than a detachment of Persian horsemen carrying the bronze eagle standards of the Medic army. Within the streets they cast back their cloaks and divided into patrols, calling upon officers and lords of the land to come without delay to the festival hall of the palace by order of the Great King, the King of the Lands.

For generations the hardy Medes had copied the protocol of the once-splendid Assyrians; they had grown accustomed to attending ceremonies at their leisure. They enjoyed the luxury of rousing slowly to be robed by the deft hands of slaves. Many of them who wandered into the hall of Astyages at all hours that morning had donned false beards to increase their dignity and long braided robes to signify their wealth. They carried no weapons except ceremonial daggers.

They found Cyrus awaiting them, seated on the carved marble throne with the battle armor of Astyages lying before his footstool.

The usual robed spearmen had disappeared from the side walls where twoscore Persians with strung bows watched the behavior of the visitors. Cyrus himself wore battle dress, and his words rang like clashing iron. He informed the army officers and lords of plantations of the surrender and captivity of their late ruler, Astyages, son of Cyaxares; he ordered them to take the oath of loyalty to himself as King of the Medes and Persians, successor to Cyaxares.

"Do so, men of lofty name," he assured the first gathering of the grandees, "and your lives and your homes, your women and your wealth will be as they were before. You will not have as many feasts; yet I assure you that you will carry out your duties. So say I, Cyrus the King."

While they struggled with astonishment, trying to understand what had actually happened, a woman's clear voice echoed above them. "Cyrus, my son, you have returned victorious as I hoped and prayed. So say I, Mandane the Queen."

She was watching from the screened women's gallery. Many of the Medes glanced up fearfully at the stone image of Ishtar, goddess of Babylon. Most of them took the oath quickly enough. One, Abradat, who had been herald to Parsagard, refused, saying that while Astyages lived he was bound to serve him.

Cyrus recognized him. "Lord Abradat, I promised you that this same Astyages would not welcome the sight of me. So it has happened." He ordered his soldiers to strip the stubborn Mede and pen him in the hunting park of the wild beasts. Abradat protested instantly, asking that weapons be given him instead, so that he might die in honorable fight in the hall of the nobles rather than be thrown to the wild beasts.

"I did not find it so dangerous when I was put among them some years ago," Cyrus assured him, and saw to the carrying out of his command. Inwardly he respected the herald for speaking without fear. "When the time comes," he told the other Medes, "I will value that man's loyalty more than yours."

It seemed to these listeners that Cyrus the Achaemenian possessed the ruthless purpose and swift judgment of the founder of their domain, Cyaxares. For the moment they were content to bow down to him. Owing to the sloth of the courtiers, most of the day passed before the last of them had taken the oath of loyalty to Cyrus, and food was brought to them in the hall. By then the outer streets were buzzing with rumors and questions. All authority, however, seemed to issue from the hall of the palace; only the Persian Asvaran could answer the questions as they patrolled the streets.

After sunset, somewhat to Cyrus's surprise, Harpaig entered the hall hastily with his body servants. The lord of the Host surveyed the gathering over the wine bowls and Cyrus solitary on the throne with archers behind him. Then Harpaig sighed in weariness and spread his open hands; he walked to the dais, glancing from right to left, and spoke softly. "Cyrus, you are a better rider than I."

Cyrus assented, and waited.

Rubbing his gnarled beard, the Armenian caressed the chain of gold with the lion's head at his throat. He looked old and tired. "It is true," he said hoarsely, "that I desired one thing above all, to force Astyages to his knees. I have seen him weep. In that I kept faith with you. Remember that in my tent I once spared your life. Think now how I can aid you as commander of the army of the Persians and the Medes. That is all I have to say."

Loosing the chain with his insignia, he laid it down and prostrated himself before Cyrus's feet, saying in a loud voice: "I, Harpaig, lord of Ani, lord of the Medic Host, give my life and all my possessions into the hand of Cyrus, our King."

Raising him up, Cyrus let him stand behind the throne, and thereafter, he kept Harpaig at his side, although for three years he gave the Armenian no separate command. Growing older and perhaps indifferent to political power, the astute Harpaig came to bestow on the young Achaemenian the devotion he had given his murdered son. Perhaps he carried out his own ambition vicariously in Cyrus. He was remarkable as a strategist and Cyrus proved to be as remarkable a ruler.

Mandane the Queen had her say about that. When Cyrus roused himself from sleep the first morning in Agbatana, he found motionless slaves waiting to pour clear water over his hands and head. When he went out to the terrace to make his prayer to the rising sun, he found Mandane, the daughter of Nebuchadnezzar, seated before her maids, and eunuchs awaiting him. Although she wore her crown and half-veil, harsh daylight showed the paint that hid the lines of middle age in her face. On this occasion Mandane chose to appear in the guise of a royal woman, not as the harlot dedicated to the Great Goddess. When Cyrus had finished his prayer, she bent her head to him.

"My son, you have changed. Wisdom lights your eyes and you stand forth in the strength of Marduk, champion of the gods. Yet

I fear for you the more. Alas, you have lost my token, even while you struggled against Evil, as Marduk fought the monstrous Tiamat who created life only with the dark strength of Evil." She peered at him closely and sighed. "I fear most of all that the Great Goddess is offended by something you have done. Perhaps you have injured some women cherished by her. The manner of your offense is not revealed to me. Cyrus, my son, a woman—an aging woman such as I am now—does not reason about the will of the unseen gods. She is either given insight, impossible to men, or she understands nothing. Now I cannot see what lies in the tablets of your destiny; I desire only to shield you, as I did during your foolish outbreak in the great hall and again yesterday when the grandees of the court were of two minds about you."

Cyrus thought that Mandane appeared little grieved at becoming a bereaved wife. He promised her that she might keep her chambers and servants and personal treasure and be treated with the honor due to his adopted mother. That seemed to please her, but she frowned and sighed again, drawing her slender body erect in pride.

"I am, of course, grateful for such an allowance. Yet the memory of Astyages hangs about these stone chambers like the smell of a rutting boar. Yea, he gorged his swelling body with spiced meat and eased his lust upon the bodies of slave women schooled in Lydian pleasures. He was a hair on my eyeballs, a hard crust in my throat. His death would uplift my heart." The dark eyes of the Chaldean princess appealed to Cyrus above the flimsy veil. "Now in Babylon my father, Nebuchadnezzar, favored of Nabu, god of written destiny, victor even over Marduk—my father once showed great consideration to a bride who was princess of the Medes, fat in the body, although she had soft hair and fine teeth like all the Aryan women; when she grieved for her native mountains, he built her a garden upon the loftiest roof summit, a hanging garden in Babylon wherein she could look down upon the great teeming city as if from the summit of her native hills. Alas, Cyrus, am I less than she? Truly my heart yearns for Babylon; the comfort of that lofty garden would solace the grieving of the old woman who is still your mother and protectress."

In his first court sitting that morning Cyrus gave order that Mandane was to be honored in her chambers but kept within Agbatana. Scribes wrote down his words, and officers bowed their heads when they accepted the written orders. In the hall of the Medic king such ceremony attended every action. When the Medes addressed him, they raised their right hands before their lips as if to shield him from the pollution of their breath—or perhaps to show that they held no concealed weapon. It merely exasperated Cyrus who liked to have things done quickly.

When he mounted a horse to go to inspect the new ziggurat tower, trumpeters trotted before him, blowing a brazen blast, and scribes gathered up their robes and tablets to hurry after him while throngs clustered against the house fronts—leaving a passage clear for him—to stare avidly at their new monarch.

The new tower was indeed completed; its summit shone with pure gold. When Cyrus halted to study it curiously, a band of earth workers threw themselves on their faces, except for one man with hard scars crisscrossing the jutting bones of his bare body. Leaning on his flint spade beside a half-planted tree cutting, he looked up at Cyrus while flies swarmed over the sores on his shoulders chafed by a yoke. Even so disfigured, Cyrus recognized the digger.

"Magian," he called, and added, "your prophecy has been fulfilled."

The prisoner at labor shook his head. "It was the word of Zarathustra." Glancing up at the gleaming tower, he went on almost with contempt: "Little wisdom was needed to foretell that a monarch of men who sought treasure rather than his own destiny would soon cease to rule."

Hearing the voice of the digger, an overseer ran up with raised whip, and Cyrus motioned him back irritably. "Magian, once you invited me to share your supper. Now I bid you join my company of friends and discuss the mysteries unknown to me."

The scarred man caressed his spade, and his voice came quickly. "Nay, Cyrus, the kingdom I seek is very different. It is merely everlasting life."

"Where?"

Brushing the flies from his eyes, the Magian said, "I do not know where—unless it is the kingdom that beholds the sun. To the east of us."

The words touched a memory, of the Aryan homeland under the rising sun. That memory was always with the Achaemenian. "By what route can you make the journey to it?"

"Route?" The scarred slave roused from his meditation and laughed, holding up the flint spade. "Take this in your hand. Dismount and tend the growing plants of life. Otherwise, whoever seeks my kingdom will find nothing."

It angered Cyrus the King that this man alone spoke defiantly to him. Like all temple priests, he told himself, the Magian uttered the phrases some master had taught him. Yet he seemed to understand their meaning. "Release him," Cyrus bade the overseer. "Bathe him, clothe him, and fill his hands with silver." Then he reined on his horse, saying to the scribe behind him, "Watch what road he takes, and tell me."

Very quickly the scribe reported the order carried out. "Great king, the mendicant asked in the caravansary the way to Bactria. Then he bought a white-nosed donkey with two silver shekels and started off on the road to Hyrcania, to the east."

It befell in the next years that Cyrus himself journeyed to the west.

He could not avoid doing so. Since the Medes were close kinsmen of the Persians, they accepted the young Cyrus in place of the aged Astyages without murmuring as long as their customs were not disturbed. Cyrus saw to that. But their dominion ran haphazard over mountains and deserts, without a hub except at Agbatana. Astyages had been content to drowse there in comfort; Cyrus was not so content. At the moment, however, he could not substitute his remote and poverty-ridden Parsagard as the center of his reign. In fact, this question of choosing a capital troubled him and his descendants for long years. He still had the instincts of a nomad. He decided this problem by ruling from horseback.

Summoning Mithradat by horse litter to the city of the Medes, Cyrus gave him its government as *khshatra pavan,* or commander for the king—the Greeks called it *satrap*. At the same time Cyrus sent the whole treasure of Agbatana, the silver ingots and precious metals and jewels, to his home city for safekeeping. He also kept Astyages there with every comfort of meat and drink. Foreign wine seemed to have one virtue; it dulled a drinker's mind.

Then Cyrus set out to ride around his enlarged dominion, to discover how its government, copied from the Assyrian bureaus, worked in the more remote lands. In doing so, he satisfied his own craving for action. Yet he did not get very far.

Tidings of his seizure of the throne passed speedily to outlying kingdoms as far as the court of the Pharaohs on the Nile. As usual, rumors rode with the news until it was said that Cyrus had appeared like a thunderbolt with an army of conquest, which was hardly the case. Embassies came from Tyre, maker of the purple dye, and Gaza—The Treasury—maker of glass, to discover the strength and purpose of the intruder upon a great throne. These merchant-ambassadors learned little except that armed forces were in motion through the mountains.

In the hot alleys of Babylon, by the waters of the river, the prophet Jeremiah had declared that the Lord was raising an assembly of great nations in the north country. He had sent out his voice to them. *"Put yourselves in array against Babylon round about. All ye that bend the bow, shoot at her, spare no arrows; for she hath sinned against the Lord. Take vengeance against her; as she hath done, do unto her."*

Because the Hebrews were accustomed to inveigh in this manner against their masters, they attracted little attention. The first to interfere with Cyrus was Croesus of Lydia, the most enlightened, as well as the wealthiest, monarch of the age. Out of that came the beginning of the disturbance that caused the great change upon the earth.

THREE

The Treasure of Croesus

IN SAMOS, an island in the Aegean, a witty slave named Aesop had gained some fame as a teller of fables. Probably Aesop did not invent his fables of the talking animals, but he told them well and a crowd usually collected in the market corner to listen to him. In the year that Cyrus became king of the Medes—the year 550 B.C. of the later Christian calendar—Aesop the slave died in unusual circumstances.

One of Aesop's tales seemed to have political significance. This was the one of the frog people who wearied of having a stupid log for their king and invited in a fine-looking stork to be monarch of the frogs, and this King Stork proceeded to rule by eating his subjects. At least this seemed to have a political moral to the energetic tyrant of Samos who had replaced the ancient council of elders. Unwilling to execute the popular storyteller, the efficient tyrant appealed to the judgment of the oracle of Apollo in the vale of Delphi, accompanying his appeal with a generous donation of money. Of course the judgment actually came from the mouth of the Pythia woman sitting above the vapors of the chasm, but the well-informed priests wrote it down beforehand and coached the woman carefully to repeat the words; in this case, the answer of the oracle was that Aesop must die, but his heirs, if any, must be compensated with blood-gold. It was all done as the oracle required.

They say that when the slave Aesop learned of his sentence he **told the fable of the old hunting dog that, cramped by age, failed** to run down and catch a rabbit for his master, who then beat him unmercifully, the moral being that a faithful hound was cast aside when his strength failed. This pitiful story did not delay Aesop's execution. Very soon after, a much more important inquiry came to the Delphic shrine, with an extravagant gift of silver ingots for the priests. This question, from Croesus of Lydia, was: *What will be the consequences to me if I lead an army across the river Halys against the Persians?*

It was hardly as casual as it sounded. The river Halys had formed the boundary between Lydia and Media since an eclipse of the sun had stupefied their rival armies in the field and the politic Nebuchadnezzar had intervened to arrange a truce between the Lydians and the Medes. What the victorious Croesus really desired to know was whether he should keep the existing peace or strike at once at Cyrus, a newcomer and an almost unknown Persian. Could he not profit by the disorder in the great Medic empire?

Croesus's high regard for the oracle came less from superstition than from reverence for the statesmanship of the priests who kept in close touch with events. The wealthy Midas kings of the mountains beyond Sardis had begun the practice of having their problems analyzed by the oracle; Croesus, the fortunate son of a conquering father, now possessed the Midas land and the gold of his native river of Pactolus as well; yet the bulk of his fabled riches came rather from the Lydian control of the trade route that brought raw materials of the farther East to the Ionian ports of the Great Sea. From those ports Phoenician and Greek trading fleets carried the finished wares into the obscure and barbaric West.

The Lydians who were advancing outward in this manner had made quite a metropolis of their inland city of Sardis, a most ancient site beneath the sacred Mount Tmolus. In Sardis they had cultivated the arts of living. Only the Egyptians excelled them in this, and the people of the Pharaohs—whoever the Pharaohs might be—clung to their life-giving Nile. Lydians had served as defenders in the Trojan War that had earned immortal fame by the songs of the Homeric poets. The Lydians desired fame but they devoted themselves to living comfortably. They had coined the first trade money by stamping discs of electrum; they had also devised dice and ball games, imported foreign cooks, fashioned small pitchers for toast-drinking, harps for their singers, and eunuchs for export to more savage folk like the Medes. Girls of their common class amassed a marriage dowry by serving as prostitutes. It is said that when the citizens of Sardis raised a dome on stone foundations to the memory of the gods who had been their first ancestors, the prostitutes made the largest contribution to the building fund. They were not Aryans.

In their government of subjected cities, the Lydians had devised the convenient method of ruling through a local tyrant—their word for an intelligent dictator. A man of such singular authority in Ephesus or Samos could carry out the wishes of Sardis—at the present moment the desires of Croesus—so long as he himself was not injured nor his subjects unduly taxed. And Sardis, in the person of Croesus, took care to be tolerant as well as farsighted.

Hence it happened that Croesus asked the advice of the Delphic oracle. Being cultured, he was a complicated man. He had learned to use wealth, not to waste it in ornaments or hoard it in a treasury —despite the tales about him—like a Scythian or Medic monarch. In his dining hall the ornaments were bits of marble or bronze shaped by the hands of artists. His statues possessed a unique quality, entirely new. They resembled human beings rather than benevolent gods or malevolent monsters. At the same time they were touched with beauty. To create something merely beautiful was quite unheard of elsewhere, unless in the forgotten Crete of Minos.

So Croesus the Lydian, avid of victories, still feared calamities; bound by his own desires, he still longed to raise up those who were subject to him; his pride craved splendor around him; his wit warned him that the gods punish grandeur in human beings. He feared the goddess Nemesis. Perhaps his great failing was that he could never make up his mind.

When he studied the response of the oracle, he found it to be cryptic. "*If you cross the river Halys, you will destroy a great empire.*" It did not occur to Croesus that the empire might be his own. He knew that he possessed no more than a wealthy kingdom;

the domain of the Medes, therefore, must be the great empire. Or so he thought.

Thus Croesus mustered an army and led it east against the Persians.

THE REVELATION OF GUBARU

Word of the march of the Lydians reached Cyrus by a courier when he was in the pasturelands of the Nisayans, preparing to journey eastward to the Salt Desert. Instead of consulting an oracle, the Achaemenian rode south at once to ask the advice of Gubaru, lord of Shushan. For years he had not set foot in the warm southland of Elam and he found it refreshed and green with young grain. As at his first coming, Gubaru advanced from the open palace gate to meet him, this time bearing earth and water in twin bowls as a sign of peaceful submission. Gubaru had aged and waxed in dignity; he waited in respectful silence for the young victor to greet him, and Cyrus thought that the Elamite was as aged and more tranquil than his father. "What is this?" he asked.

With the bated breath of ceremony, Gubaru told him: the submission of the land of Elam, which had paid tribute to the Medes, was now offered to Cyrus, King of the Medes and Persians.

Cyrus touched the earth and water, then waved them aside. He said for all to hear that Gubaru would be *khshatra pavan* for Elam henceforth and that nothing else would be changed. "You have nourished this earth, Lord Gubaru; you have increased the cattle herds; the workers sing in your fields. This has become a happy land—keep it so. So say I, Cyrus the King."

Gubaru may have been astonished; he revealed only his joy and clasped Cyrus's hand in both his own, asking what service he might render his royal guest, because he understood well that the Achaemenian had not journeyed to Shushan merely to admire the farming.

"Once you bade me consult with you," Cyrus reminded him, "at the death of Nebuchadnezzar. I was unable to do that. Now I must decide how to act toward the ruler of the Lydians, unknown to me."

When Gubaru heard the news from the northland, he said nothing until he had feasted his royal guest while his daughter, Amytis, brought delicacies of sugared dates and honey cakes. Then he said the two of them would appeal to the wisdom of his counselors. Cyrus expected to go before the Elamite's elders and Law-bearers. Gubaru, however, led him into a new chamber of the palace where several scholars pored over inscribed lambskins and stamped clay tablets. Like fragments of a treasure, these writings were set on stands against the walls, and Gubaru explained that they held a store of wisdom because they contained the record of the past.

"The last Assyrian, Assur-bani-pal, possessed a vaster library. Better for him if he had remained in it instead of mounting to the chariot of war."

Cyrus, who could not read, waited patiently for the learned Elamite to answer his question, but Gubaru proceeded, as if performing a ritual, to take up a lamp and touch his scrolls and tablets, explaining their messages. These held the secret of the downfall of the Hittites, mighty in valor, and after them the warlike Assyrians. "For their strength could not withstand calamities. They warred against each other—like the Babylon of the Sargons—and were blind to the greater evils."

Over their lands, Gubaru repeated, rode the wild Cimmerians, the Gimirrai, out of the far northern darkness. The Cimmerians plundered what had been built up, temples as well as palaces. Gubaru read from a scroll of curving Aramaic writing: *"They are cruel; they ride upon horses set in array as men for war against thee, O daughter of Zion. Anguish hath taken hold of us, and pain, as of a woman in travail. Go not forth into the field; for the sword of the enemy and fear are on every side."*

Such was the lamentation of the Hebrew, Jeremiah. Fear made people helpless for a generation of years; pestilence followed the horsemen. "Two champions arose against the horsemen," Gubaru went on thoughtfully. "Yea, Cyaxares the Mede and Alyattes, father of Croesus the Lydian. They beat back the calamity of the invasion but the fear and pestilence lingered on; Medes struggled against Lydians. Nebuchadnezzar, my master, vanquished the Egyptians. He sought to fortify Babylon against any future invasion. I labored with his engineers, building the wall against the Medes, while the farseeing Nebuchadnezzar—may his troubled soul survive in peace—made a treaty of amity with Lydia. They called him the Chaldean because he shared the foresight of the astronomers. They say he wasted the strength of his people in building the fortifications, but behind them Babylon throve in trade and wealth for a generation, until now."

Putting down his lamp, Gubaru folded his hands.

"You have told me nothing!" Cyrus cried, exasperated.

"I have told you everything, Lord Cyrus. What has happened will happen again, unless it is changed to a new course that will overcome the old."

Pondering this, Cyrus understood that the old Elamite had described the conflict of city against city, of Babylon against Nineveh, of Agbatana against Sardis, and the greater calamity of the invasion of northern nomads, whether Scythians or Cimmerians. The one thing Cyrus desired at this stage was to withdraw to his own valley, to cherish it as Gubaru had cherished the once-desolate land of Elam.

When he told Gubaru as much, the elder statesman shook his head quietly. "The one thing you cannot do is to withdraw. Your father, I believe, attempted that with rare skill. But the King of the Medes must protect all his subjects and they are many. Even now it seems that the Lydians besiege your Cappadocians in their remote citadel, which happens to be among the ruins of the Hittites." Gubaru smiled at a fleeting memory. "Has the successor to Cyaxares any choice except to march to the aid of these barbaric Cappadocians, or not to do so? In either case, can he avoid the evil of a new war?"

This stubborn reasoning wearied the Achaemenian, who cried: "I can summon my Asvaran and ride to this frontier to see matters for myself, and do then what seems best to be done."

The lines deepened in the Elamite's expressionless face. "I feared you would do that. I have tried to make clear some of the consequences. The question really in your mind is—how can the unworthy Gubaru aid your first venture into war?" He sighed. "If you will not heed the lessons of the past, come and listen to the voice of experience."

Then he led Cyrus and Harpaig before the elders of Elam. When these had heard what confronted the Achaemenian, they meditated, sitting like judges hearing a plea; they put their aged heads together and murmured together before they gave their decision to Gubaru.

"These men of wisdom," Gubaru announced, "find a great and hidden difficulty in your way. The Lydian Croesus has strengthened himself by alliances, with the Pharaoh at Saïs who profits from his trade, and with the kings of Sparta who admire him, and with Esagila—the citadel of Babylon. Thus you may face four enemies instead of one. Now the fleets of the Spartans and the chariots of the Egyptians lie far off and could not reach Sardis for many moons. Babylon, however, mighty in strength, is near at hand. Thus the elders counsel you to offer Babylon at once a treaty of mutual defense. With that offer in hand the Chaldean statesmen will be inclined to wait watchfully to discover if Croesus can overthrow you or you him. In either event, they will have in hand a treaty with the victor; they can gain by another's war."

Cyrus broke into the argument concerning details of the Babylonian treaty by saying he would not have it. He felt that a friend must be treated as a friend and an enemy as such—without a screen of deception. The elders wagged their heads in disapproval, until Harpaig hit upon the thing to do. Elam, he said, being now tributary to the Medes and Persians, could offer the treaty of non-aggression to Babylon. That would not bind Cyrus in any way, while the Chaldeans would suspect that Gubaru was seeking some advantage for himself and would wait watchfully to discover how they might gain more than that for themselves.

Leaving Harpaig to discuss the details of the Babylonian treaty with the elders, Cyrus led Gubaru forth from the palace, down to the bridge over the flowing water. He wanted to clear the clamor of argument from his mind. "My father is in his tomb," he said then. "I will adopt you, Gubaru, as my father. In this way the tie between us will never be broken."

Gubaru was startled, and affected as well. That night he gave proof that he accepted the blood tie.

When Cyrus sought his sleeping chamber that night, he found a lamp lighted within it. The daughter of Gubaru held the lamp in both hands and spoke to him. "Achaemenian lord, I believe you will be merciful to us." She raised her eyes to his, with a little smile. "Now that I am your sister, you may take pleasure from me—if you will."

In this way, Amytis gave him solace and contentment that night. By doing so, she became his second wife, although a child of hers would be inferior to Cyrus's older sons. There was no longer any question of Gubaru betraying him.

Assured of that, Cyrus began his journey toward Croesus early in the month of Nisan (546) when the horse herds could feed on the new grass. He sent ahead an offer of conciliation: *let the Lydian king acknowledge himself to be commander-protector of Cyrus, King of the Medes and Persians. Then he may rule his people and city of Sardis as now he rules them; his life and family will be as they now are, unchanged by his submission to Cyrus as overlord.*

To this in due time Croesus returned an answer, brief and contemptuous. *Croesus the King has never obeyed the order of another. Least of all will he heed the command of the Persians who were the slaves of the Medes and will be the slaves of the Lydians.*

"That's to add a written tablet to his fame," Harpaig observed and went on, "evidently he has prepared for a battle. I do not see that you have done so."

"Well, do it now."

Harpaig sent forth curt summons to the armed forces along the great north road. His Armenian hill men marched to join them at the "gate of Asia" which was the gray gorge leading down to the Zab River. There the wild Kardachi—the Kurds—rode in behind their tribal chieftains with horsehair crests tossing on their fringed turbans. Cyrus greeted them and asked what they lacked. Silver, said the eager Kurds—who had been named the robber tribes by Astyages—and he emptied chests of silver shekels into their hands. "Let them earn it first," grumbled Harpaig.

Cyrus, however, was thinking of the scorn of the Magian for the ruler who chose to amass treasure instead of following his destiny.

Experienced warriors called him a dreamer among themselves, beholding him sitting in judgment, the heavy Medic tiara gleaming above his gray eyes, aquiline nose, and short curling beard. Already he appeared older than his years. When the tidings got around that the Achaemenian made gifts to all who gained a hearing, village patriarchs pressed through the guardsmen to appeal for justice and aid. Cyrus heard them out and the silver chests became lighter in his baggage train. In the late watches of the night, hardheaded Emba grew angry and tried to pull his master away to sleep. Once the Hyrcanian spat out a mouthful of sugar cane, to clear his throat, and complained: "If you are so sweet, these dogs will chew you down."

"And if I am too bitter, they will spit me out."

Although he did not remind his servant, Cyrus took comfort in the knowledge that men who had opposed him now served the Achaemenian ruler with zest—Tabal the Germanian and Harpaig, who had sought to trick him to his downfall. Even Astyages who had wished to destroy him now dwelt in a harmless wine haze within Parsagard. However, Cyrus never imagined that destiny was drawing him away from his valley.

When his treasurer reported that the silver chests were empty as last year's wasp nests, he nodded approval. "Good—now it will cease to trouble you. Croesus, I hear, has a great burden of wealth."

His officers began longing to relieve the proud Lydian of his burden of riches. When they marched up the Plain on the left bank of the Tigris, they showed Cyrus dark walls standing over a grass-grown mound. It was the remnant of Nineveh, and beside the wide gate stood two genii of stone, bull men with kingly crowns and the upflung wings of spirits. Within, the asphalt blocks of the streets stretched empty, whipped by the mountain wind into dust clouds through which beggar folk and lepers fled into broken buildings to escape the soldiers who took no notice of such creatures. A bearded ghost, still speaking the ancient Akkadian, led the officers through halls of glazed tiles wrought in hunting scenes to the dried palms of the palace garden. The guide pointed out a picture incised in gray stone in the deserted garden.

"The favored one of Assur."

There he sat, or rather reclined in the stone portrait. Assur-banipal had discarded his tiara for comfort and loosened his long hair; with a shawl over his knees he sipped at a goblet of wine, and one of his ladies sipped at another while robed slaves brushed the flies from them and played soft music on flutes. Cyrus observed that the man's couch and the woman's chair had been set on pine cones which served to keep evil earth spirits from climbing up to the royal pair. He noticed, too, that the severed head of an Elamite king hung upside down from one of the palm trees. So Assur-banipal had made this picture of himself in restful feast after triumph. How long ago? No more than three generations ago he had raised his tablet of victory after destroying Shushan. Now the palms of his garden had become dried stalks and the sand piled up unheeded against his portrait.

What had the wise Gubaru said of this king? *Better for him if he had remained in his library instead of mounting to the chariot of war.* For Gubaru believed, and insisted to Cyrus, that out of war itself came a greater calamity. One who drew the sword would die by an invisible sword. Could any human being, unless aided by the most powerful of the gods, ride into conflict and still escape the calamity that would follow? Cyrus wondered. He had never given much thought to the consequences of his actions.

He stared for so long at the stone picture of the Assyrians that his officers wondered if a spell had been laid upon him, and the aged guide ceased begging for a coin.

Newcomers to the army on its march were surprised to discover that it carried no god with it, not even the protecting image of Nabu or Ishtar, whether captive or guardian. Cyrus, it seemed, had no such image. Nor did he take omens from sacrificed animals or released birds at the start of a day. He led two hundred hundreds of men, with their herds and ox carts and camels, to the west, along the escarpment of the great hills. At the headwaters of the Euphrates he turned up into the hills. Faring north, the army climbed to pine-shaded valleys. Sacred Mount Ararat lay far out of sight to the east. All these lands that had been Hittite and then Assyrian had come under the rule of the Medes, hence of Cyrus himself. On this road Eurybatus the Ephesian overtook him.

Eurybatus, a Greek, brought with him light chariots laden with Lydian coins and offered them all to Cyrus. His story was that Croesus had given him the money under pretext of sending it to the Delphic oracle but actually to enlist Greek mercenaries at the ports. It seemed that Eurybatus disliked the tyrants ruling for Croesus, and he liked the rumor that the powerful monarch of the Medes and Persians showed remarkable mercy. And in evidence of his good faith he gave Harpaig details of the armed forces mustered by Croesus. So many hired hoplites, so many superb Lydian horsemen——

Cyrus thought it strange that a Lydian should betray his own kind. The Armenian general shook his head over the numbers of the enemy, which he had verified by spies of his own.

"Well, what will you do about that?" Cyrus asked him.

As usual, Harpaig answered obliquely. On the march he had grown more cheerful, having no responsibilities except to teach the Achaemenian from his own experience. Now he related a fable of the slave Aesop about a wolf and a mountain goat that warred against each other. The wolf tried to trap the nimble goat, who kept out of his reach on the hillside. So they warred, with victory coming neither to one nor the other. Until the day when the mountain goat beheld his own likeness in a pool of water. He fell to admiring himself, saying, "What splendid horns I have on my head, and what fine swift legs I have on my body. Surely I have made very poor use of my strength." And thereupon in his new pride he sought out the wolf and charged at him. So the wolf caught him by the throat, killed him, and ate his fine body.

"The moral being," added Cyrus, who enjoyed a story, "that I am such a mountain goat, admiring my strength. What if I continue to run away on my hillsides?"

"We will all live longer."

By then they were entering the dark plateau of Cappadocia, where the Lydians awaited them.

THE HELMET THAT FELL DOWN AT SARDIS

Cappadocia—Katpatuka as the Persians called it—was the heart of the vast peninsula of Anatolia. Its lofty tableland, pressing against the clouds, offered an avenue leading down to the headwaters of the Tigris and Euphrates in the south, to the mountains of the Armenians in the east, and to the trading ports of the Greeks along the shore of the Euxine Sea in the north. The earliest Greek Argonauts had named the peninsula Anatolia, or the Eastland; much later, when they discovered the size of the continent beyond it, they referred to it as Asia Minor. So, in seizing the Cappadocian tableland, Croesus had made a strategic conquest, but not a very profitable one.

His army found that the fortified cities proved to be the ruined citadels of those industrious builders, the Hittites. The capital, if it could be called such, was the walled Alaja with women-headed sphinxes standing guard at the gateway. Still, it appeared as if the prophecy of the Delphic oracle had been fulfilled; after crossing the Halys River, Croesus had conquered Cappadocia. The inhabitants fled away to the wilderness of cliffs and red rock towers. There they hid in caverns with their sheep. Although unquestionably victorious, the Lydian soldiery obtained little spoil except hides and Greek-trade vases and some girls they carried off. Such spoil excited neither the civilized mercenaries from the flourishing Ionian ports nor the high-spirited Lydian cavalry searching for a worthy enemy to ride down.

The summer wore on and the army of Cyrus failed to offer battle. Fragments of it appeared to harass Lydian foragers or to assail the caravans from Sardis with flights of arrows. When a Lydian column marched out to search for the Persians, Nisayan-mounted warriors raided its encampments at the dinner hour. It was useless to pursue these barbaric riders; the well-trained Lydian war horses could match the pace of the Nisayans, but the enemy riders spewed back deadly arrows; the Lydian lancers carried no bows. They claimed a victory in every combat, but the Medes and

Reconstruction of Achaemenian shrine on the open height of Parsagard, probably finished late in the reign of Cyrus. Achaemenian architecture, preceding the Periclean Age of the Greeks by about a century, is an example of the first western Aryan art, showing as yet little "oriental" influence. (The altars are not shown.) By F. Krefter; from Herzfeld—Iran in the Ancient East.

Simple tomb of Cyrus the Great, Parsagard, as it appears today. Six steps lead up to the gabled chamber of stone blocks. (The outer columns are later construction.)

(Left) Gold rhyton, or ceremonial drinking vessel. The superb, stylized lion's head blends almost naturally with the paws and sharply detailed wings, curving to tips in the Achaemenian manner. Probably of a date after Darius I, the rhyton formed part of the imperial treasury at Agbatana (height about 9″). Reproduced here for the first time. *(Right)* Ceremonial gold dagger ornamented with lion and ibex heads. This, with the rhyton and bowl, was owned for a time by the Metropolitan Museum, then purchased by the Iranian Government (length 16½″.) *Courtesy Archeological Museum, Tehran.*

Persians kept them from taking the food in the Cappadocian hide-outs, and they wearied of eating hard barley and pickled dolphin's flesh. The dark volcanic soil offered no harvests to be gathered in. The Medes and Persians seemed to have no spoil worth fighting for.

When autumn storms penned the Lydians in their occupation camps, Croesus's generals reminded him that winter would presently put an end to the campaign and that the cavalry chargers could not endure a winter on the snowbound plateau. Accordingly, Croesus set up wreathed victory columns in Alaja, and his army started the long march back to its homeland and better barracks, there to prepare for a renewal of the war in the coming summer.

When the first snow fell from the gray sky, the Medic commanders reminded Cyrus of the same hard facts. This barren plateau, lean in harvests in any case, had been stripped of supplies by the Lydians. The Cappadocian farmers could outlive the winter by grinding up acorns or dried fish, but they had nothing to share with the Medes and Persians, who must return to warmer valleys.

Cyrus listened to them while he inspected the deserted walls of Alaja and the trophy columns of Croesus. His Armenians wished to hibernate in their home villages; his Medes longed for the warm halls of Agbatana, while his Asvaran argued about the quickest way back to Parsagard. After all the spokesmen had given their advice, Cyrus meditated upon it and spoke himself. For the first time he overruled his veteran commanders.

"We will pass the winter," he said, "most comfortably in Sardis."

For the first time they felt the iron in his purpose. He drove them west over the frozen red earth, across the Halys, out of the drifting snow, down to the warmth of the olive groves where reared sacred Mount Tmolus.

When Croesus returned safely to his chambers that looked across the ravine to the height of Tmolus, he paid off and dismissed his mercenaries who marched away to their home ports on the Ionian coast. Having saved their pay for the winter in this manner, he took pains to notify his allies across the sea and in Babylon that he would expect their armies and fleets to assemble in five months in readiness to invade the Plain of the Two Rivers, Tigris and Euphrates. Whereupon, as he returned to auditing his accounts, he ordered a shield of solid gold to be made by his artists as a worthy gift to the priests of Delphi from whom he expected other services.

One prophecy of that noted oracle, however, the astute Lydian kept to himself. Or at least he never discussed it, nor did his courtiers speak of it in his hearing. Among Croesus's many anxieties, his deepest worry was the case of his youngest son. The boy, comely as a Greek ephebe, had been born deaf and dumb. No intervention of a kindly deity had healed the dumb boy, although Croesus had devoted hours to prayer and sent gifts to the temple of Artemis at Ephesus as well as the shrine of Apollo by the spring under Mount Mycale. He had hoped for much from this last, since legend persisted that Apollo had sired a son, Branchus, by this spring. The great Pharaoh Necho had honored it with a gift of his garment worn during a victory over the Jewish king Josiah at Armageddon. Afterward, Jewish slaves died by the thousands in the labor of building a canal to allow Necho's ships to pass from the Great Sea to the Red Sea. Possibly the alert priests of Delphi had learned of Croesus's donation to the rival oracle of Apollo Branchidae, because their answer to his inquiry about his afflicted son had been enigmatic, if not hostile—so much so that Croesus did not mention it again.

> *Never wish to hear thy son's prayed-for voice.*
> *For on that day woe will befall thee.*

This troubled Croesus's orderly mind; it joined to the puzzling dictum of the Greek philosophers, Solon among them, that he could expect no joy in his life until after death. He had fitted his splendid environment to his taste, ornamenting his city and not forgetting to add columns, fluted in the Milesian fashion, to the domed tomb of his ancestors, toward which the prostitutes had contributed so much. Surely he found joy enough in a sane, healthy manner, except for his beloved deaf and dumb child——

The news that reached him first, that the Medes and Persians were descending from the mountain road, he brushed aside as a rumor. No army, Croesus believed, could make the journey from the Cappadocian ridge in winter. Then, too, Croesus had never beheld this elusive host. The next message, however, came from the lookout on holy Tmolus—that the barbarian horsemen, resembling starved centaurs, were in the valley itself. His valley, dark with fragrant grapevines.

As the crisis grew, Croesus felt the strange unreality of it, and the futility of averting it. The hoplite mercenaries could not be recalled in time. The swift galleys he dispatched from Smyrna could not return in time with the fleets of his Spartan and Egyptian allies. He listened to the invocation of the women bacchantes on the slope of Tmolus, and to the eager advice of his military advisers to muster the Lydian cavalry for battle. The officers were glad that at long last the barbarian horde had massed in the open fields below the city to meet the lances of the victorious Lydian horse——

The tidings of the battle that followed had the same unreality about them. Waiting in the shrine of Cybele in the palace garden, Croesus heard that his lancers had charged the foe with their customary spirit, only to have their horses frightened into flight by the apparition of monstrous, roaring beasts. His brave Lydians had managed to dismount, to throng into the ranks of the infantry with their lances and swords. Yet they could make no stand afoot against the death-dealing arrows of the Medes and Persians who rode around them as if they were cattle herded together.

(In the advance down the Lydian valley, Harpaig had noticed that the native horses fled away from the sight and the smell of the camels carrying his baggage. These beasts of burden from Elam and the Iranian deserts had not appeared before on this coast. In drawing up his forces for battle, Harpaig took care to place a line of unladen camels, with their drivers, in front of the Persian horsemen. The camels were familiar enough to the Nisayan steeds. The first confusion caused by the fright of the Lydian horses grew into disorder when the dismounted lancers tried to push into the ranks of the spearmen on foot.)

The fugitive forces of the Lydians all sought shelter within the walls of Sardis, closing the gates behind them. After one vain attempt to rush the gates, the army of Cyrus pitched its tents in the wide battlefield by the lake, to rest the horses and forage the fertile countryside. This plain was known thereafter as the "field of Cyrus."

In fact, as Croesus watched from his eyrie, the valley beneath him seemed to become the grazing ground of Cyrus. No conflagration seared the garden suburbs; no blood flowed from doorsteps, and no bands of captives were roped together as slaves—as had happened during the invasion of the Cimmerians. The invaders acted as if they had forgotten the war. They held horse races in the wide field beyond their tents; they climbed the terraced hillsides to assist the peasants in gathering the last autumn yield of grapes. Yet they paid no attention to the wine jars in the shops and filled their own jars with the water of the clear-running Pactolus stream.

The anxious Croesus heard that his enemies performed one strange ritual on the bank of the stream. After building twin rock altars there, they lighted fires upon the altars, and priests in white felt hoods tended the flames with aspen rods, covering their mouths while they poured out symbolic offerings of water and honey. A Cappadocian captive in the palace told the Lydians that this was done for a water goddess, Anahita, favored by Cyrus.

It impelled Croesus to perform a ritual of his own. Surely the Great Goddess was omnipotent in the Lydian lands—worshiped as Artemis, the bow-bearer, the woman self of Apollo, or in the guise of Cybele, the earth mother. In the palace of Croesus her shrine was served by eunuchs and priests in woman's robes. At the shrine his wives and companions put aside their veils to pray and to chatter there beyond his hearing. There might be more power than he suspected in this goddess, protectress of his women. Croesus prepared a symbolic sacrifice in the open court before the portico of the shrine. He ordered slaves to build a pyre of dry wood, interlaid with brush, and let it be known that he meant to immolate himself on this pyre if his enemies won their way into his city. He would not wait like the aged Priam to be cut down by a soldier's sword.

And he ordered the eunuchs to put to death all his wives and mistresses when they beheld the pyre lighted.

Even while he sought celestial aid, Croesus reassured himself by the logic of philosophy. If the Spartan and Egyptian fleets did not arrive in time to raise the siege of Sardis, the city wall might hold against his foes; if the outer city fell, his palace on the height over the river might prove to be impregnable. And if not, he might always escape by flight. The thought of fleeing like an escaped slave became a torment to Croesus.

He spent the days in an agony of mind.

The catastrophe, however, occurred within two weeks, and it was caused by the quiet on the walls.

A palace sentry walked casually along the outer parapet at dusk of a windy day. He stopped to peer over the edge and his helmet was blown off, to bounce down the rock face and lodge a few spear lengths below. Since the palace buildings crowned the height of Sardis, no wall had been set here at the brink of the cliff that fell to the stream. The Lydian sentry hated to lose his helmet, and he laid aside his weapons to climb down to it by footholds in the soft pudding stone. Retrieving it, he climbed back again. A Mardian warrior on a round of sightseeing below watched with interest and reasoned that where one man could climb another could do likewise. The Mardian, a mountaineer, soon satisfied himself that the soft cliff was climbable with a bit of step cutting. Where one could go, a hundred might follow.

The Mardian explained as much to his commander, who took him to Harpaig. It was worth a try, Harpaig decided, because failure would cost no more than a score of lives, while the capture of the palace pinnacle with the Lydian king would probably bring about the surrender of the city. Cyrus offered rewards to the first to make the climb.

In the quiet of the next evening the Mardian fighters climbed the rear of the height and crouched along the parapet, letting down ropes to aid others up. Some time passed before the Lydian sentries, who paid little attention to the cliff, noticed that strange warriors were walking into the palace. Then an outcry and clash of weapons resounded at the royal chambers still lighted by the sunset. The splutter of igniting torches, the screaming of women, and the panic rush of frightened slaves filled the corridors. When Croesus and his nobles hurried out to the courtyard, the funeral pyre burst into flame, lighted in obedience to his orders.

Indecision held him in a vise of pain; he was aware of eunuchs hurrying to the doors of the women's chambers, drawing their knives to cut the throats of the veiled inmates; body servants crowded around him, gaping. He could not articulate a command. His officers shouted at armed men filing past and yelled again when these were seen to be hooded Persians. In the confusion of sound, a strident voice cried at him, and it was his deaf and dumb son, clinging to his arm, uttering senseless words.

The conflict around him had the unreality of a dream. Croesus raised his arms and stood without moving. The guardian eunuchs threw down their weapons. The Persian warriors noticed the burning pyre and pulled it apart with their axes, casting water on the fire.

So fell the citadel of Sardis with hardly a battle worthy of the name. In after years, Greek poets embellished it with the legend that Croesus died in self-sacrifice on the pyre, although some put it that Apollo had appeared on the scene and mercifully called down rain from the sky to preserve Croesus's life.

The next morning, as Harpaig had anticipated, the lower city opened its gates. A band of noble Medes and Persians walked up the courtyard steps. In the portico they stopped to admire the view. Croesus stood in his doorway, wearing ceremonial robes; he called out to the victors, asking them not to burn the palace after looting it. From force of habit, his interpreters waiting with him translated the words.

One of the officers, sunburned and restless in riding cloak and trousers, turned to look at him and asked: "Why should I burn what is mine?"

Uncertainly then Croesus led them into his reception hall with the rare paintings on marble and the lovely pictured jars from Caere. In the library he pointed out the new-style Corinthian paintings—not one a fake. In the festival court he led the victors to the huge gold meat bowl shaped like a Nicaean craft, with

Neptune astride the stern, with silver rhytons ranged around it. Down in the crypt of his bullion treasure, he opened the brazen doors artfully shaped to lock fast together when the triple keys were withdrawn. With something like pride, he motioned for his captors to take what they desired of the gleaming bars of silver, electrum, and pure gold. In quick relief he fancied that the barbarians might leave him his paintings when they carried off his precious metals.

When they had looked around them, they began to laugh at something one had said. They seemed to be merry. From behind them the traitor Eurybatus—who had absconded with the money entrusted to him—stepped to Croesus's side, whispering, "Cyrus the Achaemenian asks why he should relieve you of the care of such a great burden as this?"

After Cyrus and his staff had departed to inspect the city streets, Croesus took his young son by the hand and went to rest on his couch. The boy was speaking at last in this day of woe, as the Pythian oracle had foretold. Croesus reminded himself that he should make some extraordinary gift to that oracular shrine; then he reflected that he could no longer make such a donation—he no longer possessed a single talent of silver. Like Priam he had lost the city that had been his life. Worse, he had failed to make his last moments immortal in fame by ascending the funeral pyre; after meditating on that, he convinced himself that the Persians had prevented him from doing so. Then he imagined building a notable mausoleum by hewing it out of the rock summit of holy Tmolus, above the burial mounds of his ancestors. One comforting thought crept into the lethargy of his weariness. There was nothing more that Croesus, last King of Lydia, could or need do. He had no more decisions to make. What his fate would be he did not know.

Stretched on the couch by the deaf boy, he slept quietly.

Although Cyrus allowed him no authority henceforth, he kept the Lydian beside him for questioning. Free of his brooding, Croesus proved to be a witty companion, with a good ear for harp playing. The victorious Achaemenian kept the great treasure locked in its vaults and appointed the lord Pactyus, collector of revenues under Croesus, as the receiver of new money in Sardis, while he named the forthright Tabal the Germanian to command the garrison and watch Pactyus.

Croesus made opportunity to send an envoy without gifts to the oracle at Delphi to protest that the ambiguous prophecy had caused him to lose his own dominion instead of conquering that of the Persians. Whereupon the Delphic priests returned a caustic answer—that Croesus had lacked the common sense to inquire of them *which* empire would be destroyed. Thus Croesus discovered that a captive king did not receive the courtesy the shrine bestowed upon a reigning monarch. He never consulted an oracle again, and he found a certain contentment in becoming the guest-captive of the unpredictable Achaemenian.

On his part, Cyrus was badly puzzled by the behavior of the Greeks on this Anatolian coast.

CYRUS ENCOUNTERS THE SPARTANS

An afterglow hung over the coast. As the sunset lighted trellised gardens, this luminosity of an earlier age touched the habitations of Aeolians and Ionians alike. In the shadows of an empty hillside theatre, youths and maidens clasped hands to dance to the strains of half-forgotten music. An actor donned a satyr's mask, although no such creature survived on the ripe Anatolian coast. The afterglow came, as the sunset did, from the sea and its islands. At Knossos in Crete ghosts hovered over the tombs, and the daring youths and maidens who danced before the Minos kings had disappeared from the smooth gypsum floors, now occupied by businesslike sea pirates. But the Ionian coast was intensely alive, while newly discovered wealth preserved its ancient heritage of culture. The people were conscious of this heritage and fearful of its loss. Children in the pastures sang together: *"Forty-five artisans and sixty apprentices—worked for three years to bridge the river—each day they built it up, and each night it fell down!"*

When he could leave Sardis, the Shepherd of Parsagard rode down to the port of Smyrna that linked the Lydians with the great western sea. He beheld the tideless water of the bay, crowned by the twin mountain peaks; he puzzled over the circumstance that the white buildings had been demolished, except for the quays which were lined with Greek galleys and black Phoenician cargo craft. His interpreters explained that the Lydian kings, in conquering the coast, wished to keep the city of Smyrna from becoming a rival to Sardis, while they desired to make use of the port. As for the sacred peaks, one held a shrine to Neptune who exerted power on the great waters; the other served Nemesis, a sea-born goddess who avenged herself on mortals who became proud of their power. The interpreters made no mention of Croesus.

If the Greek-speaking inhabitants of these minute, lovely cities at the edge of the sea puzzled Cyrus, they in turn were stunned by his unexpected appearance among them. This *Kyrios*—as they termed Cyrus—seemed to be a gentleman in barbaric woolen-sleeved shirt and riding trousers; he asked questions of philosophers, while statesmen had no means of judging his power or policy concerning themselves. He had come, as it were, out of nowhere. Native Anatolians and immigrant Greeks alike had never known the yoke of the Assyrians or Babylonians. True, each city—except for proud Miletus—had submitted under more or less force to the conquering Lydians; but the Lydians had been quite understanding and had linked the sea trade of the fertile coast to the caravan trade of the hinterland to their mutual profit. And now the hinterland had appeared among them in the person of *Kyrios* with his baggage on camels.

The Ionian cities heard his demand to submit to his rule. They answered that they would first require a guaranty of the conditions they had enjoyed under the Lydian kings. Then Cyrus told their envoys a story. "A piper came to the shore of this sea and piped to the fish to come out and dance with him. The fish then said no; they would not do it unless they enjoyed the same conditions they had in the water. Thereupon this piper put aside his pipe and got a net. With the net he hauled out the fish, and then indeed they danced vigorously for him." Unlike the dead slave Aesop, Cyrus did not explain the moral of his story but the Ionians understood it perfectly. They temporized, because they had sent an urgent appeal to the Lacedaemonians of Sparta to muster a fleet—as allies of the defeated Lydians—to defend the coast against the strange Persians.

This the Spartans, after due consideration, refused to do. Yet they sent an envoy with a message of warning to Cyrus. He received the Spartan, Lacines, seated in state in the hall of the Lydian palace, wearing the high tiara and braided purple robe of a King of the Medes. Lacines gave his message word for word: let Cyrus the Achaemenian take care to do no harm to the Greek cities on the Anatolian coast, or he would draw upon him the anger of the Spartans.

When the message was interpreted to him, Cyrus lost his temper. He remembered vividly what he had seen of Spartan merchants on the shore of Colchis in their bargaining for gold. And he answered: "I have no reason to fear these people who meet together only in a market to dispute about food and try to cheat each other about money. If I keep my health long enough," he assured Lacines, "the Spartans may have to complain, instead of the misfortunes of these Ionians, of their own misfortunes."

Lacines took his answer to Sparta, with an account of what he had seen on the Anatolian coast. No punitive expedition sailed east from Sparta.

Cyrus never forgot or forgave the stupid challenge of the Spartans. If he had journeyed farther into the west, he might have become master of their city and written new pages in history. But the sea confronted him, and his Asvaran would not forsake their horses to go upon a wooden deck to ride the great waters. As for the other allies of Croesus, they caused him no immediate anxiety. The Chaldeans were bound to him by a non-aggression pact, while the nebulous Egyptians showed no inclination to send an army to aid a completely defeated monarch. Ships from the Nile continued to moor alongside Greek vessels, taking on cargoes of ocher and alabaster, timber and iron, wine and dried fruits of this rich coast.

More than the sea, however, the minds of the Greeks baffled Cyrus. "Here," he told his counselors, "we are the fish out of water."

That happened whenever the Persians—or the Medes, for that matter—ventured out of their native mountains. In the far Sea of Grass they had found themselves among such strange plains dwellers as the warrior women. In the lowland of Shushan Cyrus had trod warily, relying on the wisdom of his adopted father, Gubaru. Otherwise the dominion behind him remained as it had been under the Medic kings, the great highlands that linked themselves together above the plains—of Parsagard itself, Media proper, Armenia, and Cappadocia. All of them lay apart and above the centers of ancient civilization. Each of them Cyrus had given to the charge of a trusted Persian as *khshatra pavan*, or *satrap*, as the Greeks pronounced it. His new satrapy of Saparda he kept under his own hand that winter, using Croesus for a mentor. The pleasant valley beneath the palace pinnacle yielded the richest foods, cheese instead of milk, olive oil instead of sesame oil, pheasants instead of Iranian chickens. Croesus took pride in the cooks who served up pungent dishes seasoned with sweet sauce, to be washed down with wine, not water. But the valley of Sardis was out of sight of the sea, and the Lydians were Aeolians, eastern folk who made music on harps and scorned the flutes or pipes of the barbaric Greeks who had intruded along the Ionian—Cyrus called it the *Yavana*—coast.

Croesus could relate the Aeolian tradition, which seemed somewhat like the Achaemenian, because the hero-leaders had been Aryans in the earliest time—that of the Midas kings, the "Mita" Phrygians who had dispossessed the Hittites "of the land of Hatti," and King Priam who had defended his walls for a long time against the barbaric sea rovers of the western king, Agamemnon. For all of ten years, Croesus said, and Cyrus found it hard to believe.

"What did these sea wanderers do with Troy after they captured it?"

Croesus believed they sacrificed some Trojan women to their gods and sailed away in triumph with rich spoil. At least Troy was no more than a picturesque ruin now, with a customs station at the water. A customs station, he explained, collected tolls from passing merchant ships.

"A deserted place becomes a desert," Cyrus agreed. "For no one cultivates the earth."

He had seen ruins enough during his journeys; it seemed as if the dwellers in the lowlands were forever building great strongholds, to store them with treasures, whereupon the citadels were broken into for the treasures.

"That is Fate."

"What is Fate?"

With a sigh Croesus asserted that it was a mystery not revealed to mortal knowledge, although the Hellenic—the Greek—philosophers believed that invisible goddesses spun, wove, and cut the threads of mortal life. It seemed childish to Cyrus to believe that unseen deities shaped like men or women manipulated human lives like threads on a loom. After cross-questioning Croesus and the Lydians, Cyrus did not anticipate great difficulty in dealing with the luxury-loving Aeolians, and he set their portion of the coast aside in his mind as a satrapy to be ruled by a sympathetic officer. It included the offshore island of Lesbos where even the women became poets; at least one, Sappho by name, retorted in verse to the advances of men and challenged Fate by consorting with other Lesbian women.

The Achaemenian had learned not to interfere with local customs. In Anshan the tribes had managed their own affairs and judgments. Their Shepherd had taken their gifts and guided the mass of them in time of danger; the laws he attempted to carry out were the laws of the Persians themselves. On this fertile, teeming shore there appeared to be no threat of danger. The Cimmerians— creatures of hell, said the Greeks—had vanished over the horizon three generations before. Therefore, in Cyrus's exacting mind there seemed to be no problem in the government of the coast except to make the inhabitants act together for their own protection and welfare.

He asked only one thing of them: unconditional submission to his sole authority. That he had to have if he was going to hold so many cities and lands under the rein of one authority.

When he came to consider the Yavans of the southern shore, however, Croesus ventured to disagree with him.

"The Greeks," he said, "will agree only on one thing, that they will never agree among themselves."

"They must meet in a tribal council."

The Ionians, Croesus declared, came together only at Sardis, where their artists were best paid. For one painting on wood he had paid its weight in gold. They did hold religious festival under Mount Mycale. They were no longer tribes; each of them dwelt in a separate *polis*—a communal city—and each warred at times with another *polis*, while maintaining rivalry with the rest. The rivalry, of course, extended to their trade over the paths of the sea. Croesus insisted that he had treated the Ionians generously, building a porticoed temple for Artemis the Many-Breasted at Ephesus, even while he was forced to besiege Phocaea. Moreover, new tides of Greek immigrants were seeking the shore from their motherland, from Corinth and from Athens of the goddess Athena. Yes, the tyrant Pisistratus of the Athenian *polis* rid himself of political antagonists by shipping them to Ionia, while fetching back in his ships asphalt and gypsum and cedar-tree trunks to raise a new portico on the rough stones of his acropolis.

Cyrus decided that the Greeks were energetic and imaginative. They excelled as stonecutters and painters; they could impart beauty to small objects, but what was the purpose of their building and what did they seek to create as a whole?

To discover that, he summoned the Ionian tyrants and philosophers to Sardis. But he called them in separately from Smyrna itself, from Phocaea, Teos, Ephesus, and Miletus, as well as the island of Samos that had been the home of the slave Aesop.

THE WISE MEN OF MILETUS

When they met face to face, Persians and Ionian Greeks were aware of a mutual likeness. They looked, as it were, into the faces of distant cousins and heard familiar words. But that blood kinship of remote Aryan descent was almost lost in the greater differences of their ways of living. The migration of the Iranians had been over the vast hinterland, moving with their herds; the migration of the Dorian Greeks had brought them to the shore of the sea and they had settled in the small ports that became thriving cities. The Persians, accustomed to emergencies, were the more versatile, more forceful in action; the Greeks were better schooled, more covetous. As warriors, the heavily metaled, shielded Greek swordsman on foot differed entirely from the Persian horse archer.

From the beginning, Cyrus had distrusted these traffickers who flitted about the sea with fragile wares to sell. Even their aristocracy, as they named the noble families, seemed to be merchants, while their workers were slaves. The Phocaeans and Teians boasted of their trading ports. In Parsagard trading was left to the caravaneers who came through from the far Indus to Shushan and to Babylon. The first Greek he had encountered, Eurybatus, appeared to be a shrewd traitor. Yet Eurybatus might have betrayed Sardis to serve his own city of Ephesus. He kept urging Cyrus to honor the Ephesians as allies, while treating the other cities as subjects.

Pactyus, the revenue collector, also praised Ephesus as the shrine of Artemis the Many-Breasted.

"If that is your Great Goddess," Cyrus demanded, "why is she different there than here, where she is called the Earth Mother?"

At times the quick-witted Greeks found the questions of the Achaemenian difficult to answer. He seemed to expect a simple explanation of complex matters. He had the delusion that whatever gods existed must be the same in all corners of the earth. Pactyus merely observed that the mystery of Artemis of the Ephesians was shared only by women—that in the yearly festival they departed from their husbands to worship their goddess by offering their bodies in ritual to strange men and to contribute the gifts of the men to the shrine, which had increased greatly in wealth and honor.

"If that is so, then some of the coins you receive each year from Ephesus come from the hands of these Yavan women?"

"As the Great King is pleased to declare, so it is. From them, and the port tax."

When he departed from Sardis to visit one of the Ionian cities, Cyrus passed Ephesus and Phocaea and Teos. Riding south to the winding Maeander River he followed it to the coast, to Miletus, last and most famous of the ports. He dismounted in a luminous valley between hillsides terraced into gardens. The Milesians had no tyrant to manage their affairs and to greet the royal visitor. The leaders who offered token gifts to Cyrus called themselves philosophers and scientists. Without argument they acknowledged him as their king—which they had failed to do in the case of Croesus—and merely asked what he required of them. They explained they were too busy to be bothered by politics.

Cyrus never understood what the Greeks meant by politics. It seemed to be an ingredient that stirred up all their activities. A tyrant might follow after this *policy* or that, compelling his people to do the same. Otherwise, they obeyed no code of law or any authority that Cyrus could distinguish. He understood that the Milesians left both politics and policy to him, which seemed reasonable enough as he was their monarch.

In the way of tradition the Milesians had little to show except what they called their independence. Their ancestors had migrated by ship from an isle of the west, Crete. The Milesians claimed that they looked ahead toward achievements, and not behind them at memories. But Cyrus noticed in their streets the four-wheeled carts and harnesses of Shushan; they wrote their words on familiar lambskins of the Aramaic-speaking tribesmen; they hewed beams with the double-headed axes of Sardis. Such tools they had got from the eastern peoples. They possessed also the sun clocks of Egypt—dials that marked the hours by the shadow of a gnomon, a pointer set toward the north. And they had made a map of all of the world they knew.

Then, too, their men of knowledge, or *scientists* had delicate instruments affixed to great rings to follow the movements of the planets as apart from the stars of the sky. The scientists took Cyrus to the marble tomb of one of their kind, Thales, who had been a salt merchant, traveling about with Croesus. In fact, Thales had calculated and predicted the eclipse of the sun that had stupefied the Lydian and Median armies forty years before. Thales had worked with the tables of the Chaldean astronomers which determined the great cycle of the sun's eclipses of some 26,000 years.

What interested Cyrus deeply was the Milesian theory of the

earth as a single body surrounded by everlasting fires through which the outer universe could be perceived at times. In that vast outer space, they maintained, other invisible bodies whirled through orbits unchanged by time. Life, they believed, had its origin from water, and life—at least on their earth—was developing toward something even higher, through the aeons of time. How long had it taken fish to become men walking the surface of the earth?

"Anaximander has said that if man had been then, in the origin, as he is now, he could not have survived."

All this touched upon memory in Cyrus of the majesty of the sun, supreme over gods, of the celestial nature of fire, and of the life-giving attribute of water. Moreover, since the Milesians worked with practical instruments, the Achaemenian could follow their calculations in his mind, although this was not easy without writing down the numbers.

He liked particularly to believe that human beings might develop themselves into a better sort, instead of being shaped by an invisible Fate. He noticed that the Milesians irrigated their gardens well and piped flowing water from mountain springs—a mechanism unknown to the Persians. Instead of taking tribute from them, he gave them a chest of Pactyus's coins to purchase more instruments and—expecting a return of courtesy—asked for a Milesian scientist to accompany him to Parsagard. The Milesian elders looked at each other and complained politely that both Thales and Anaximander were recently dead, while their only disciple of promise was a wildly dreaming youth, Pythagoras, self-exiled on the island of Samos. The truth was, as Cyrus suspected, that no Milesian wished to leave his city and the revered shrine of Apollo Branchidae down the coast.

On leaving Miletus, he decided that some Greeks could be bought over, but not all of them. Their Apollo oracles might be relied on to give an answer favoring the person who made the costliest gifts. Taking Croesus's suggestion, he dispatched massive ingots to Delphi and the shrine by Miletus as well. That city, at least, had acknowledged his rule. The other Ionians obviously waited to see what action Cyrus would take.

Convinced of that much, he acted. Before the coming of grass, he departed from Sardis with the bulk of his army and all the baggage train including camels loaded with Milesian water pipes. He gave out that he was journeying to Agbatana and farther east and he took no hostages with him except Croesus and the deaf son. The army of Medes and Persians ascended the highlands as far as the citadel of the Midas kings, where Cyrus halted to encamp, to wait—as he explained—for better grazing in the upland pastures. In reality he was waiting to discover what action the Ionians would take in his absence.

In the next moon a courier arrived from Sardis to report that Pactyus had slipped out of the city with the money in his possession; Pactyus was enlisting hoplite mercenaries in the Ionian ports. A rebel army had broken into Sardis and was besieging Tabal, the commander, in the citadel guarding the treasure.

HARPAIG, SATRAP OF IONIA

Straightaway Cyrus sought out Croesus and found him casting hucklebones, one hand against the other, between sips from his wine goblet. "Of what use are slaves to you?" he asked.

Putting aside the bones, the Lydian explained that slaves served the owners of wealth by handwork in mines or fields, or simply about the house. Although a slave might save money and buy himself a share in a mine, or a hectare in a field, he remained in the slave class.

"Is there any reason," Cyrus then asked, "why I should not sell your Lydians off as slaves or transport them to Agbatana to do such useful work?" Thereupon he told Croesus of the revolt of the hired army and the siege of Sardis. "Otherwise, what good does it do me to hold you, the father of the Lydians, if the children turn against me?"

Sensing the anger of the Achaemenian, Croesus blenched, fearing for the first time for his life. "Punish Pactyus, my lord king! Do not——" he rallied his courage and changed his words—"do not lay waste a noble city for the crime of one man!"

Cyrus remarked that it was the Greeks who laid waste in Sardis. Croesus had an agile mind and he gained confidence because the downright Cyrus had been inclined to question him. "If the Lydians are indeed my children," he ventured, "you can make sure they will never arm themselves against you again."

"How?"

"Perhaps they are their own worst enemies; yet I do believe they never meant to be yours. You have seen that they are full of repressed desires. Then grant them what they so desire and take away the means by which they harm themselves. Take all weapons from them; let them wear only tunics beneath their mantles; let them take their harps in hand to console them and tend only their homes, cooking pots, and shops. Then they will be harmless as their women."

Croesus laughed a little to point up his jest, while his fine eyes pleaded with the Achaemenian conqueror. Without a word, Cyrus left him to summon his commanders into council, with the chieftains of tribes and all Law-bearers. They came at once because the impatient Shepherd had a way of appointing another officer in the stead of one who absented himself. Most of them advised their king to turn back with the army and suppress the revolt down the length of the coast. One, Mazeres, an elder Mede, did not agree. He had long experience in the service of Astyages.

"A revolt is a nuisance, not a war," Mazeres argued. "Civilians herd together like animals in such a case; by killing many of them you can cause the survivors to flee. That may or may not stop the revolt. Now a herd only follows after its leaders, and if they are taken away the others will return to their habits of action because they are no longer in danger. I say, send a small force to relieve Sardis—for that is the stronghold we cannot lose—and join with the Lord Tabal's garrison to hunt down all leaders of the uprising."

Cyrus gave his opinion. "I have no wish to wage war down this coast. Greater evil than the revolt might come out of that."

And he sent Mazeres west on the road with a column of fast-marching Medic spearmen carrying long bows. He gave the veteran officer firm orders to capture Pactyus, who had betrayed his trust, to enslave the soldiery under arms, and then to await the results in Sardis.

Before Cyrus reached Agbatana, he received tidings from Mazeres. At the appearance of the Medic detachment, the Lydian Pactyus had fled down to the coast; the besiegers had scattered, few being captured. Mazeres and Tabal thereupon had remanned the wall of Sardis and dispatched a small force of cavalry to hunt down Pactyus. Whereupon Mazeres had confiscated all arms in the Saparda satrapy, issuing a proclamation that householders who played harps or games, tended shops or cookeries would not be molested. Mazeres finished his report—neatly written by a Lydian scribe—with the announcement that now harps could be heard at all hours in all the streets of Sardis. Cyrus reflected that the old general thought only of carrying out orders, regardless of consequences.

Mazeres's reports followed the Achaemenian on his journey of the ensuing months. Each one related some fact——

The Lydian fugitive Pactyus sought refuge at the seaside city of Cyme, an Aeolian city.

The citizens of Cyme sent inquiry to the shrine of the Apollo situated 135 stadia south of Miletus as to what they were to do about the Lydian Pactyus. The oracle of this Apollo Branchidae said give him up to the Persians. Thereupon, a young nobleman of Cyme, Aristodicus, hurried to the shrine of the oracle. Aristodicus walked around the shrine, stripping the swallows' nests from it. A voice was then heard from within, warning him: "Impious man, spare my suppliants who are these birds!" Thereupon Aristodicus made answer as follows: "And do you command the Cymaeans to give up their suppliant?" The voice made answer: "Yes."

Whereupon the Cymaeans secretly sent Pactyus away by ship to the island of Lesbos. Unable to reach Lesbos, having no ship, Mazeres then sent a demand to the Lesbians to give up the Lydian Pactyus. He offered them silver in return.

Discovering this negotiation, the Cymaeans interfered, sending a second ship to convey Pactyus thence to refuge on the island of Chios.

Mazeres then offered the Chians a tract of shore on the mainland, called Atarneus, for harvesting. Pactyus went to a sanctuary in the temple of the guardian goddess of Chios (Mazeres was not certain of her name). From this temple, the Chians dragged the fugitive Pactyus to deliver him to the Persian mounted patrols in exchange for a grant of the shore named Atarneus, which they took in the name of their goddess. The patrols brought Pactyus back to Sardis where he was carefully watched.

(Cyrus made a mental note that the Chian Greeks had sold a man who had taken refuge in their sanctuary.)

Mazeres closed his account with the remark that he had sought out the hoplites who carried arms against Sardis and ravaged the lands of their villages, forwarding the men under ample guard to Agbatana.

This was his last report because the veteran Mede died from sickness.

Cyrus was far distant in the east by then. After meditating over the reports of the dead Mazeres, he called in Harpaig and repeated them to him. Mazeres had been a good soldier but a poor governor, and he imagined that the Armenian, now accustomed to his ways, would do better in Sardis.

"For I am unable to understand these Greeks or to satisfy them in their own minds. Their coast of Yavana is the brightest and richest in soil I have ever seen; they need nothing but peace to prosper and play their games and music and invent useful machines. The Milesians seem to be doing that; the others will not." He ransacked his memory and added. "In Miletus they told me that Thales, a Phoenician merchant, advised them all to join together in one government at Teos, their central city, and devise laws to share among themselves. Was it not wise advice? The Yavans would not take it. Mazeres was wrong in likening them to a herd, for each city must go a way of its own, and each dweller in a city must follow a destiny of his own toward some kind of Fate which they do not seem to understand. I mean to set a single authority over them, as Thales proposed, and make Sardis their ruling city, and you, Harpaig, their Guardian of the Country."

So the aged Harpaig journeyed back to Lydia as satrap. Cyrus, having full confidence in him, gave the Armenian no specific orders, merely requesting him to do the best he could.

In little more than a year, Harpaig subjected the Ionian coast more by guile than by force. He made no use of the oracles or traitors. He summoned each city in turn to submit to the rule of Cyrus their Great King. In Teos of the far-ranging fleets the inhabitants sailed away in a mass with their treasures to found a new city beyond the sea. In Phocaea, Harpaig asked only that the inhabitants pull down one section of their wall and dedicate one house to the service of the Persians. The Phocaeans asked for time to consider their answer and embarked on their ships with their families and belongings under cover of the truce; they sailed only the short distance to the island of Chios, but the Chians refused to sell them land, fearing they would build rival trading posts. Then the Phocaeans divided, and half of them sailed back to their deserted city to attack the outpost Harpaig had left in it. The others made the long voyage to the west, to Corsica and the River Rhone where they set up remote trading posts.

It seems that a solitary Ionian, Bias, spoke to other leaders at the religious festival under Mount Mycale—for the Ionians held their festivals as well as games during this crisis—urging them to join their armies in mutual defense of their coast. They would not agree. They prepared to stand siege in their separate communities. However, Harpaig indulged in no siege operations. He built earth ramps supported on timbers, in the fashion of the vanished Assyrians, to the summit of their walls. When his armed men advanced over the ramps to the walls, the citizens were forced to surrender.

Harpaig met with savage resistance only in the far south, among the native Anatolians, the Lycians. By then he had Ionian hoplites serving beside the Medes in his command. It did not surprise Cyrus that Greeks would go out to meet Greeks for pay. The northern coast along the Hellespont, with ruined Troy and the Phrygian farmlands, he entrusted to a mild satrap, Mithrobat. So all of Anatolia was joined together for the first time and the word of Cyrus became its law.

That, however, was not immediately apparent to the Aeolians or

Ionians. They accepted Cyrus the Achaemenian as the successor to Croesus the Lydian, perhaps more dynamic and certainly more remote. Harpaig consolidated the highland peninsula in his own way; after buying the good will of the oracles at Delphi and Mycale, he pensioned the local tyrants with portions of Croesus's treasure. Such tyrants proved to be useful in two ways; as individuals they could always be called to account and as governors of the separate city states they could be made to plan for the well-being of their indwellers as a whole. A tyrant needed to please or at least pacify the *demos*, or muster of the people, which the noble merchant class took no thought of doing. In one island, Chios, a rough constitution of law was drawn up for all inhabitants.

Since the Persians had not ventured beyond the tidewater mark —they called the coastal lands "Those on the Sea" in contrast to "Those Beyond the Sea"—the Greek islands suffered no change at all, except that their commerce increased with the new activities of the coast. Aramaean-driven caravans appeared from the red plain of North Syria and Palestine. Midas-land sent its ores to the western shore, with the horses and cattle of Cappadocia. Then, because the Achaemenians were constantly bothered by the Babel-like speech of their new subjects, Cyrus named the Aramaic as the common language of trade and government. It could be written more easily than the wedge stamps of Elamite or Akkadian, and it was easily read by those other far-ranging traders, the Phoenicians and Hebrews. The Persian speech, of course, had no written form except the borrowed wedge marks, and the Aramaic script fitted it better, as well as the native Anatolian dialects. This had important consequences, because the ancient cuneiform of Assyria and Babylon began to die out and the scriptures of the Hebrews and Aramaeans became prevalent.

Thus the Greeks of the coast hardly noticed that the rule of the Shepherd had been laid upon them. They expected Cyrus to return to visit them but he did not appear again. He had merely ridden around these new territories of the far west, from North Syria and Cappadocia to the sea at Miletus. Now he disappeared for five years into the vaster regions of the east.

COMING OF THE GREAT CHANGE

While the Asiatic Greeks sensed nothing new at hand, the European Greeks were aware of an alteration in the eastern horizon. Black Phoenician galleys anchoring on the beach of Phaleron brought tidings as well as dyed stuffs and carved ivories. Thrones, they said, were toppling; the ancient gods were descending from their eyries of the heavens to their shrines on the mountain summits.

Pisistratus, being tyrant of Athens and thereby responsible for the cleaning up and beautification of his city, remembered that Solon had predicted enlightenment would be found in the east. The Phoenician traders showed him specimens of enameled tiles with brilliant colors burned into them by intense heat. By piecing the new tiles together, the figure of a crowned and marching archer took shape. It was strange to behold an ordinary human figure that still seemed to be part of a larger design.

Antenor, the moody sculptor, complained of copying out-of-date figures of gods. Antenor dared cast up disparaging eyes at the gilded and flesh-tinted statue of Athena, their guardian goddess. "Sixty-six cubits of old-fashioned stupidity," he remarked, "with a silver spear and amethyst eyes. The only female statue in the city is a jeweled warrior."

They told him that the giantess of the Acropolis served as a beacon for mariners at sea, and he declared that a lighthouse would serve better. Secretly Antenor worked at another marble woman—forbidden by law—and beneath the garment folds a human figure revealed itself; the face lacked the staring eyes of a goddess; it appealed in the manner of a prostitute.

Vessels coming from the Hellespont and the far Euxine Sea brought the usual barbarian slaves, grain and tuna fish, and also bits of delicate bronze and silver work. These were made for wealthy Scythians who liked ordinary things to be shaped by artists. Knives and hones, bow cases, belt plates, caldrons, and bowls—all the nomad possessions were portable, while their women craved mirrors and clasps and armlets. All these bore designs of racing stags or entwined beasts and winged birds of prey. The Greeks studied their designs, and the vase painters of Corinth began to make figures that were human but with a style of their own. Secrets of such arts were not passed from hand to hand by tales of distant glories; they traveled with small objects of trade.

The smallest of all were the tiny seals of translucent chalcedony and agate. They had miniature scenes carved upon them with incredible skill—scenes of suppliant men before enthroned deities or of guardian spirits protecting noble, tamed animals beside the Tree of Life. The first Persian seals to arrive in Greek hands revealed a Shepherd, a crowned king astride his horse in combat with a wild animal. The skill of these carvings, as well as the natural animals, stirred Greek artists to emulate them. Such masterly designs appeared also on the small vases brought by merchants from Ionian Caere. The loveliest pottery came from the island of Rhodes. Artists of primitive Athens realized that they had more to picture than the ritual exploits of Hercules or the affairs of the gods upon Olympus. Enlightenment, as Solon had predicted, was coming to them from the east.

So, too, masters of unknown science arrived from Ionia-way. Physicians from the islands of Cos and Cnidus taught that medicine had nothing to do with magic and that health might be protected from disease. The intolerant Pythagoras left Samos after a quarrel with the tyrant there who found his theories dangerous. After visiting the masters of mathematics in Egypt, Pythagoras journeyed to Crotona in southern Italy to teach, in a school of his own, that the human soul might be changed to other forms and that mathematics could be used for other purposes than trade accounts. (Most of his disciples were massacred later on by the citizens of the Greek cities, but the Pythagorean theories endured.) Men of the wealthy Alcmaeonid family arrived from the coast of Asia with medicine from Cos; some of them joined the Pythagoreans at Crotona. (Later on, they were known as "friends of the Persians" and accordingly traitors.)

A blossoming of the arts began in European Greece after the middle of the sixth century. Pisistratus told the young men sunning themselves on the steps of the Agora, "Take ship to the east and school yourselves in the East-land; then return to work for your city."

The bridge of the Greek children's song, that forty-five artisans could not build across the water, was built at last. Across it, from island to island, came the innovations and new thought of the Anatolian coast. The impulse of the eastern continent made itself felt in Corinth, Athens, and Thebes. Only Sparta the unchanging held to ancient ways. Not that artists in the homeland copied the models from Shushan or Sardis; they used them to create masterpieces of their own.

Perhaps the first great change in Anatolia itself was the peace. The internecine wars of the little cities came to an end. People spoke vaguely of the unalterable laws of the Medes and the Persians. The laws, it seemed, prohibited using weapons. They called for tolerance of other men's gods; they placed by some invisible balance a wealthy olive-oil merchant on the same level with a peasant renting the merchant's lands to feed animals. Only the Milesian scientists understood such laws, but the Milesians—so said the Ionians—always shifted their sails to changing winds. Now that the wind was blowing from the hinterland of Asia, the Milesians faced that way.

It was useless to debate the new laws or discuss the politics of a government that remained invisible. This government spoke to the Greeks very seldom, and only when a messenger came—who might be a Cappadocian, Armenian, or even Hebrew—and said that this was the command of Cyrus the Great King. The messenger simply repeated words that had been told him; if he actually had an order, it was written in Aramaic, the trade lingo that needed to be translated into Greek.

The Greeks were familiar with the empires that had been Lydian, Egyptian, or Assyrian. But this new dominion of all the lands and peoples seemed to be nameless. The shrewdest political thinkers did not expect it to endure more than a couple of years. Only a few people, the Milesians among them, suspected that the first world state was coming into being.

Cyrus had started east by the road from Sardis to Shushan that soon became known as the King's Road. It took him homeward by the steppe of northern Syria, across the grain fields of the upper Euphrates and the Tigris. Where he passed in this fashion with his armed host, the territory became Achaemenian; he left officers in each town to see that it remained so. At the same time—and it must have been because they planned it so—Gubaru, his adopted father, marched west from the Sealands across the lower Tigris. Gubaru's Elamites reached ancient Lagash and Uruk, the city of the goddess Ishtar near the Euphrates. So between them that summer they harvested the outer food-producing areas of Chaldea, and this had consequences that soon appeared.

For one thing, Babylon in the central region felt the lack of food. And Nabu-naid, its king, hurried out of Syria the next year— 545—to Babylon. Mighty Babylon felt the approach of hostile forces. Along the walls upon the great street, the Processional Way, certain Hebrews of the resistance group wrote words in their strange script: "*Mene, Mene, Tekel, Upharsin.*" The words meant that the days of the kingdom were numbered, but the people of Babylon could not read them.

THE MADNESS OF CYRUS

The Shepherd passed by the fortified zone of Babylon that summer. He left Croesus at the Agbatana palace with his Lydian servants and a token guard of Medic spearmen to honor him as well as to watch over him. Cyrus regretted that the language barrier kept Croesus from discussing matters with his other royal charge, Mandane. As long as he had his own chefs and his deaf son at his side, Croesus appeared to be content, although he complained of the olive oil. While the restless Mandane complained that Cyrus, for all his conquests, had not granted her one wish—to betake her aged bones to the palace suite of the hanging garden in Babylon.

"Does the Great Goddess, your guardian, desire it?" Cyrus asked.

"Assuredly," said Mandane.

"Then why do you think it will not happen?"

Cyrus hardly waited to rest at Agbatana. After conferring with Mithradat on the state of the roads, he told his servants and captains to prepare to take the familiar way south to Parsagard, with the mounted forces of Agbatana and his own Thousand of the young Asvaran. While his saddlebags were being packed, a palace scribe came in and stood stubbornly by the terrace door. The man's face was familiar and he held in both hands an old-fashioned clay tablet of writing. When Cyrus looked at him twice, the scribe began to intone his titles, adding that of monarch of Lydia and the Euxine Sea. Cyrus stopped this by demanding what he had on his mind.

"Lord of All the Lands," responded the secretary, "the pilgrim, the Magian."

He had been given an order to track down the wandering of this Magian. Accordingly he reported at this first opportunity that the said Magian had journeyed on toward the rising sun, to the Two Rivers of the East, and on toward *Aryan-vej*, the ancestral home of the Aryans. "And there," related the scribe, "the said Magian turned on my agent who followed his steps and he cried out in utter disrespect of my lord: 'Ask the Shepherd who sent thee how long he will search after Evil in darkness: how long will he fear to turn to the light?' My agent wrote down the very words quickly, lest they be mis-said." The scribe held out the tablet. "Will my lord give command to yoke this criminal now or"—his downcast eyes lifted hopefully—"to flay the skin from him and hang it to the gate tower of Bactria where he dwells now?"

Impatiently Cyrus turned away. Not for years had anyone ventured to ask if he was afraid. Even in his anger he marveled at the delicacy of the Median chain of communications which reported to him the exact words of a wanderer a hundred camel-day stages away. "No!" he called hastily over his shoulder, and then remembered to caution the dutiful secretary. "I give no such command; yet I do say to thee, cease tracking this Magian—call off your hounds. Do you understand?"

Respectfully the scribe drew in his breath and bent his shaven head. "Your slave has heard and understood."

Cyrus thrust the small tablet into his girdle. It had been stamped with the official seal of the Achaemenian wings and the head of a crowned king, but Cyrus could not read it. Its message seemed ridiculous. How could a human being turn away from Evil, which was always waiting at hand? A god on earth might find refuge in some dwelling of light, but such gods did not exist.

When Cyrus rode into his home valley, he found it changed more than usual during his absence. Children ran out as before, laughing, with offerings of cherries and flowers. Emba limped out to seize his rein at the main gate. It occurred to the Achaemenian that Emba was growing old. And beside the entrance stair two winged bulls of white limestone stood guard. Although smaller and more graceful than the stone beasts of the Assyrians, these figures still had the same crowned human heads. The architects had erected them hurriedly in his absence. They looked imposing enough. After studying them for a moment, Cyrus accepted their presence and asked his old servant, "Emba, do you believe now that I am no small king but a lord of many peoples, many lands?"

The Hyrcanian rubbed his hands against his leather trousers and rubbed his shaggy head. "Cyrus," he admitted, "there is no *name* like yours. But," he added slowly, "I said that once of Astyages, who is now in his grave, and no one cares. Still, you know that I am stupid."

"I do not think so," Cyrus said.

A multitude lined the familiar walk through the park to the *apadana*, the hall of audience. Like a stand of wheat under the wind, the heads of the crowd bowed down at Cyrus's approach. He noticed piles of cedar trunks from the Lebanon, fragrant wood from Karmania, and black marble from the isles of the sea. Gold of Sardis filled the treasury. The great hall itself stood completed, with the slender pillars rising pallid white from the black marble bases. There was, Cyrus thought, no king's hall like this, within an open park. When he walked on, he found the familiar fire altars standing at the end of a great marble terrace open to the sky.

Smoke rose from them because the priests offered sacrifice at his coming. They prepared the ritual meal for him swiftly, and this time on shining copper plates that must have come from Egypt. Cyrus partook again of the mess of figs, terebinth, and sour milk—the peasant's fare that reminded him he was no better than the people he ruled.

Cyrus sat on a portable ivory throne while he ate, and he observed that the ivory arms were neatly carved in symbols of the Seven Guardian Stars. He heard the priests ask the blessing of the twin altars, of Atar and Ahura. When they had finished, he demanded what the name Ahura meant.

The priests did not answer readily; they murmured that it was wrong to devote the two altars to one spirit, Atar the Fire. Surely there must be another spirit present, and surely this must be Ahura's. "The Master who created us, who is supreme," they said, beseeching.

"What Master?"

"The one, the Lord of Wisdom. So hath Zarathustra said."

Cyrus did not relish the strange name intruding upon his home altars. Atar, he reflected, was present in the hearth fires by which they all lived; Anahita dwelt in the rush of clear waters. In childhood he had felt their presence. But Ahura-Mazda was no more than a name spoken by a refugee prophet. It signified nothing to him. In the end he allowed the altar priests to voice their prayers as they wished. They would do that, he realized, in any case.

He could not accustom himself to the change in Parsagard. When he sat in audience—and he did so for most of the day—the Law-bearers did not give their opinion unless he requested it of them. The familiar chieftains of the Ten Tribes were almost lost among the spokesmen of his satraps and envoys from courts that he hardly remembered, and he had a very clear memory. It seemed as if people unknown to him had brought hither their problems of plague, drought, flood waters and hostile raiders, poverty and lack of trade—always with the question, what would the Great King do about it?

While doing his utmost to give judgment and aid, Cyrus felt the great difficulty of deciding matters beyond his sight. Such troubles and aspirations—he could not always distinguish the one from the other—should be dealt with by experienced men on the scene. At once he hit upon a remedy, naming his representatives to go from Parsagard to settle the problems of the different regions. To meet such varying needs, engineers, soldiers, physicians, accountants, or simply diplomats might be sent. Yet he realized that this vicarious assistance did not alter his own responsibility for the result. In later years he sent out reporters with the operative officials—men who became known as the "king's eyes and ears." The Assyrians had relied on such informers, although they had not been in the personal service of the monarchs. Cyrus was beginning to have a healthy respect for the statesmen of Assur, although he detested their method of driving the multitudes to build their cities, whether Assur itself or Sargon's City or Nineveh. He told himself there would be no ruling city in his lands.

Cyrus had no least desire to rule like an Assur-bani-pal. The Egyptian architects who brought him a model of the image of the guardian spirit to be placed at last—as his father had failed to do—beside the entrance of the hall were startled when he smashed the clay model to pieces on the ground. They had designed an Assyrian genius with four wings and royal diadem, an armed, bearded warrior. Cyrus had seen one like it in the ruins of Sargon's City.

The architects flung themselves on their faces. "What, then, does the Lord of the Land desire?" one ventured to whisper.

"Does a spirit stride in boots and wear a crown? Does he carry a sword to protect him?"

"Nay, certainly."

Cyrus thought of his own fravashi, who had not come to his side during the journey to the west. "I do not believe that any of us has seen the likeness of a spirit," he observed. "My masters, make for me the image of a good spirit coming from the sky without mortal gear or weapons. By the Seven Stars, must you carve out a sledge hammer to picture power?"

"Nay, most certainly! How great is the wisdom of our Lord!"

When Cyrus was gone, the architects did their best. Upon a white limestone slab they carved a strange figure; it had the four Assyrian wings, and a single simple robe; it had bare feet that touched no earth, and instead of a crown it wore rising flower stems that resembled Egyptian lilies. It raised empty hands in blessing, or prayer. Nothing like Cyrus's door guardian was ever made again. (By a strange fate this guardian of the entrance survived after Parsagard vanished into the earth, except for some marble paving and steps and a few fragments of columns. After long centuries it remained to puzzle archaeologists of the modern world who described it as an extraordinary demon, or perhaps a strange portrait of Cyrus himself.)

The madness of Cyrus came upon him during the early hours of one night.

He had found no rest in his home. Kassandan nagged him when he appeared in the living quarters. His first wife had grown heavy with eating and her servitors filled all the chambers; she shone with a star gleam of jewels, yet she implored him to think more of his royal glory and to transport all captured treasures to his home—and build a walled treasury to guard them. Although Kassandan did not mention it, she felt jealousy of the other woman, the daughter of Gubaru who accompanied him in his travels. She asked, as if casually, if he cared so much for Shushan that he neglected Parsagard, the city of his first-born son, Cambyses, his acknowledged heir. To satisfy her, Cyrus ordered his engineers to begin building a wall of stone on the hills above the sprawling town that Parsagard had become.

Cambyses, too, bore no resemblance to the boy who had tended ponies and gone forth proudly with Cyrus to hunt. Now Cambyses, more than twenty years of age, stood silent behind his father in the audiences. Nervous and intent, he fidgeted during the long discussions carried on through interpreters. Being educated by foreign masters, Cambyses could read and speak the languages of the realm—Persian, Elamite, and Aramaic. He understood all that was discussed, yet Cyrus noticed that in deciding a problem his son turned to his counselors or a writing of tradition.

All at once Cyrus wanted to take his son on his next journey. The two of them riding over strange territory might come to share their thoughts. As it was, he knew less of Cambyses's mind than of the aged Harpaig's, thirty horse days' stages away. Kassandan, however, besought the Law-bearers tearfully, and they reminded Cyrus of the law that the heir of an Achaemenian throne might not leave the land with his father.

That night when the sunset came, the Shepherd did not leave his ivory throne to sit down to food in his residence as usual. The chamberlain who carried the long staff with the gold eagle's head ushered the courtiers from the hall, but since the Achaemenian remained seated, many of them waited outside in the portico.

Cyrus wanted to be alone when the sunset glow left the hall. Slaves, however, put away their fly whisks to light the silver Mannean oil lamps. The flames danced on the white pillars that rose into darkness. The voice of the river rose in the silence. Years before, the Achaemenian had listened to it as the voice of Anahita. Now it was no more than the rush and ripple of water over stones. Perhaps the wise Amytis, bred in Babylon, had taken the place of the foam-dancing Anahita.

Cyrus felt the change taking place about him, and he no longer understood it.

A sense of foreboding came over him, as if his fravashi had uttered it. His old friends were dead or scattered among posts beyond his sight. His dream of uniting the mountain people had vanished in the realization that the sheltered mountain regions had no end. The heights of Anshan joined to the Elamite foothills, and they to the fields of Babylon. The dominion of the Medes had neither frontier nor purpose. His set purpose to bring each different people into friendly accord proved impossible; beyond the Armenians waited the Cappadocians, and beyond them the Midas-folk who joined to the Lydians and they to the Greeks of the sea. What else waited in the west? He had never visited the regions to the east beyond the citadel of the Germanians. Then, too, the wise men of Miletus had disturbed his mind. He wished that a single Greek scientist had remained at his side to discuss what should be done during the journeys.

The truth was that in the west Cyrus had dwelt too long in the cities of mud-brick walls. Still nomadic by instinct, he felt the strain of caring for people in a mass. The city dwellers massed together by instinct. Cyrus had been accustomed to caring for animal herds. Could human beings be treated as herds, to be fed, slaughtered, bred, and moved about? It was a mad thought, and suddenly it filled the Achaemenian with fear.

The sense of being afraid made him angry and drove him to the relief of action.

"Stop, fiends!" he shouted at the robed slaves who were doing no more than holding their fly whisks to shield the lamp flames from the fitful breeze.

Striding past them, Cyrus came out on the portico, where the officials bowed to him—since he had left the seat of audience to make a new appearance. Cambyses was chatting with a group of nobles from Sardis, all of them amused by some jest; their amusement vanished at sight of Cyrus.

"Cambyses," he commanded, "do you stay within the limits of Anshan. Act for me, consulting the leaders of the Ten Tribes. Send to me only if there is need."

His glance ran over the staring scribes, interpreters, and envoys. "Stay here," he bade them briefly and looked for one to carry out an order. A captain of the Asvaran had been examining the chamberlain's staff, and Cyrus beckoned toward the soldier.

"Go thou to the encampment of the Persians. Let all the horsemen there make ready for a journey of many moons. Let all be ready with equipment and supplies for the road. Gather at the river gate—the inflowing river gate." He reflected and nodded. "So say I, the Achaemenian, the king."

The soldier hesitated and the anxious chamberlain murmured a question. What day would it please their lord to set forth? How many days to prepare for such a journey?

Cyrus looked at the bearer of the staff. "Five hours, not days." He pointed at the tall soldier. "Now understand this. Tell it as you go. At the stroke of dawn I will ride out, toward the summer sunrise. All who are ready at that time will accompany me. All who are not ready will remain here."

So it happened that Cyrus began his journey into the east, with Emba following, with the spare Nisayan steed, and with Amytis, not in a covered wagon but astride a mountain pony. The guards came, to a man, with their supply wagons and herds. The Hyrcanian horse galloped after, because their faces were turned homeward, and some Cappadocians straggled in with huntsmen and mastiff dogs.

Of those that watched this riding out, the foreign envoys surmised there must be a new war to be waged; the Law-bearers explained that Cyrus, who habitually journeyed along his frontiers, felt the need of visiting his eastern domains. Others whispered that madness had come upon him.

Cyrus could not have told them why he was going. He believed that he could depend on this small following. And when they emerged from the river ravine to the plain of grass covered only by the clouds on the horizon, he felt at ease for the first time in many years.

FOUR

At the Fire of Bactria

KAVI VISHTASPA

THE Crystal Mountain stood over the gate to the eastern lands. They watched it for days until they left it behind. No matter how far they rode in a day, the aspect of the sentinel peak changed very little. Winding around it on the caravan track, they did not feel the winds that drove a white plume from the snow crest of the Crystal Mountain (Mount Demavend).

Scientists among the Achaemenians could not explain the meaning of the white plume, so far above the early morning clouds. Nor could they name the god that dwelt within the summit. They said that since the Assyrians had called this peak the Crystal, they must have seen it during their age of power when the armies of Nineveh thrust up through the higher mountains, seeking to carry off horses, cattle, and slaves. But those armies seldom got far among the mountain people, who fought them off.

"It is clear," Cyrus replied, "that the gods of that lofty mountain opposed those Assyrian armies; whatever they may be, they have not stood in our way as yet."

His own *lashkargah*—his moving camp—hardly resembled an army. During the day the horsemen scattered over the plain to hunt or forage, relying on a screen of scouts to give warning of any danger. The baggage train also pressed ahead during the afternoon, and when Cyrus and his companions arrived at the stream selected for the night encampment, they found the leather tents pitched for the officers, the horse lines marked out, and fires started.

In contrast to the day's journey, strict order ruled the night encampment—with the Asvaran quartered in a circle around Cyrus and their horses within the circle. Horsemen always required an interval of minutes after an alarm to find and saddle their mounts in the darkness and to form up with their squadron mates. Thus the footmen and the wagons ringed in the riders to protect them for the necessary space. Huntsmen and local tribesmen camped outside the main lashkargah and they took the mastiffs with them. The trained dogs kept watch even if the watchmen slept.

When the march began, Cyrus saw to it that the foot soldiers were given small shovels and billhooks, with their bows and javelins. Where the road had broken down or become blocked by slides, the men of the advance put aside their weapons and took up their tools to repair it. The Asvaran—who would not labor in the earth—were equipped with short axes to clear the way where it was overgrown. Engineers escorted a wagon train laden with timber and flat-bottomed boats with chains for the bridging of rivers.

Here they were on a main east-west caravan route. To the west of the Rhagae junction, it circled the Hyrcanian Sea to reach Lake Urmia and the ports of the Euxine. A branch led to Agbatana and from there westerly to the gorge that descended to the ancient Assyrian lands. The Persians turned their faces east.

Beyond the Crystal Mountain no immediate danger appeared. The Achaemenian command passed by fields of alfalfa and plowed earth. Peasant folk came from the mud-brick and thatch dwellings to watch without fear. They said this was the land of King Vishtaspa who punished raiders. And Cyrus gave order to barter for meat cattle and not to seize them from the peasants. These were Aryan settlements, where the headmen invited strange riders to dismount, eat flesh and drink milk, and sleep under their roofs. Yet it seemed that the good will of the folk must have some other reason than the command of the local king.

One sunrise when the wind rose from the north, Emba sniffed the air more eagerly than the white Nisayan he led. "The sea!" he shouted. "The sea of my home!"

That was the morning of the first evil. The Persians were threading through a dark ravine of red rock leading north; they followed the track of the last Medes to resist them, the swordsmen of Lord Abradat who had refused to take the oath of fealty to Cyrus at Agbatana. Abradat's force had retreated across the highland plain and had turned north, apparently to take refuge on the far Scythian steppe—although Cyrus did not believe that such a Sea of Grass would be the best refuge. So he judged that the unyielding Abradat had become desperate and might abandon the struggle if the stronger Persians rode in on him.

Accordingly Cyrus went ahead with the advance of the Asvaran who happened to be mostly veteran Germanians. He rode gaily, pressing on the warriors as if it had been a stag hunt—for such a morning on the trail stirred his blood. The encounter came without warning. Ahead of them the ravine narrowed to a rock pass, boulder-strewn. Around this gut pressed the fugitives who had been unable to keep their pace through it. Seeing that they were cornered, they turned, raising shields and lances. On one shield shone a gilded griffin, the symbol of Abradat who had been the herald of the Medes. He had kept with the rear of his men.

Immediately the eager Persians charged the rebels. They did not wait to use their bows; the shock of the charging Nisayans broke through the rebel array, flinging the horses of the Medes against the sides of the ravine, sending the riders to earth. In a few minutes the Medes were dead or helpless with wounds.

It brought fierce exultation to Cyrus, as if at the slaying of a swift-running stag. In this ravine he had put an end to the one noble Mede who resisted his rule. Emba, leading the spare war horse, sensed an omen in it. "Red are the walls of rock; red is the earth beneath."

The shield of Abradat was brought to Cyrus, but the body of the chieftain could not be identified among the dead, although he had surely been with his men. The Persians hardly knew his face, and the Medes refused to point him out. Then as the main force of the lashkargah came up, Cyrus beheld Amytis walking toward the battlefield, holding the hand of another veiled woman.

"If you seek Lord Abradat," his wife called to Cyrus, "here is one who will find him."

The other woman was a Lydian, younger than Cyrus, who had

kept close to the covered wagon that he had given his Elamite wife since she became pregnant on the journey. Amytis had asked his consent to take a companion, a Lydian called Pantheia. Cyrus remembered that more than once his wife had urged him to send a pardon to Abradat, saying that now Astyages had been taken to his tomb, Abradat was released from his oath of loyalty and he might consent to serve the Achaemenian monarch. Yet Cyrus had not been willing to ask this service of a man in arms against him.

"How will this woman find him?" he demanded.

"Pantheia is his wife."

They watched the veiled woman moving swiftly among the men. Her dark head was bent to look into the faces of the bodies being stripped of weapons and iron tunics. When Pantheia dropped to her knees, Cyrus touched his wife's arm. "There. Go you to comfort her. Say that I, Cyrus, offer to send her with honor where she will. I meant no harm to women."

"Your mercy," said the daughter of Gubaru softly, "comes too late."

When Cyrus ordered back his men and went to the side of Pantheia, he saw that she had found her husband. In both slim hands she gripped his sword. The veil hid her face as her body settled down upon his, and the dark lifeblood stained the linen, flowing from her throat.

"You see," said Amytis, "all this long way she followed after her husband. It is indeed too late now, Cyrus, for you to honor her."

So it happened that the Achaemenian and his riders were pursuing the surviving fugitives when they encountered Kavi Vishtaspa. And much thereafter befell the Persians and the world because of that.

They were across the watershed, dropping from the Red Ravine to foothills drenched by sun-brightened rain. Although winter was at hand, until then they had not felt rain for the days of a moon. Emba pointed to sleek herds of cattle and beehives ranged among terraces of wine grapes. He showed his master the blue expanse of the sea along the horizon, and truly they felt the warmth of the inland Hyrcanian Sea. Cyrus judged that the warm moisture

miskals of silver and turquoise? Astyages even mentioned gold. I have none of that. It comes here from the east."

Cyrus had considered this delicate matter of tribute, and he requested one sixth of the crop yield and of the herds in good years, against nothing at all in lean years of drought or plague. At need, he promised that he would give his cousin assistance from his western granaries and stock farms.

"A fox," Vishtaspa snorted, "told the pheasant, 'I will protect thee against danger, and I will feed thee in starvation time!' Easy to say, hard to do. There are no lean years in my Hyrcania. Do you know why? Because we are a safe distance from the death of the earth where empires are built and demolished! *Ahi*—where armies slaughter each other and all growing things as well and enslave peasants of good lives to make them build mud palaces and towers to reach strange gods."

After evenings of such negotiation, the amount of tribute was agreed on, to Vishtaspa's secret satisfaction. He believed that Cyrus would keep his spoken word. On his part, Cyrus instructed the other Achaemenian to build granaries and to channel off his flood streams. Not until the winter ended did he ask the question that rankled in his mind. "Why, my cousin, did you greet me with the title of Liar Prince? That title no one else has given me."

"You inherited it. Astyages made use of the lie. Are you not his successor? And Croesus was a pleasant liar, like all other monarchs of the barbaric West."

Cyrus had wondered how the rude-appearing Vishtaspa gained such accurate knowledge of happenings in the West—until he remembered how many Hyrcanians served in the armed forces of the Medes and Persians. Cyrus himself kept in touch by the couriers that came in almost daily from the post road with messages from Harpaig and the other satraps. He felt some anxiety because his son sent nothing on from Parsagard.

"Did you ever think," he asked, "that such ancient evil might change to something else?"

"Yes," Vishtaspa agreed and was strangely silent for the time milk takes to boil. "So said Zarathustra."

CYRUS FOLLOWS THE TRACK OF ZARATHUSTRA

Vishtaspa always took thought before he spoke of Zarathustra, who did not seem to be a noble Aryan, or a Magian, or a priest. "Not a harvest passes," he observed once, "without a savior of some kind coming by to be fed and proclaim some new god arising into power." Again, he paused. "Nine years ago Zarathustra fled hither from the soldiers of Rhagae. I hid him and fed him and listened to him. He was son of Purrushaspa—of the Gray Horses—from west of the sea. His clan, I think, was Spitama, the White. Once he also had been a soldier. At least he knew how to draw a Parthian longbow—the kind you wedge an end against your foot to draw. A Parthian shaft can pierce an iron shield."

Cyrus wondered how the prophetic Zarathustra had got his name. *Golden Camels* seemed to have no sense, because a camel had nothing to do with gold, unless indeed the beast were carrying a load of it, and that in turn hardly applied to a man. Oddly, other people never managed to describe this vagabond prophet, although they were quick enough to quote him.

"One night," said Vishtaspa, "I went forth to watch for the first light of Sirius the Bright. Zarathustra was there also, waiting. He sighted the star first and flung out his arms. '*Who fixed the way of the sun against the stars?*' So said he. '*Who makes the moon wax and wane? Who upholds the earth from below and the stars above from falling? Who gave swiftness to the wind that drives the clouds like sheep before it? What artificer divided light from darkness—and gave to man, who understands it not, an awareness of the whole of his creation?*'"

Vishtaspa rubbed at his beard. He spread his legs to the hearth fire where the sheep dogs drowsed, and his seven-year-old son Darayous—the one the Greeks called Darius in a later time— climbed on his legs. Holding Darius firmly, huge Vishtaspa spoke on. "I asked, 'Have you a vision perhaps?' Then Zarathustra cried at me, 'I have no vision, only a torment.' He went on asking the stars his Who and What and, most of all, Why? He departed at lambing time toward the east, over the Choara, with the torment still in him. I think he had been condemned to death for mocking some kavi. But that did not seem to be the cause of his torment."

"I believe"—Cyrus thought of the peculiar tranquillity among the Hyrcanian homesteads—"he converted you."

"At the time, no." Vishtaspa laughed with a rocking of his body, and the boy Darius held fast to him. "He converted my wife. My first wife, Hutaosa." Again the pause. "Yet, Cyrus, my cousin of Anshan, when he was gone I *felt* him. I heard his voice crying in the garden as if a fravashi wailed at me."

The voice again. Cyrus questioned in his mind if the elusive Zarathustra were really a man and not a voicing of thought, good or evil.

"The road guards were after him," observed Vishtaspa.

When the ground hardened, Cyrus devoted himself to training the Hyrcanian and Parthian youths on horseback. He made the Parthians forsake their huge bows and learn to wield a small deeply curved bow from the saddlecloth and to direct their shafts at targets behind as well as before them. They became much attached to him.

Their king, the new satrap of Hyrcania-Parthia, did not relish this training in warfare of men taken from useful work in the fields. Or so he said.

"Some day the Scythians will come," Cyrus answered. "And then who will you call upon to do useful work?"

Vishtaspa suspected the truth, that the Achaemenian king meant to take the local recruits with him when he marched east. So Cyrus did; yet he left his Elamite wife at Zadracarta. She had not been at ease in mind after the deaths of Abradat and Pantheia, and a woman far along in pregnancy could not go on the road with warriors. Hutaosa took her under her care. Besides, his wife would serve as hostage to reassure Vishtaspa. And Cyrus valued his friendship as well as the fertile lands around the Hyrcanian Sea. However, he missed Amytis. She did not appear in the evening hour of rest to listen to him worrying aloud over the problems of the day. She was the last of his former companions, and when Cyrus set his face toward the red heights of the east, he felt that the more his power increased, the more he was left alone.

The thought of Zarathustra also disturbed him. Under the veil of his prophetic speeches, the man was a rebel against authority, a man of the rabble, as Harpaig had said. No sooner had Cyrus hunted down the rebel Abradat than this other appeared in his way. Amytis could have told him how to deal with Zarathustra but Amytis was no longer at his side.

EVIL COMES TO THE FESTIVAL

Their way led the Persians up again to familiar red earth and pine trees and cold winds of highlands. Climbing to this Choara, they breathed deep and looked about them for some notable peak upon which to offer sacrifice to their sun god Ahura on the first day of the New Year. And there the second evil of the journey befell them. Cyrus judged it to be the fault of Farnaces, although he knew himself to be unjust in deciding so.

The inhabitants of the lofty Choara, being savage cattle keepers and hunters, gathered together to resist what seemed to them to be an army of invasion. The hill folk took their stand on a low ridge across from the advancing army. Observing the mass of them, Cyrus knew they had done a stupid thing, because their slight elevation could not shield them from the Iranian arrows nor check the rush of the Iranian war horses. Accordingly he ordered his Asvaran veterans not to advance, while he sent the new recruits, the Hyrcanians and Parthians, off to circle around the ends of the Choara array and scourge it with their bows. He knew that untrained men, attacked by weapons they could not ward off, would run away. And their flight would clear the caravan road for his column. He had no desire to slaughter the hillmen; it would suffice to teach them a lesson.

This maneuver was carried out at first as he had ordered, although the young warriors pressed in fiercely on the wings to display their courage. When the Choara mob began to flee, however, the sight was too much for the mounted Thousand of his guards, commanded at that time by Lord Farnaces, a veteran who bore the device of a leaping panther on his shield. Once let go, the Nisayan chargers broke into a gallop that swept over the ridge of the fighting and carried them through the mob of fugitives, leaving bodies thick on the ground behind them.

When Cyrus called Farnaces to judgment for disobeying an order during battle, there were no Law-bearers to attend the hearing; only the commanders of the hundreds seated themselves around the king-judge and the plaintiff. Nor did Farnaces make a plea, as he might well have done, that he could not check the charge of the Thousand. He held out his arms, stripping back the loose sleeves to show the scars of combat upon them. He gave, as Persian law entitled him to do, the account of his achievements in battle to be weighed against this one serious offense.

He had made the ride with Cyrus from the Sea of Grass to Parsagard nineteen years before; he had led the cloaked horsemen through the gate of Agbatana; he had scaled the rock of Sardis——

After the tale of twenty years of service, Farnaces made his plea to Cyrus. "Because of the evil thought of one minute, will my lord the king send Farnaces from his brothers-in-arms and from sight of the lashkargah, his home—will he bid Farnaces go from this place to the door of a house without honor, there to say to his family: 'Cyrus will no longer have me with him'?"

Cyrus knew what the man was driving at. Farnaces wanted to be reduced in command but to stay with the lashkargah. After the first month of the journey, Cyrus had replaced most of his high officers who had failed to adapt themselves to the hard conditions of the march. But a leader like Farnaces could not be kept on as a captain. Instinctively Cyrus longed to spring up and cry that the one offense was forgiven. Ten years before he would have done so. By right of the old Persian law, he should do so now. In his mind, however, the Achaemenian measured the distance he had come from Parsagard—more than forty camel day stages (eight hundred miles). Here among strange peoples his army was held together only by his personal authority, despite the loyalty of most of his followers. If he overlooked disobedience in Farnaces, how could he call a Parthian to account for an offense? And the Parthian recruits were watching the judgment from the hillside. When he had meditated, Cyrus gave an unjust decision.

"No," he said, "Farnaces of the Mardian clan, commander of the Unchanging Thousand, will yield up his command and depart this day for the city of Agbatana. There he will take charge of all armed forces until I, Cyrus, say otherwise."

Cyrus wondered briefly why he had singled out Agbatana, the center of the Medes, instead of Parsagard. Agbatana, his own base, had become more important to him than his home town. He told himself that there Farnaces would hold high command with honor and would not actually be an exile from the army.

Yet the veteran took the decision as a condemnation. He started to speak, hesitated, then pulled the golden wings from his headband; he let his shield fall to the ground and started to walk away in silence.

Rising quickly, Cyrus pulled the brooch from the cloak on his shoulders and fastened it on the shoulder of Farnaces. This gift was a sign of the king's favor. Farnaces inclined his head and went on. His long curling hair, Cyrus noticed, was streaked with gray.

The Persian warriors took advantage of the halt to make the New Year sacrifice to the sun lord on the nearest rocky height. Some of them drank more wine than they poured out, and at the sunset hour they began the ceremonial dance around the fires—quickening to the wail of pipes and the beat of drums until they leaped and whirled with swords swinging about their shields. Although they fancied this to be the dance of ritual, it was no more than the Aryan war dance of their ancestors after a victory.

On the battlefield itself, however, some strange people appeared. They carried torches and wore white hooded smocks, and they resembled dressed-up peasants. Oddly, they sought out the wounded Choara men, washing the blood from them but keeping the stained water from dripping into the earth. While they did this, the white figures sang softly in the manner of a hymn.

When Cyrus called for their leader to account for his actions, several of the white-robed came to his tent, unarmed. They denied that they came from any clan, district, or king's rule. "We are merely the White Congregation. We have come to heal where the *ratheshtaran* have harmed."

Cyrus had trouble understanding the language in the east, far from the Greek or Aramaic or Hebrew speech. The Persian leaders could follow many of the Aryan dialects, yet the spokesmen of the White Congregation used ancient words that were half-forgotten in the west. Ratheshtaran meant "chariot-driving nobles" of a day when chariots were still used. Cyrus did not relish the word because it stigmatized his horsemen as members of a noble class. "Whose orders do you obey?" he demanded.

The spokesmen laughed as if at a jest. "No kavi or captain or ratheshtara, certainly," they cried.

So they were masterless men of a low-class cult.

"Tell me, jesters," he asked at a venture, "do you obey the prophet Zarathustra?"

They ceased laughing and took thought. "We follow the way he has gone."

"Whither?"

As one, they pointed to the east.

"To what city? Maracanda?"

"Nay, to the City of Gold—the city that beholds the sun."

The Magian had sought that same place. Something in the words also reminded Cyrus of Vishtaspa. He saw himself standing again in the Red Ravine, over the bodies of Abradat and his wife, while his own wife still remained at his side. In that ravine, Cyrus had gone headlong with the charge of his horsemen against the rebels— as Farnaces had done on this red height. "Where lies this marvelous City of Gold?" he asked abruptly. "Or is it one with Kangdiz?"

They understood the word for the ancient castle of the gods. No, they said, it was nothing like Kangdiz. It was really there, on the river called the Gold Bringer, the Zarafshan, that flows into the great River of the Sea.

Having got nothing sensible out of these disciples of Zarathustra, Cyrus dismissed them with a token gift, reflecting that in some odd fashion the word gold seemed to be a clue to the elusive prophet's nature and whereabouts. The token of the Great Goddess also had been fashioned of gold, but Cyrus believed he had left her and her worshipers far behind.

During the journey he had kept his bearings by use of a small sundial in the manner of the Chaldeans. Then, too, the masters of the passing caravans gave him details of the country ahead. Some of the strings of laden, two-hump camels had come from afar, beneath the rising of the summer sun. These brought precious loads of carved jade and ivory, flimsy silk and gold itself. Cyrus knew himself to be on the caravan track that passed through Maracanda (Samarkand). The mounted guards were squat nomads resembling Scythians, but not speaking like Scythians. The owners offered gifts to the Great King, appearing to think that was required. Cyrus assured them that their goods would need no guarding on the road to the west, over which he had come. Henceforth the King's Road would be safe to travel. To his surprise, one chief of a westbound caravan told Cyrus that he had crossed the headwaters of the River of the Sea. He pointed to the north of the summer sunrise—the direction Vishtaspa had warned the Persians not to take. This river, the man said, got its name because it actually flowed into an unknown sea, due north of the Great King's encampment.

An impulse that he could not define made Cyrus leave the caravan highway to journey north toward this river. In a few days the highlands fell away, and the Persians found themselves descending into a vast plain unknown to any of them.

When they reached the River of the Sea, it drove everything else from their thoughts.

TERROR OF THE RED SANDS

They were not prepared for the river because by now they had journeyed beyond the limits of the empire of the Medes. Moreover, their native plateau had only small mountain streams, fed by scant rainfall. Accordingly, any flowing water held almost mystical significance for the Persians. And here before their unbelieving eyes a vast gray river, a giant of waters, moved majestically across the dry waste of a plain. An Amu Darya—a Sea River!

The strongest archer, using a Parthian longbow, could send an arrow no more than a fifth of the way across the Amu Darya. The strongest walker could not keep pace with its current. Engineers, measuring the high watermark along the eroded banks, declared that in flood the water increased one half again in volume. This immensity of water came from no visible source; it passed on to no known end. And it fascinated the Persians.

One warrior swore it was the twin of the River Nile that sustained life through all of Egypt. Cyrus called on his natural scientists to account for the miracle of the Amu Darya. They conjectured that it must rise in remote mountains where snow lay deep; it must discharge into more than a lake—into an inland sea like the Hyrcanian. That was probably the reason for its name, the River of the Sea. In fact, as the Persians journeyed along it to the north, they had to detour around bays and swamps where the Amu Darya formed a delta in the waste of the plain.

"You have a treasure in it," Cyrus told the inhabitants, "yet you do not bridle it to make use of it."

"Who could bridle the river?" they responded. "Nay, it flows where it wills."

These were the Chorasmian people. They dwelt in clay-thatch villages, cultivating a little land at the edges of the swamps, because their settlements might be washed away by fresh floods or left dry when the arms of the Amu Darya changed their channels. They were as submissive as the Caspians of Cyrus's ancestral Anshan, although they did not believe their misfortunes came from Fate, as did the barbaric Greeks. They explained that no caravans traveled along the route of their river because it led north into the steppes of the nomads they called Dahians, which meant simply the Enemies.

It exasperated Cyrus to behold the wealth of water passing unheeded through the Chorasmian land. He assured the village chieftains that the river could be bridled and kept within channels that would water an immensity of fields, and forests of hardwood as well. If that were done, he pointed out, the Chorasmian people could build dwellings of stone and timber, and if they prospered, trade caravans would seek them out. But the Chorasmians had an answer to that. If they enriched the land and themselves, it would bring the Dahians in to ravage them.

"These Dahians must be kin to the Scythian nomads," Cyrus said, "and I shall keep them henceforth from all the lands of my rule."

He was thinking of the inroads of the bestial Cimmerians, who had been turned back, after years of terror, by Cyaxares the Mede. This land of the beaten folk who lived little better than their animals, beside the matchless river, could be made the first new satrapy to the east, a new domain of the Achaemenians.

For these reasons, but chiefly because it challenged him, Cyrus began his attempt to curb the great Amu Darya. He had a way of attempting what seemed to be impossible and of finding some means to accomplish it. But the river proved to be an insatiable antagonist.

His engineers selected a broad basin that might be dammed at the outlet. It could be turned into a lake, with the outflow set in channels that would in their turn drain a delta of swamps. The dam itself defied them for a long time. The clay of Chorasmia would not harden into burned brick like the earth of Shushan. The Persians fashioned new kilns to give greater heat to the burning. They pressed thousands of the peasants into the labor yet could find no material strong enough to stay the flow of the mighty waters.

Months went by while Cyrus and his host and the folk of the land labored on the river.

"Nothing will avail," the Mede who was the oldest of the engineers told Cyrus at last. "Brickwork will not hold. For this, only hard limestone or granite will serve—set in asphalt."

"Well, then do it that way."

The oldest of the engineers wiped his hands in the air and growled, "It is easy for the Achaemenian king to say 'do it.' In this desert I have seen no trace of hard rock or asphalt." He pointed south of east. "The nearest granite lies in the quarries of Maracanda, that way. Twenty days' journey." He pointed to the west. "The nearest asphalt lies surely on the far shore of the Hyrcanian Sea where burns the everlasting fire. How far that is from here I know not."

"Ninety days, for laden beasts." Cyrus told him and considered the problem. "The great caravan road from Maracanda to Rhagae crosses our river not far above this place. Collect drivers, go up to the road, visit all relay stations, take the draft camels and horse-drawn four-wheel wagons. The ox carts of the peasants are too slow-moving and cannot cross loose sand. Draw payment for the transport from Vishtaspa on my order, against his next year's tribute. Do not tell me again that nothing will avail, but search instead for something that will!"

Another New Year came before the arrival of the first loads of black asphalt. The Iranian engineers, however, excavated the side foundations of their dam and filled in the crushed stone. Cyrus and the Asvaran explored the sea at the river's end, discovering the reason for its name, the Island (Aral) Sea. Its blue waters were shallow and set with innumerable isles of clay and rock. The scientists of the expedition decided that in a remote age, known only to the gods, all these inland seas had been joined together, stretching to the great mountain ranges.

When Cyrus crossed a watershed and looked out on a new horizon, he thought that this also would be a part of his domain. Generations before, his ancestors had wandered across these virgin plains, seeking game or spoil; now he, the first civilized king of the Aryans, was returning to the wilderness, not to despoil it but to rule it.

In such a mood of pride he felt the approach of the power of hostile gods.

Fishermen of the Island Sea gave him warning. The Enemy, they said, was coming again from the north. When he returned to the encampment on the river, he found it swarming with refugee families from the eastern settlements. Two nobles of the Maracanda country sought him out at once.

They were spokesmen from the caravan city; they explained that nomad hordes were in motion toward the settlements, driving off the animal herds—themselves as unthinking as the beasts—roping together women and strong young children, slaying all others. The path of the nomads was marked by the smoke of burning farms.

Surviving families were crowding into fortifications of Maracanda itself.

The invaders were Massagetae, ruthless as fiends. This year, said the spokesmen, the chieftains of the nomads would take no ransom payment to spare the city. The Massagetae chieftains had brought their women and their wagons and had sworn an oath to their Great Goddess to make a burned offering of Maracanda, and there to sacrifice a thousand horses and a thousand captive men to their insatiable goddess.

From all this voicing of fear, Cyrus and the Persians conjectured that the raid was in some strength and might be aimed at the rich plunder of the caravan route. Cyrus told his officers to assemble the Chorasmian mounted warriors with the Hyrcanians and Parthians, as well as their own regiments, and to have every rider take a week's food in his pack. No supply wagon would accompany the army. "We will find enough to eat in the wagons of the tribesmen," he decided. "Since they have brought their women and wagons, they will be under the disadvantage of defending them in some spot, while we may move where we will."

He remembered the Sarmatian women warriors who had tried to safeguard their tombs in the Sea of Grass. He did not lead his reinforced lashkargah to Maracanda, because if he drove away the nomads the great city would be safe, while if he took his army into Maracanda, they might be besieged there by the horse archers of the steppes who were peculiar but dangerous fighters.

Thus Cyrus set out to the east by long marches, across the plain called the Red Sands by reason of its dry loess soil. This eroded earth rose in billows like the swelling of the sea in a storm; but the thin spring grass offered grazing to the horses. The disciplined army of the civilized state met the nomads in the outer foothills of Maracanda.

That day the Achaemenian tasted the bitterness of defeat. The warriors of the steppes did not appear in an array. They drifted like wolf packs over the ground swells. Hunched in their furs and leather on shaggy swift horses, they whirled against the Persians in masses that discharged arrows and broke apart, to come in around the hillocks. Their shafts tore into shields and the metal scales of body tunics.

Like animals, the Massagetae appeared to be insensible to wounds. Bleeding, they whipped on their racing mounts to keep up with their fellows. Bent low in their saddles, they offered poor targets to the powerful Persian bows, the best weapon of the Asvaran. Shouting no war cries, they kept up a deep ululation, voicing their rage and exultation. Gold gleamed on the arms and necks of their chieftains. Swirling dust covered them and they emerged from it unexpectedly to slash deep into the ranks of the soldiers. When a Persian hundred of riders sallied out at the nomads, they parted in front of the charge and raked it with arrows from the sides.

At midmorning, by voice and signal horn, Cyrus called back his regiments. He took his stand in a long shallow valley. It was screened from the foemen by a brush-grown rise, but Cyrus knew that hidden watchers observed the movements of his Persian warriors. He knew as well that he had lost too many men, and that it was useless to carry on a combat in this manner of the nomads. They must have observed his approach. He remembered a saying of crafty Harpaig that a foolish courage was fatal to warriors. For a space, while the Massagetae decided on their next move, he let his men find their places again under the vociferation of the captains of hundreds, while their horses breathed at rest. As they did so, he rode from one end to the other of the column.

As the regimental commanders cantered out to him, Cyrus bade them all follow after him. "With bows in cases," he ordered, "and lances in hand. No man is to draw a bow or let go of his lance. No hundred is to break away from its thousand." Cyrus wore a jeweled diadem that flashed in the sun beneath a crest of white plumes—a poor sort of helmet but easily seen. "Follow this," he said gleefully, raising his hand. "We are going where only the brave will ride and the cowards will flee. We are going this time to victory."

It was no more than a chance saying, but Cyrus knew that his men would be roused by it—as surely as he guessed that the no-

mads, puzzled by his withdrawal, would be waiting in their bands
to find out what direction the Persians would take next.

Accordingly, when he galloped to the head of the column, he
started it off at a trot to the side. A ring of lancers formed around
him to protect him. It would appear to any watchers that the
Persians were retreating toward their encampment. However, they
had no baggage encamped. Cyrus set his Nisayan steed into a
canter. He was counting off the minutes to himself, trying to estimate what the nomad chieftains would be doing in this interval
and how soon they might assemble together to attack him. As he
counted, he felt the pace of the horses behind him quicken.

He led his column around the rise of ground and reined his
charger toward the Massagetae.

As he had hoped, the nomads were all in view, their dark masses
merging together. Cyrus loosened his rein and the experienced
Nisayan snorted, starting to gallop toward the enemy. Behind
him, his commanders threw out their regiments to form a battle
front. It swept forward, with lances down along the front. Slowly
at first the nomads began to give ground to form their packs. But
they did not have the swords or lances of the Achaemenian's riders;
they did not have the will to stand their ground and struggle, body
against body. The Persian charge broke through them.

Then the dark packs of the Massagetae drifted away, farther
and faster. Cyrus beheld their encampment for the first time, with
the standing wagons, the tethered beasts, the masses of herds and
captives. When he turned toward it, the Massagetae galloped in
between the Persians and their camp. Their ululation changed to
screaming rage as they struggled to hold off the attack and went
down before it.

Disheartened by the charge they could not face, the nomads
drew apart, seeking to save their property or their women—who
wielded bows savagely among the wagons. Once they began to flee,
no force could assemble them again.

By the end of the afternoon the Massagetae had vanished in
bands toward the northern horizon. Cyrus called off the pursuit
before sunset to return to the disordered encampment, free the
roped captives, and round up the frightened cattle. The wagons of

the Massagetae were packed with loot of the countryside. The women who had been freed from slavery wept joyfully as they hastened to prepare food by the campfires for the wearied warriors. Cyrus dismounted—he had been fourteen hours on horseback—to eat a little milk curds and dried apricots moistened in a bowl. "Did I not foretell," he demanded of his men, "that we would find supper in the wagons of our enemies?"

"Ay, truly!" they shouted, admiring him. "In very truth thou art our Prophet and our Shepherd, leading us from harm to plenty!"

Cyrus did not remind them that they had been at the edge of disaster that day. He wished that his son or his Elamite wife had been at his side that evening because he could have spoken his thoughts to them. Or could he? Amytis had changed toward him since the slaughter in the Red Ravine. Since the throng around him waited on his words, he flung both arms toward the darkening sky. "Up there they shine—the Seven Guardian Stars that watched over us. Will they not guide us to new victories?"

THE MOVING OF THE FRONTIERS

When Cyrus rode in triumph into Maracanda the grateful merchants of that caravan city held a festival of rejoicing in the terraced gardens spread with carpets and lighted by Chinese lanterns hung in the fruit trees. They seated the Achaemenian on a chair of silver, with silk beneath his feet. Their poets chanted his praise as one greater than Achaemenes, a brother to Jamshid, who conquered the fiends of the north. His death-dealing sword, the poets sang, had brought a most memorable victory to the heroes of Iran over the ancient foemen of Turan. Such a victory, they cried, as had never been gained by mortals before that day.

While he listened patiently, Cyrus reflected that he had been too preoccupied that day to draw his sword from its much-decorated sheath, and that to gain a decisive victory over the Sarmatians and Massagetae would be a task more difficult than bridling the Amu Darya.

Intoxicated by wine and relief, the magnates of Maracanda pressed around Cyrus to bow to him as their king and swear that they would erect a palace of jade and chalcedony for his dwelling, and fill it with ten talents-weight of silver for his treasure and the choice of their noble maidens for his pleasure. Cyrus thanked them for their good thoughts but requested instead that they find for him a thousand two-hump camels, a thousand ox carts and a thousand artisans, and as many hardy youthful warriors. These, said he, would aid him in the work he meant to do for Maracanda.

On his part he made Maracanda the capital city of a new satrapy, of Sogd. That was the ancient name of the vast land between the two rivers of the east, the River of the Sea and the River of the Sands. He named a Sogdian as satrap to rule for him. Here in the east, as in the case of Vishtaspa, he left the government in the hands of a native noble. In the west he had replaced Astyages and Croesus and the others by trusted Persians, Medes, or Armenians.

"A few days ago," he told the nobles of Maracanda, "you called on me to aid you in defending the walls of your city. Now I will move your frontier a month's journey to the north. Henceforth you can carry on your trade in peace, for that is what I think you are best able to do."

It was a novel idea, to the merchants of Sogd, to defend their walls and caravan route by removing their enemies, the nomads, and secretly they doubted that the Persian king could do anything of the kind. He did it within a year. He drove all nomad encampments north, beyond the barrier of the broad Aral and the Syr Darya, the River of the Sands. That river took its swift course from the high ranges near Maracanda for six hundred miles to discharge into the Aral. Nomads could never bridge such a river barrier, and they could be kept from crossing on rafts and inflated animal skins. To keep watch on the Syr Darya, Cyrus built seven forts—as many as the Seven Stars—with horse relay stations on the track connecting them. As control point of this new frontier, he built the fortified town called Cyrus's City, or simply Cyra. These outposts would give early warning of a raid or invasion, and an army of defense could assemble at Maracanda.

The year after the erection of Cyra, the engineers finished the bridling of the other river, the Amu Darya. In floodtime a lake filled behind the new stone dam; five sluice gates released the water in five channels that irrigated the countryside as far as the sea. The satrap of Chorasmia controlled the flow of the waters and collected a tax from the settlements given water. No tax paid, said Cyrus, no water.

Then on the morning of his departure from the plain, a warning came to him. He woke before the first light, conscious that someone had entered his tent, thinking that it was an attendant busy with the packs—for Cyrus always took to the road at sunrise. No one stirred near him, and in the stillness he heard the guards of the Thousand talking, low-voiced, by the entrance.

Presently he was aware of a darkness against the dimness of the pavilion's wall. Silent on his pallet Cyrus made out a standing figure, and it did not move. The pallor of a face showed above the black-draped body, and Cyrus drew in his breath to shout to his men. As he did so, the figure spoke to him in words that he barely understood. *For the second time . . . he brought harm . . . to her people who harmed him not.*

The measured voice did not come from a man. It recalled Tymiris in anger—Cyrus thought of the Great Goddess—he started to rise. In the next seconds he was struggling with a straining body, catching at a flailing arm, feeling hot breath panting against his face. Tensing his shoulders, Cyrus flung his antagonist back. The figure vanished. The breath was still.

Something had dropped on the matting at his feet. Feeling for it, he grasped the soft metal of a heavy dagger. Then he strode through the entrance curtain to confront the two spear-bearing guards who stared at him curiously. "Who went out before me?" he demanded.

The young warriors exchanged glances, and one explained diffidently that it was only a woman wrapped up in a cloak—a fair woman with unbound hair.

"Did you see her enter?"

This time they answered promptly together, "No. Not in our watch."

They were staring at Cyrus's right hand. In the glow of the night lamp he saw that he clutched a dagger of deep-hued gold, and he felt in his fingers the familiar image of Ishtar and the lioness. Such a token of the goddess he had cast away long ago, in the Sea of Grass after the slaying of Vartan. That had been after the spoiling of the Sarmatian tomb and the defiance of the Sarmatian princess Tymiris.

No deva of the goddess had visited him; almost certainly it had been a Sarmatian and perhaps Tymiris herself, voicing her hatred of him, stealing in shrouded during the last moments of darkness when the encampment was beginning to stir. Anger seized upon Cyrus, and he shouted, "Blind watchdogs—to allow a nomad wench to go by your post!" When others ran up with weapons, at his call, Cyrus ordered the young guards to be killed with their own spears. This was done at once. When the anger left him, Cyrus repented it.

The dead warriors had believed that the shapely woman slipping out of his pavilion before the first light had left his couch after serving him for a night. And perhaps the goddess, protectress of the women, had laid her spell on them at that moment.

PERIL OF THE PEAKS

A slight thing drew the Achaemenian on to the east. Yet in turning his horse toward the sunrise, he followed his own craving to seek new lands. He did so, although the fourth winter of his journey was at hand and the couriers brought urgent pleas for the king and the army to return to Agbatana.

It was no more than the appearance of servitors of the White Congregation to carry off the bodies of the slain guards for burial. "They flock like kites to carrion," growled the aged Emba. Exasperated, Cyrus summoned the white mendicants before him. "You who obey no captain or kavi, you who boast of your City of Gold where the sun seems to shine always—it is time that you guided me to it. I have silver enough by now; yet I must have some gold also. Where is this place with its river called the Gold Bringer?"

In truth, now that he needed to provide for regiments of the eastern peoples, Cyrus required more treasure in his coffers. The Ishtar dagger of pure gold reminded him of that.

Like their fellows in the Choara, the white mendicants smiled at him as if they shared some jest beyond his comprehension. One said, "A crawling leper may find our city and stand erect in it; a pigeon with a broken wing may fly over it, but a king of the earth will never find it."

"Riddles like that," Cyrus said, "are not meant to be solved. They are meant to hide the truth, and that is what I mean to discover."

He commanded the spokesman, the most powerful and most amused of them, to be bound at the arms and set on a pack animal to accompany the army. This mendicant gave his name as Haddu but did not name his father. He did not seem downcast at being trussed up to serve as guide. Cyrus himself gave the direction for the march up the Amu Darya to the east. He believed he had two clues to the secret the White Congregation guarded so well. Caravans certainly brought their gold from a region to the east. And the White Congregation at Choara had spoken of the river of their homeland as the Zarafshan, the Gold Bringer, flowing into the Amu Darya. Most probably that would be up at the headwaters which the Persian scientists believed to be far off and surely in the higher ranges where snow lay deep.

The army began the march readily enough because the veterans were fond of going after treasure, and by now all of them obeyed Cyrus without question. In the wilderness his personal wish became their law.

Almost at once they left the caravan track to follow the great river up through the red loess hills, through the narrowing gorges to the heights where they found no habitations. They climbed past the shoulders of mountains so vast that the summits were hidden in cloud. Each day the cold increased.

Now the man Haddu became fearful. He came to kneel before Cyrus to beg him to turn back.

"Whither?" the king demanded. "Which way leads to your home?"

Deeply troubled, Haddu hung his head. "Great King of many, you may not pass through these valleys. Turn back before the snow closes the way."

He said nothing more about lepers crawling. Cyrus noticed that the few birds were wide-winged eagles or ravens; the trees were dwarf pines bent by the wind. Yet a track wound up by the dwindling river. Animals and men on foot had passed over it. It must lead across the mountains. But whither?

Far ahead and above the ascending army the river roared over a fall. The sound came and went with the wind, like the roaring of an angered beast. Cyrus felt almost physically the anger of these heights, loftier than the mountains of Parsagard.

Late one day a great wind cleared away the veiling of the clouds around the Persian army. From the depths of the ravine below, dust swirled up in a devil dance. Above the ravine lofty summits appeared, shrouded in snow. Under the battering of the winds the snow swirled from the peaks in a dance of its own.

Men and beasts clung to their footing on the rocks of the trail, leaning against the wind, half-blinded. It seemed as if the level earth had turned, to rise above them and descend to unseen depths. Haddu cried that the wind would bring a storm.

Yet toward the end of the day the wind ceased; the sky became clear behind the pinnacles of the mountains. The level rays of the sun dazzled the marchers without warming them. The hard blue of the sky appeared menacing and no longer beneficial. And where the trail left the ravine it divided, one track rising to the waterfall, the other circling to the right. The Hyrcanian leaders of the advance riders came back to ask Cyrus which track they should follow, and he could not tell them. They had all pulled up their felt hoods and wrapped their mantles close against the bite of the cold. Cyrus called for all commanders to discuss their situation by the one fire his servants managed to light from the scant tree growth. "Now the storm is near us," the mountaineers warned him.

"Then release the prisoner, Haddu," he ordered, and added softly, "watch where he goes."

Because they were allowed to speak their minds in such danger, the chieftains and officers, each in turn from eldest to youngest, voiced their fears: that the unknown gods of these heights barred the way to them; that the cherished Nisayan steeds could not survive another three days without grazing; that they no longer knew which road to follow or what people awaited them beyond the summits. Cyrus judged that two anxieties weighed upon all of them—fear for the horses, without which they would be left helpless afoot, and dread of the coldness of the sun, abode of Ahura, god of the Aryans. By now all of them longed to turn back.

Cyrus did not speak his mind until darkness closed in and the white peaks stood like ghosts above them. Then he asked which way the mendicant had chosen to escape.

"The man Haddu," an officer responded reluctantly, "slipped away on the trail to the right hand."

Leaving the glow of firelight, Cyrus climbed to an outcropping of rock and stared in that direction, south. There a single point of light showed in the utter darkness. It might have been a solitary lamp near at hand or a great fire far off. It did not move, and the Persians decided that it was a fire on a distant mountain summit. If so, it must be tended by human beings.

"The mendicant swore he would never guide us," Cyrus observed, "yet, unwittingly, he has done that very thing."

"Not unwittingly," put in the officer morosely. "For when I cut the ropes from him he warned me to turn back down the road or leave my body to be food for the kites."

It crossed Cyrus's mind that the Hyrcanian officer might have invented that, being desirous to return to his homeland. A Persian would not have lied. "Still, we have sighted a beacon to follow," he said sharply. "Let your thousands rest and sleep if they can. At the first light the lashkargah will march to the south, toward the fire beacon."

Before the hour of their start, the starlight dimmed and snow flurries struck them. Feeling the force of the hard snow, Cyrus roused his followers at once to set out along the path to the right hand. As he had feared, the snow hid the distant light. Keeping the wind at their backs, they went forward, leading their horses and feeling for the path underfoot like blind men.

WHERE ZARATHUSTRA RULED

By the second day they had descended to a valley shrouded in snow, where the animals could feed on rock lichens and brush. That night the men could sleep again around fires sheltered by dense pine growth. There Cyrus called a halt until stragglers in the storm came in to the fires. But all the sick and wandering bands did not rejoin the army's column, and the army itself had become an array of hungering wanderers. These had one thought, to reach the beacon that gleamed fitfully through the storm. On the third day the snowfall ceased, and they felt the warmth of the sun again and heard water running beside them.

The valley widened, descending to a fertile plain where water shone in a lake. Yet when he looked back at the white summits they had left, Cyrus realized that his followers could not return on their tracks as long as winter held. When the Persians trotted forward along the trail, it widened to a cart road, and upon it stumbled strange companion travelers, who proved to be either blind or lame. They lifted their faces toward the warmth, crying that if they could not behold the sun they could feel it. A fur-clad patriarch, crawling with a staff, shouted that they were within the kingdom of the sun. Beside him a leper dragged himself forward, keeping away from his fellow's touch.

Cyrus asked the maimed ones who ruled this kingdom.

"No one, neither kavi nor king," they insisted. "This is the land of Zarathustra."

"And where is he?"

As one man the afflicted pointed at a blue summit on the far side of the valley. "There!" The leper added with authority, "There by the Fire of Bactria."

Cyrus fancied that fire might be the beacon they had followed out of the storm. As he rode on, the pilgrimlike throng increased, and they gave him puzzling answers to his questions. Where was the temple, the place of the gods? He could not find it, they assured him, because there was no such thing. Then where was the place of blood sacrifice? Nowhere, insisted the pilgrims. Whither were they going? To renew their life.

Never before had the Achaemenian entered a country without a temple or altar of sacrifice attended by priests. Once as he passed a roadside hut he reined in to watch a powerful man busied with pigeons and pheasants in cages. Occupied in binding a splint on the wing of a pigeon, the man kept his face averted, but Cyrus recognized Haddu and called out, "You spoke the truth concerning the lepers and broken-winged birds. Yet you see that I the King have found my way to this valley of—Bactria."

"May Ahura-Mazda avert the evil of your coming!"

Then Haddu bent over his feathered patient in silence, and after a moment Cyrus reined his charger on. It occurred to him that the mendicant was renewing a bird's life, as if that were important. Meanwhile his men were easing their hunger with fresh milk and meat; his horses were cropping the rich grass. Before he reached the end of the great valley, Cyrus and his scientists decided that the depth of the valley gave it warmth in winter; the immense ramparts of snow above gave it endless flowing water and guarded it from invasion as well. Yet because the White Congregation had endeavored to conceal the road into it, there must be another hidden way leading out. To the eyes of strangers a mountain range offered only a barrier; the inhabitants would know the passes through the ranges.

The inhabitants spoke of it with conviction as the valley of peace, but they said little of what lay beyond it toward the east. "The lands beyond the mountains," they responded briefly. By patient persuasion Cyrus learned that there the headwaters of the Indus River led on to cities that had been prosperous in ancient times. Cyrus longed to explore farther into this *India*. He suspected that the Bactrians traded with the merchants of the Indus valley; they had so many exotic articles and sheer fabrics in their homes. Their physicians made use of medicines unknown even in Babylon, although they had no more skill at writing than Cyrus himself. The people themselves seemed to come from many lands, and perhaps they were refugees, but all united in keeping their secrets from Cyrus.

When he sought their city—thinking that he would find in it the real rulers of the country—he merely came upon hamlets ascending the slopes like bird's nests on a huge tree. Everywhere he was offered fresh food in gold vessels, but the spokesmen of the villages insisted they paid no taxes to a court or temple.

Cyrus did not believe it. "Why do you mine such a quantity of precious gold," he asked, "if you make no use of it?"

The Bactrians replied that they did make use of the soft metal to fashion fine vessels, useful in the homes. They were proud of their goldsmiths and they brought one of the masters of the craft to Cyrus to show him a specimen of his skill—a miniature winged horse leaping up with flowing mane and tail. Every feather showed on the outspread wings. No statue in the treasure of King Croesus had been so lifelike, yet perfect in detail. Cyrus coveted it instantly and asked the goldsmith what price he put on the winged horse, but the man refused to sell it, saying that he had made it with his utmost skill as a gift to Ahura-Mazda, and he could not make another like it.

"Then why do you not place your offering in a shrine to Ahura?" Cyrus demanded.

"At the altar of the Fire?" The bearded goldsmith shook his head. "Nay, for Zarathustra hath said the shrine of the Wise Lord is at every hearth, or nowhere."

Such riddles exasperated the Achaemenian. Although the Bactrians concealed their shrine from him, they made no secret of the source of their gold. It was not dug out of mines but screened from the sands of the river that flowed from their lake, the one called the Zarafshan. Remembering that the Zarafshan flowed into the Amu Darya, Cyrus knew that it must offer a second way out of the valley, open in winter and probably used by the trade caravans that brought the rare goods from India to exchange for gold of Bactria. He wondered then if the seemingly dull Haddu had not outwitted him by pretending to believe that the long and dangerous track over the high summits was the road into Bactria.

From the first, Cyrus realized that this land without visible authority was more benevolent than his paternal kingdom of Anshan. It had neither Caspian serfs nor the slaves of the Greek coast. Its treasure of gold might be greater than the bullion stored in Croesus's vault; yet this wealth lay scattered among the hamlets. The valley's fields were well plowed, the cattle herds pastured properly upon the mountainsides. The lake offered a self-sustaining reservoir of water. His Persians already spoke of it as a true paradise, except that the shapely young women had no eyes for strangers.

It seemed impossible that such good life could be maintained without inflexible authority—despite the protestations of the inhabitants. And that authority must be hidden from strangers. The restless Cyrus had no patience with mysteries, and in his apparently aimless questioning and wandering he had narrowed the mystery in his mind to two unknown factors—the elusive prophet, Zarathustra, and the mount of the perpetual Fire that *somebody* must tend. He reasoned that Zarathustra, a fugitive, could be hidden on the solitary mountain. This appeared to be uninhabited, and none of his village hosts had offered to show the Great King of the Medes and the Persians a way to ascend it. Nor did Cyrus let them perceive his interest in it.

When the eve of the New Year was at hand, Cyrus showed himself at the horse racing and dancing of his soldiers, and when they prepared for the feasting of the night, he withdrew to the quarters he had chosen on the shoulder of the mount of the Fire. He told the guards at his door that he felt weary after the sports of the day and must not be disturbed. In his sleeping chamber he put off his weapons and insignia and put on a short dark mantle. Then he summoned Emba, his oldest servant.

"We are going," he explained, "to see what is kept hidden from us."

By the time they reached the rock face of the mount, the moon rose. Both men were skilled climbers, and Cyrus had marked a route to the summit the day before. In fact they found themselves on a path that others had used. Where the rock rose sheer, the path ascended a cleft. With his head close to the stone of the mountain, Cyrus heard the echo of voices rising and falling. It sounded like a hymn and he heard it with satisfaction. He had guessed that on

the night of the beginning of the New Year the disciples of
Zarathustra must hold some sort of ritual on their eyrie.

With the glow of the fire above them increasing, the climbers
ascended a last flight of steps cut into the rock. They came out
on a terrace of white limestone, gleaming in the firelight. Cyrus
stared out at the circuit of snow peaks. A man stepped to his side.
A voice asked, "What seeks the Great King?"

It was a familiar voice, and Cyrus recognized the Magian who
had labored at the tower of Agbatana. This wanderer appeared
to be taller than in the bygone years, perhaps because he wore the
robe of the White Congregation.

Many of them waited beneath the pinnacle on which the fire
shone. It bore no resemblance to an altar. Wood that must have
been carried up from below lay stacked at one side of the rock
pinnacle. There was no sign of a man-made sanctuary. When Cyrus
had observed all this, he responded, "I seek the prophet Zarathustra
where you have hidden him."

Without a word the Magian led him forward to the rise of dark
rock. There he stopped and touched a square slab. He said, "Here
we buried him."

It was a strange light on the place, mingled of moonglow and
fire gleam. The white hermits seemed to take no notice of Cyrus
and his servant. They sang their hymn again, and Cyrus followed
the words:

> *From the lands he fled*
> *From the nobles, his companions, and priests,*
> *He fled from the Liar Princes*
> *And the weapon-bearing men,*
> *Toward the light.*

Cyrus had attended many rites of many gods, but no such simple
ceremony as this. He asked no questions and the followers of
Zarathustra kept on with their hymn, while at times a pair of them
climbed up to put more wood upon the fire. After they had done
so, they picked up familiar balsam rods and raised them to the
four quarters of the night sky.

It did not seem long before the horizon altered to the east. Sunrise grew into flame behind the distant summits. The full moon dimmed in the west. Then the White Congregation ceased their hymn singing and prepared to go down the path into the valley. The hamlets below were still dark because the inhabitants slept late after the festival. Black goatherds and gray herds of sheep, however, moved on the green shoulders of the mountains. After two of the hermits had taken their post by the fire, Cyrus went down with the Magian. He thought of his twin fire altars raised to Ahura and Atar on the splendid marble shrine at Parsagard, above his new palace hall.

When he asked about the tomb, the Magian told him that Zarathustra had been slain by raiding tribesmen a few years before. His disciples had brought his body to the seclusion of the valley toward which he had been fleeing.

"Then you do not call him prophet?"

The Magian appeared to be surprised. "No, he was our teacher."

Cyrus asked, "He taught that Ahura of the sun is the greatest among the gods?"

They were at the well-stream of the village, and a woman drawing water into a jar took no heed of them. Around her, chickens flocked hungrily and a dog came out to stretch and throw himself down in the sun. Again the Magian said, "No. The name Ahura-Mazda is one name among many for the god who exists alone."

"In this valley of yours?"

"In every valley."

The Magian, older, had more authority in him. Although he seemed to have no duties to perform, he felt a responsibility that weighed on him. At parting from Cyrus, he bent his head and made a plea. "Great King of the lands afar, you have come among us unbidden. The peace of the fields is disturbed by your army, and you cannot restore peace to us. But leave Bactria as you found it, and do not seek to add this land to your dominion." He stretched out his arm to the west and looked into Cyrus's eyes. "I have seen too much of evil—there. Of all the princes who rule, you are the most humane. You have the will and power to change the flow of rivers and perhaps to heal the plague of the cities. You do not have power to heal what you understand not. Leave us the peace we seek, for our souls."

The word *soul* was strange to Cyrus. He supposed it was some patter of cult priests, and it angered him. Never before had the royal Achaemenian been accused of lack of understanding. "Until now I have had no trouble understanding truth," he cried out. "I, Cyrus, have no liking for lies!"

The Magian raised his head defiantly. "We serve the Truth! The Lie is our enemy."

Cyrus looked long into the eyes of the pilgrim. Then he uttered his judgment as master. "I have heard that said often enough. Now, Magian, your people must prove it to me. Give your testimony and by the good and evil disclosed by it, I, the King, will decide the fate of Bactria."

Not until later, when he stretched out on his couch for a short doze, did he reflect that he had used a word of the Greeks—*Fate*. Emba put away his mantle, muttering, "These hymn singers have too much gold to expect to be left in peace."

CYRUS JUDGES THE BACTRIANS

Cyrus heard the testimony of the Zarathustrians, sitting on the porch of his house in his hunting shirt, without Law-bearers or scribes to keep a record of the questions and answers. He remembered it all well enough, and it failed to satisfy him. A throng of mixed folk gathered at the steps of the porch, so eager to testify that he summoned them to speak in turn. The Magian did not appear. Instead Cyrus heard an elder of the White Congregation, who claimed to have beheld the Truth, and a peasant woman who babbled that the suffering of tame animals had been healed, and a leper who believed himself to be cured of his sickness.

Listening to them patiently, Cyrus concluded that they denied the power of the ancestral Aryan gods, even of Anahita and Mithra, supreme in judgment and war. (Yet the goldsmith had fashioned the image of the winged horse that once had borne Mithra toward the sun.) The sun itself they believed to be no more than the great giver of light. (And Cyrus bethought him of the philosophy of the Milesians who envisioned the vastness of a universe around the orb of the sun.)

"Nay," many voices cried out, "this Mithra of the blood sacrifice turns the wise into Liars; he desolates the pastures, his lordship favors the devas—the demons—who destroy with weapons, with sickness, with suffering. Mithra is served by Evil more than Good."

"Then," questioned Cyrus, "is not Ahura supreme over such gods?"

"Ahura is indeed Lord of Wisdom, unknowable, unseeable. Who can gaze into the sun? He is verily the Master, but not supreme."

"Tell me then who is supreme?"

"He who created us and is forever beyond our knowledge."

A pilgrim from India spoke of the Fire as the sign of the uttermost of the gods. He termed it the Fire of Vishnu.

"Well," Cyrus asked, "what is this mysterious thing within you, a soul?"

They said it was the gift of the supreme creator who also caused the sun to sustain life. A soul was the spirit life in each one of them. It might renew its life after the death of the body. It might never die.

Cyrus judged that they meant the fravashi, the disembodied spirit that accompanied him on his right, good side and spoke to him at times. Certainly his fravashi was aware of mysteries concealed from a mortal. However, Cyrus could not imagine his fravashi as an immortal being, living on throughout the length of time itself.

The Zarathustrians explained that after the change of mortal death the fravashi-soul ascended to the Bridge of Judgment. If, at that point, the soul had been blessed by good thought and good deeds, more than evil, it would pass over the Bridge to renewed life.

Cyrus thought he detected in this the ancient law of judgment of his own Iranians: that a plaintiff was entitled to name the sum of his good deeds against evil.

"Well, bring me proof that life endures after the body's death," he requested.

The Zarathustrians consulted among themselves and sent for a man named Ashir. Cyrus waited expectantly until peasants appeared, carrying a litter of branches on which lay a frail elder, white of hair and thin of flesh. Members of the congregation explained eagerly that Ashir had gained the name of Destiny because he had been a disciple of their teacher—he had followed the steps of Zarathustra from the homeland by the Caspian Sea to the house of the disciple Vishtaspa. Now Ashir was at the edge of death. In the hours before the New Year a vision had come to Ashir.

"In his sleep?"

"Nay, his eyes were open as he awaited death."

On the litter the aged man held up his arm for silence. He raised his head to look at Cyrus and said, "I was awake. It was the change of light at the fading of the moon and growing of the sun. Another came into the room and he was Zarathustra. Thus said he: 'Thou wilt lose life to gain it anew—thou, the faithful servant of the Lord.'"

Cyrus reflected that this prophet Zarathustra had met a poor kind of death himself, by the spear of a warrior, at the command of a kavi. "Do you yourself," he asked, "believe you have gained immortality like a god, by serving?"

The thin, sunburned face expressed joy, and the eyes of the sick man brightened. "That is the blessed truth."

Cyrus motioned to the litter bearers to take Ashir away. "Then am I, the King, condemned," he said without thinking, "for I may serve no one. I, who judge all matters, cannot be judged."

Ashir tried to protest, and the bearers would not move on while he spoke. He cried out that the judgment of the Lord would be upon kavis, princes, and kings of the earth. Upon Cyrus, ruler of the Medes and Persians, as well as the shepherd who watched over a flock.

Cyrus said: "I could not keep my oath as king of my people if I served another. Farewell, Ashir—I do not question your vision." He rose to tell the congregation that the hearing was over.

As he waited for his huntsmen to come with the mastiffs, he thought that he had been given the name of Shepherd at his birth.

It was a simple matter to care for a flock of animals or for a farming folk like the Bactrians in their fertile valleys; to govern Persians, Medes, Armenians, Cappadocians, Lydians, Greeks, and all the very different peoples of the east was quite another and much more difficult matter. Had they not called him "the people's king"? When Emba ran up with his Nisayan charger accoutered in gold, Cyrus decided that the Zarathustrians must be reckoned with as more unyielding than the Milesians.

His information agents assured him that they numbered converts among the distant nations of India, as well as in Vishtaspa's Hyrcania-Parthia.

Rising early, as he did each day at sunrise, Cyrus often heard the singing of his Asvaran, renewing the hymn to the dawn which he had not heard for many years. Men of so many lands had entered his armed host that the hymn singing had been abandoned. Now it joined that of the Zarathustrians.

Cyrus decided that he must depart from the valley as soon as he learned of a practical road out.

Actually his army made the move necessary. Although men and beasts fared well in the valley, it was not possible to keep thousands of warriors inactive, quartered upon the villages. He always had a bad time when his host wintered near a great city like Sardis or Agbatana. The soldiers gravitated toward the streets of the prostitutes, winesellers, or junk merchants. Here in the plentiful valley they sought out the nubile girls or simply started fights among themselves, and they tried to cajole or buy up the amazing amount of vessels of pure gold. Cyrus intended to lead them on to the east by the road of the caravans that must bring him to the great River Indus. In doing so, he meant to turn Bactria into a base of operations like Maracanda.

It was the Magian who managed to change Cyrus's plan abruptly. That wanderer disappeared from the villages after the hearing. He returned by way of the Zarafshan trail at the head of an entire band of government couriers. Those hardy riders from the western courts had failed to find the tracks of Cyrus's army after it ascended to the higher passes, now closed by snow and ice. The Magian had sought them and brought them in by the open way from the banks of the Amu Darya.

Cyrus, heedless of many things, had not worried because he had lost touch with the satraps of the west. He had enjoyed the exploring of the mountains. But now he had to sit for long hours while learned scribes read the sealed messages from his lieutenants.

He had been absent too long. The picture of the familiar west outlined by the reports came as something of a shock to him: Harpaig dead—the satraps of Anatolia appealing for his intervention—Gubaru beseeching him to return, to stem the plagues arising in Babylon where the death of the earth increased while Belshazzar feasted. Cyrus had to ask who Belshazzar might be and learned that he was eldest son of the king Nabu-naid.

He was deeply disturbed by tidings from his home city of Parsagard. Cambyses, in the fourth year of Cyrus's absence, planned to lead an army against the Pharaoh of Egypt, one-time ally of Croesus. There was no report from Cambyses telling of this plan, although his son dutifully stated the yearly total of the treasure under his hands and expressed his hope for the well-being and continued victories of his royal father. Cyrus regretted anew that he had not kept Cambyses at his side. It was natural that his son, left in command at Parsagard, should long to make use of the armed forces that served him. But Egypt!

Cyrus had the scribe read a second time the message from Amytis, who had given birth to a girl child in Vishtaspa's hospitable home. She prayed for the health of her lord-husband, and she expressed a wish in guarded words—the daughter of Gubaru could make her thought clear quite easily—to remain at the castle-farm of Zadracarta. In such a peaceful home the child thrived. It astonished Cyrus that she desired to remain apart from him with the child that could not inherit the glory of the Achaemenians. It seemed as if she had become a convert to the Zarathustrian faith.

When the scribes had finished reading, Cyrus left them to meditate by the hearth. The room filled with officers, waiting for him to give them orders. Cyrus meditated for the time milk takes to

Silver mountain goat, or ibex, forming handle of vessel. Stylized yet lifelike, it shows traces of the "animal style" of the Scythians and unmistakable touches of Greek artistry, yet the whole is typically Persian.

Achaemenian wine bowl with strikingly simple design of opening lotus blossoms. The cuneiform inscription is in three languages of the empire: Babylonian, Old Persian, and Elamite. Probably of the time of "Xerxes." *Courtesy Archeological Museum, Tehran.*

Sole surviving figure, hewn into limestone, of Cyrus's palace at Parsagard. Almost human in body, this guardian spirit bears four wings of Assyrian design and Egyptian-head symbols over flattened goat's horns. An inscription reads "I, Cyrus, the King, the Achaemenian." This caused it to be taken at first for a portrait of Cyrus himself. It is, however, his signature as builder. *Photo by Ettela'at, Tehran.*

boil; then he commanded that the army be summoned to its ranks to return to the west.

So Cyrus began the long march to his homeland. On leaving Bactria he made it a new satrapy to adjoin Sogd. He named a Lydian of understanding to rule it, setting a moderate tribute figure. With him he took no more than ten talents weight of the oversupply of refined gold.

On his own account he took the winged horse of gold and the artist who had made it. He left with the Bactrians a pledge that he would defend them against any enemies—as he had done in all the conquered regions.

There was no protest or demonstration, whether of joy or sorrow at his leaving. The Bactrians, like the Greeks, seemed to look upon his passing as a measure of their destiny that could not be altered. When Cyrus went down the steps of his porch to mount his horse, he summoned the Magian and waited until the white-robed pilgrim appeared.

"You have your wish," Cyrus told him, "and I am going from the valley. If you have any need of me, come to me yourself. I shall hold myself ready to assist Bactria, the most hospitable of my lands."

The Magian bowed his head in acknowledgment. "I hear," he said without expression, "the command of the Great King, King of all the lands."

When they rode down the winding bank of the river, the bringer of gold, Cyrus looked back at the first night camp. Under the stars he beheld the beacon of fire, burning as when it had guided him out of the blizzard on the heights.

The army followed a new route home. On the way, new provinces were made out of Aria and Drangiana. Fresh forces joined the army. When it reached the Salt Desert, it numbered five tens of thousands of warriors.

Cyrus arrived at the familiar highlands of the Germanians, the easternmost of the Persian tribes, with a mighty army at his heels. Behind and ahead of him lay an empire of vast extent. The poets who hastened to greet him declared that no man since civilization began had ruled so much of the earth.

Yet when he came in sight of the river of Parsagard, Cyrus thought less of his dominion than of his home valley. Within it he had always found rest. When he beheld the white of the fire altars above the green of the valley, he cried out in gladness.

As the days passed, however, his joy left him. The valley seemed to be unchanged after five years but much within it had changed during his absence. Secretly, one by one, the sly servants who were the "king's eyes and ears" came to tell him of the evil they had beheld and overheard: of the pride of Kassandan who bade all visitors bow down to her slippered feet, of the treachery of the officers who served Cambyses, his son—who sought to draw the heir to the throne out from Parsagard to a campaign of conquest that would eclipse his father—and the jealousy of Cambyses himself, who had hidden his torment of mind while writing bland letters of congratulation to the king, his father. While face to face with Cyrus, neither Cambyses nor Kassandan, doting on her son, revealed their thoughts. Yes, regardless of the law, Cyrus should have taken his son with him to the Eastlands.

Cyrus was not aware that he himself had changed. Seated in state in his apadana, he was troubled by memories of the valley of Zarathustra, as if distant voices besought him. Sometimes in his musing he failed to heed the voices of petitioners before his throne seat. He remembered the anxiety of his plodding father who feared that the rule of an empire would end the peace in their valley. One sunset hour when the apadana slaves came to light the lamps, Cyrus could endure the strain of listening no longer. He rose abruptly to end the audience and ordered the attendant guards not to accompany him. He let the purple robe slip from his shoulders and went out the rear colonnade, turning into a garden path that led to the old gate where in his boyhood he had listened to the teachers of wisdom. The impassive stone winged bulls stood there now. Beneath them the aged Emba gossiped with a stout Aramaean wrapped in a shawl who cried out to Cyrus that he had racing horses to sell. Ignoring them, Cyrus went on toward the river.

He came to a knoll where he could hear the whisper of the river water, perhaps a bowshot away. Standing on the knoll, he stared at the fire of sunset beating upon the western hills, and the flaming of the sky was like the torment of thought in his mind. Waiting there he longed for the familiar voice of his fravashi to counsel him, and he heard no more than the rush of the water, he saw no more than the dim figures of Emba and the horse trader who followed irresolutely after him. He could never be entirely alone. Another figure came nearer and spoke. "Great King, in other years I warned you."

This man, bent with age, leaned on a staff; the sunset lighted the thread of gold in his cloak. A silver ring shone under his earlock. "Yea," he went on, "I brought you the first word of the coming of Harpaig, who is now dead, and of the host of the Medes which now serves you."

Bending down to see his face, Cyrus recognized the Hebrew merchant of Babylon, who had indeed befriended him. "I remember," he assented. "And now?"

"I waited at the out-gate for I have word for Cyrus alone." The dark eyes of the merchant peered up at him anxiously. "In Babylon the king, Nabu-naid, has joined his firstborn son, Belshazzar. Now together they make strong their walls; now they summon up their host of spearmen and chariots from Gaza to the Sealands. They summon their strength against Cyrus the Achaemenian."

By force of habit, Cyrus wondered what motive lay behind this gratuitous warning of the Hebrew—for he knew there was one. Indeed, others reported that Nabu-naid had become estranged from his son. Cyrus pondered that and suddenly laughed. Those very words might have been spoken of himself and Cambyses. And what was the truth? In considering the truth of the warning, Cyrus sensed an opportunity to end what troubled him. Why should he question such a chance? He struck his hands together, saying to the Hebrew that again he was grateful. He said to Emba that again the old servant would follow him forth, and he cried to the Aramaean that he would buy the racing horses and use them himself.

With fresh hope in him, Cyrus strode back to his audience hall, where courtiers and servants awaited him in the portico—eyes watchful of his every move during these hours of uncertainty. They drew aside at his coming, and Cyrus went straight to Cambyses, now taller than he, a strong-bodied warrior, even if no more than that. Throwing his arm around Cambyses, he kissed his son in joyful greeting, saying for all to hear, "It is time that you held the reins of command of our armed host, of the regiments from Saparda and the Eastlands alike. It is time that you led them forth, before snow in autumn closes the mountain passes. Come, and suffer me to advise you. For we will take the same road this time."

FIVE

Babylon Is Fallen

ASPECT OF THE CITY

DURING the winter of the year 540, word came to Babylon that Cyrus, King of the Medes and Persians, had returned from the east to his mountain fastness. It was said, too, that hordes of mounted tribesmen followed him.

Probably the best-informed coterie of the great city were the bankers of the Exchange by the docks. These careful appraisers of events outside the walls—their class stood below the nobility of the court, and the officials of Esagila's temple, and the over-seers of labor—remembered that Cyrus had been an illiterate man, son of a ruler of peasants; as for his tribesmen, they had managed to overrun the distant deserts like the Cimmerians before them, but presented no danger to the metropolis fortified by the far-sighted Nebuchadnezzar. That autumn the men of the Exchange were more disturbed by the continued slump in building, the still-rising price of grains, and the prevalent epidemics attributed by the destiny-seers of the temple to the anger of Marduk, who was Bel-Marduk, the supreme god of Babylon.

That year ended as usual with the symbolic death of Marduk and mourning by his servants. The New Year—that came to be recorded as the year of the great disturbance—began with the feast of Nisan, carried out with more than ordinary splendor. It was in fact unusual in many ways. Nabu-naid the King, who had been absent at New Year for most of his reign, was present in person to ascend the steps of Esagila's sanctuary and to go forward to grasp the hands of Marduk in evidence of the loving kindness of the god and the devotion of the king. Marduk's fearsome figure had been adorned with a head wreath of lapis lazuli and a breast wreath of pure gold in visible token that he had been revived to life and power.

Yet the bankers took note that on the eve of the twelve days of the feast, officials of the Esagila bank remarked in the portico that the anger of Marduk against Nabu-naid remained unchanged, and the blight still lay on the lands of Chaldean rule. Such gossip in the portico was more meaningful than the formal talk over the counting tables. The bankers also made a mental note that a double ration of wine was given the soldiery at the feast, not jars of common date wine, but wine of grapes imported from the Lebanon. This was done by order of the crown prince, Bel-protects-him—called Belshazzar by the Hebrew money-changers of the Kebar canal.

Such details served, in the estimation of the financiers, to measure the antagonism between the temple priests of Marduk and Nabu-naid, who was, of course, high priest as well as ruler. Gossip had it that Belshazzar, commander of the armed forces and ruler in all but name, waited for some public display of weakness on the part of his father to poison Nabu-naid and ascend the dragon throne as a second Nebuchadnezzar, heroic defender of Babylon. To accomplish this palace revolution, Belshazzar would need at least a token victory over a well-known enemy. There had been peace at a price—and the bankers knew the price—along the frontiers for a generation. Yet now that the headstrong and untaught Achaemenian had appeared again, Belshazzar could conceivably obtain from Cyrus the victory he needed.

Against any such expectation, however, the devious mind of the elderly Nabu-naid must be weighed. The king was no true son of a daughter of Nebuchadnezzar; his mother, although a Chaldean, had been a priestess of the moon-god Sin at Harran. He had gained the throne by the successful murder of the pretender who grasped it.

Now before the feast Nabu-naid had carved a prophecy upon a tablet of chalcedony: "At my feet Cyrus the Persian shall bow down; his lands shall my hands seize; his possession shall become my spoil." When the tablet was set up, Nabu-naid observed to his attendants that if Cyrus ever saw it he could not read the wedge marks.

This tablet was really a clever piece of work and very useful propaganda. After reading it, the courtiers of Esagila realized at once that by means of it Nabu-naid had stolen his son's thunder. If Belshazzar now gained any sort of victory over the Medes and Persians, the credit would go to his father who had foretold it as the dispensation of the gods of Babylon. Under their porticoes the Exchange bankers quietly offered even odds that Belshazzar would die before his father. The prince was too fond of wine.

And then on the day of the New Year Nabu-naid scored an unexpected triumph.

The mighty ones, the ancestral gods, seemed to aid him in staging it. Not a cloud of ill omen appeared in the shining sky; not a dust devil stirred in the windless air. The gold tip of the pyramid Tower of Babel gleamed as if with fire. Babylon stood in stark splendor above its myriads of inhabitants. Multitudes of them swarmed with their families or slaves to the wide Processional Way. There, from the bronze lions of Adad Street to the blue towers of the Ishtar Gate, they crushed together against the backs of the royal guardsmen. As usual, the branded slaves filled the dark alleys. Freedmen, peasants, herders, and porters were permitted to crowd behind the guard cordon of the Way; the higher classes, metalworkers, bakers, and butchers occupied streets of their own. Scribes, merchants, bankers, and overseers filled the stands, some of the wealthiest shaded by red canopies. In balconies and on the flat housetops the noble families sat at ease in scarlet festival robes adorned with wreaths—of flowers for the children and jewels for the elders—some of them traced their ancestors back to the first great Sargon of Akkad.

A Greek vase merchant exclaimed at the splendor around him: "Say I, the wonder of the court of Sardanapalus was a dungheap compared to this!"

The barbarian meant to flatter his hosts of the Exchange, but many of them laughed because his Sardanapalus was merely Assur-bani-pal, the collector of books and hunter of captive beasts, the last of the Assyrians.

Through the multitude of spectators along the Way percolated the casteless ones, sellers of charms, prostitutes who bore no mark of Ishtar, incantors of illegal hymns, interpreters of omens, and simple thieves or spies of Rimut, watchdog of Nabu-naid. There were also Hebrews from the Kebar quarter who claimed that their fathers had dwelt beyond the Two Rivers in the time of Ur.

Then for a little while all the multitudes forgot anxieties and hunger when Marduk came forth from the open gate of Esagila, with the sounding of massed trumpets that sent swarms of pigeons circling into the sky. In his chariot car drawn by rows of chanting priests, standing erect upon his dragon, the god of Babylon emerged from his sanctuary, restored to life and to the eyes of his worshipers.

The harps of the women sounded, with the kettledrums of the men musicians, and myriad voices chanted, rejoicing, invoking the aid of the reborn Marduk. For in Marduk were united the powers of all the older deities:

Nergal of the city of Babylon,
Nergal is Marduk of the battles,
Zababa is Marduk of the slaughter,
Enlil is Marduk of the counsel,
Shamash is Marduk of justice——

Then as Marduk turned into the Processional Way, something unwonted followed after him. The critical spectators had looked for the symbols of Nergal and the other ancient deities. Instead they beheld the actual gods, each in a chariot drawn by white mules—the demon Sin of Harran, the Shamash of Sippar on his winged, fire-darting lion, and Ishtar of Uruk, veiled and armed.

This procession of deities lengthened until the wiser heads among the watchers realized the truth: here they beheld all the gods of Babylon's dominion. They had been brought from their cities to the capital to a gigantic theophany. Surely Nabu-naid himself must have done this, and not merely to add to the New

Year rejoicing. Had the strange gods been brought into the citadel of Esagila for safety's sake? And if so, what event portended? Or had they been carried hither to increase the power of Babylon? If so, against what contingency?

All the day of the festival until the candlelighting the multitudes repeated the questions. There was no one to answer them. The interpreters of omens and the destiny-fixers reaped a rich harvest of silver and cheap jewels for their surmises which few hearers actually believed. A mystery always intrigued the Babylonians, and this was a notable mystery.

During the evening rejoicing at the laden tables a rumor came from the sanctuary of Ekur, where Marduk rested again after the procession. The rumor claimed that Marduk now held supremacy over all lesser gods—as the watchers had seen. But Zeria, the master of the temple, would say nothing. Since Zeria was spokesman and creature of the king, this meant that Nabu-naid himself chose to give no explanation to his people. A strict ritualist, he had withdrawn from sight after taking the hands of Marduk.

Members of the Exchange decided that the astute Nabu-naid had stirred up the expectations of his people. Whatever happened during the coming year would be attributed to his ritual at this festival. All in all, the financiers believed that Nabu-naid had scored again over Belshazzar's party.

That night festive lamps shone at the doors of the fifty-three temples of Babylon, the three hundred shrines of the earth divinities, the six hundred shrines of the celestial divinities, and all the uncounted shrines in the recesses of the walls along the streets. The illumination aroused hope, all the greater because it could not be defined.

Outside the ramparts of Imgur-bel and the guarded gates, the tenements on the dark Kebar canal did not share any such hope. The Hebrew workers had been allowed no temple in their quarter by the canal. They gathered at such times in an empty chamber over the water for the ritual of their prayer in the dark and in whispers that did not break the silence. That night the whispers repeated the saying of the zealot Isaiah: *"Bel boweth down, Nabu*

*stoopeth, their idols were upon the beasts . . . they stoop, they
bow down together; they could not deliver the burden. . . ."*

The words, if repeated to the agents of Zeria, could not be con-
strued as treason. Yet to those who had beheld the procession of
the gods upon their animals following after Bel-Marduk, the words
held a meaning. Such a parade of idols could not relieve the city
of its burden.

Along the stagnant water of the Kebar canal the odor of death
increased. Each day after the New Year the armored guardsmen
of Rimut hunted through the streets to find and herd before them
the beggars, lepers, blind, and plague-ridden or simply starving
creatures who infested the alleys. Rimut called his scavengers the
Sanitation Guard. They drove their scourings of the alleys out the
east gate of Imgur Bel down to the refuse heaps along the canal
and left them there, bidding them eat and drink their fill. So the
human filth lined the canal, brandishing their arms at the gathering
vultures and wailing to the passers-by who sometimes tossed bronze
pence to them to see them fight for the tiny *shees.*

At rare intervals men passed along the canal, scrutinizing those
who mourned by the water and saying to the strongest of them:
"Lift up your eyes to the hills; thence will come your aid."

Few of them did so. Only on a cool and windless day could
they make out the hills in the east beyond the outer wall and
the stretch of green plantations. It did not occur to any of the
afflicted and dying to try to leave the city. The instinct that had
drawn thousands of them to the walls of the city kept them there.
Even Rimut's guards made no attempt to drive them beyond the
canal because they would certainly crawl back to the refuse piles
and the water of the canal.

It was during the moon after the feast that the beggars of the
Kebar beheld the miracle.

They beheld the noble Yakub Egibi, fat with good living, gripping high his fringed robe with one beringed hand while he held a
vial of sweet scent to his nostrils with the other—Yakub Egibi of
the Exchange, with a tall black slave holding a parasol over his
shaven head and a short white slave wielding a staff to beat back
the screaming beggars. They watched him step around the spots of

contamination and they shrieked: "Aid, mighty one, favored of Marduk—give aid to the starving!"

Instead of throwing out shekels or even shees, Yakub Egibi turned into the door of the Hebrew prayer house where nothing could be seen in the dark or heard in the silence. At the door his staff bearer held back the beggars, and Yakub Egibi let fall his robe and told them, in the words of the Hebrew spokesmen, "Look to the hills for your aid."

Then this wealthy banker skipped into the hidden room of the Hebrew captive colony.

WHAT JACOB EGIBI BEHELD

Yakub, or Jacob Egibi, senior member of the ancient House of Egibi, dealing in loans and discounts, took some pains to investigate the mysterious circumstance that drew him, against his better judgment, into the conspiracy of that year. He had all the wariness of his mother, daughter of a Jerusalem captive, and the acumen of his Babylonian father; he spent a large share of his profits on his inquiry agents who remained unknown to the spy network of Rimut and for the most part to each other. From their reports he pieced out the true story of the horse traders. It cost him a tidy sum to satisfy his suspicions in this manner, but Jacob did not begrudge the silver because his life was at stake.

With all the reports before him, he discovered that the first circumstance of that day after the feast was the meeting of the two youthful lovers, Nusku, the brickmaker, and Ealil, the free prostitute. There was nothing remarkable in that because the witless young people had spent all their coins during the feast and were hungry. Apparently the girl Ealil warned her lover to stay away from the loan brokers, while he made her promise over again not to sell her body to another man. On leaving Nusku at the bridge, Ealil proceeded to go her own way, following after an Aramaean horseman.

Ealil defied the laws by wearing a scarf over her fair head— prostitutes were forbidden to appear veiled in the streets—like family women—and by swinging an amulet of Ishtar in her slim hand. Although not a registered temple prostitute, she realized that men were drawn to a girl from the temple, and she was probably very hungry. Experience had taught her that a tribal chieftain riding a costly horse—rarely seen in Babylon—usually carried a pouch heavy with coins. This barbarian rider was fat with good eating and followed by a sword-bearer clad in clean felts, also well-mounted. Ealil trailed the visitors up Adad Street to the Esagila citadel where they stared at the great Tower and then dismounted to inspect the tablets erected in the vast asphalt-brick courtyard of the royal palace. The tablets lining this courtyard told of the victories of Nabu-polaser and Nebuchadnezzar. The one recently set up by Nabu-naid, third of the Chaldean kings, told his mockery of the unknown Cyrus. A few curious souls had stopped to read the new tablet. Here the horsemen also stopped to stare.

Seizing her opportunity, Ealil pushed forward, shaking the scarf aside from her face and catching at the Aramaean's thigh as if for support. One glance, and she knew the bearded chieftain desired her. Quickly she spoke in Aramaic, courteously explaining the nature of the new tablet. It seemed to surprise the tribesmen. "What are the words on it?" demanded the tall sword-bearer, also in Aramaic.

Ealil, who could not read, asked the spectators and explained to her visitors: "'At my feet Cyrus the Persian shall bow down; his lands shall my hands seize; his possessions shall become my spoil.'"

Hearing this, the bearded Aramaean smiled. Encouraged, Ealil told him of Nabu-naid's jest: "If Cyrus ever saw this he could not read it.'"

This time the servant shouted with laughter, gripping his sides. "Well, perhaps he couldn't," he cried out. "Yet by Anahita and Ahura, by their names and power, he would contrive to have it read."

Ealil did not know those particular gods. The Babylonians around them stared uneasily; the Aramaean suddenly became fearful and drew the laughing sword-bearer away. Ealil followed, exasperated but still hopeful. She pretended they had summoned her.

At the waiting horses, before the curious guards of Esagila, the servant gripped her hand. He looked at her not lustfully but thoughtfully and said, "Girl, we'll buy your voice instead of your bottom. Come!"

He spoke as if with authority. Ealil could not read his gray eyes; she could not decide whether both men wanted her, or neither. Whereupon the servitor opened his other hand and showed her six coins of Lydian gold. These, she calculated at once, were worth twelve times their weight in pure silver—more than she had managed to earn in all the time before pledging herself to Nusku. Obediently she tripped along beside the riders, so that the soldiers at the gate would not observe the sheen of gold. Such was the testimony of the prostitute Ealil.

At that moment Jacob Egibi faced the youth Nusku across his counting table, considering the boy's request for another loan. Jacob attended to such small transactions himself, although he kept an Amorite bodyguard at call because debtors sometimes attempted to stab him. Nusku looked hungry rather than desperate. While he considered, Jacob sent a counting slave for Nusku's record tablet. On the table beside a pitcher of clear water lay the notices of the day: sesame seed had risen to eleven shekels a gur, and the best grape wine to the unheard of quotation of nine shekels a medium jar. A landowner might buy it; the poor could suck their dates and dream of wine that gave forgetfulness. "Why did you change your name?" he asked idly.

Nusku muttered that he hoped that Nusku, god of fire, would aid him in the kiln heating.

"Your family had no trouble making bricks or enameling them; you can't manage to sell them—that's all."

When the tablet came, Jacob turned over the clay cover impatiently; it was written up for Rimut's inspectors to examine. The inner tablet bore the secret and correct account of the shekels—ten—given Nusku at interest—forty per cent—on security of the seven freedmen laborers of the upper Euphrates brickyard and the sheepherd—thirty lambing ewes—that helped feed them. Jacob's own code marks showed that by now, owing to accumulation of

unpaid interest, he owned the laborers and the herd as well, since
he fed the men a minimum of barley and dates, while selling the
meat and lamb yield of the herd.

"Ten shekels more," he offered, "on security of the land. The
yard is worthless." This land on the river bank, well within the
Median wall, would gain in value with the rise of inflated prices.

"Give me at least twelve!" cried the boy.

Without answering, Jacob began to dictate to the waiting slave
who marked the damp clay of a fresh tablet rapidly. The boy waited,
biting his lips, to hear the price. Then the Amorite guard stirred
uneasily; the small prostitute Ealil ran into the chamber, catching
Nusku by the arm and crying to him to yield nothing for silver
because they could have *gold* in their hands.

"Why do you lie?" Nusku demanded harshly.

The girl dared speak in the presence of her lover and the banker.
She rattled on, saying that two Aramaeans, or at least two tribesmen with wonderful horses, offered gold for voices, and Ealil believed they must be spies or mad, but Nusku must come quickly
to aid her or the strangers might carry her off.

From anger at her entrance and suspicion at her story, Jacob
Egibi fell into deep meditation. Tribal horse traders were not
usually mad, while spies from Egypt or Lydia might have gold to
spend, and he—Jacob Egibi—might render a service to the powerful
Rimut, which would need to be repaid in kind, if he gave information leading to their capture inside the walls of Babylon.

The girl persuaded Nusku to go with her. When the curtain fell
behind them, Egibi ordered his Amorite to go after them. After
waiting a moment, he called for his mule to be brought to the
door. Mounting to the pad of the ambling animal, Jacob looked
around for the curled head of his big bodyguard and found the
man moving through the wicker bales of the docks toward the
bridge. He followed, still wondering if he had not been misled by
a girl's dramatics.

Ealil and her Nusku were on the bridge, deep in talk with two
prosperous-looking riders who seemed not to care if they obstructed
traffic. Without trouble, Jacob edged his mule up to them and
learned—for he understood Aramaic as well as Hebrew or Ak-

kadian—that the strangers sought to know the flow of the river in
different months and what god resided in it.

"My lords of the plains," put in Jacob amiably, "people here
made sacrifice to the god of the waters in ancient times. But now
in their prosperity they have forgotten him."

"Then they are stupid," grumbled the Aramaean master, "because without the river, what would the city be? Buildings set on
sand!"

"Rather notable buildings, don't you think?"

The servant looked at the mighty summits gleaming as with
gold leaf, although they were actually, Jacob knew, yellow tiles.
"This land is sick and tortured," he said. "How can the dwellers
upon it be prosperous?"

"That is the secret of Babylon." Jacob was puzzled by these
strangers because the servant spoke like a man of wisdom, the
master like a herdsman. "Other cities have their day of fame," he
added amiably, "and the unseen gods destroy them. Babylon, beloved by Marduk, endures and will endure when your seed has
vanished in death into the earth."

The crush on the solitary bridge compelled them to move on.
At the far end, the servant paid the eager Ealil with coins of pure
gold—minted at Sardis, Jacob thought. Although men so outspo-
ken and careless could hardly be paid agents, he wondered where
they quartered themselves and whom they served. "If you have
riding horses to sell," he suggested, "I might look at them, although
mules and chariot wild asses are the beasts favored in Babylon."

From force of habit, Jacob belittled the worth of a commodity
he meant to buy. The two Aramaeans looked at him pleasantly,
smiling. "We have some good horses," declared the master. "We
will take you to them," offered the servant, "if you, my lord, will
tell us more of the wonders of Babylon on the way."

Again the strange reversal of castes: the servant making an offer
for his master. Jacob noted it silently and added other items of
strange behavior to the sum in his mind, which would decide
whether the Aramaeans were unusual spies or unusually naïve tribal
horse traders. He prided himself on his quick evaluation of strangers. Moreover, he rather enjoyed playing the part of a guide. In

his divided nature, Jacob was conscious of the evils of the immense city, as if he saw through the eyes of his mother, yet he felt a perverse attachment to it. Wherever they rode, they never lost sight of the gold summit of the Tower and the green of the palace roof garden that seemed to hang suspended above the line of the ninety-foot wall of Imgur Bel, its jutting towers shielding the impregnable inner rampart of Nimitti Bel.

Even the visitors were silent when they recrossed the Euphrates on the ferry barge nearest the wall. They watched the play of the long poles of the barge slaves thrusting against the current and the flow of the gray river through the arch in the wall. Jacob explained that this flowing of the river through the city itself gave ample water to the Babylonians in case of siege by an enemy; the vast granaries built by Nebuchadnezzar provided food for everyone in need. Yes, Nebuchadnezzar had declared to his people that while Imgur Bel and Nimitti Bel stood together, no foeman would set foot in their city.

The servant tossed a straw into the water and watched it move away. "And yet you have all forgotten the god of the river," he mused.

Water seemed to fascinate him. At a canal where ascending rows of slaves hoisted buckets to an irrigation channel, and an inspector checked the amount of water taken out, the servant reined in to seize the chin of one of the thinned brown figures straining at a hoisting pole. The eyes of the slave were white and blind.

At the gate of a plantation the horses of the tribesmen shied violently—yet the riders kept their seats easily. The flayed skin of a man, still damp, was nailed to the gate.

"Was that a slain enemy," demanded the servant, "or a rebel?"

Jacob glanced back at the inscription under the skin. "He stole a sheep and reported it lost."

After that, Jacob led the visitors quickly past the mud-brick barracks that served as breeding pens for children sold by dealers to the weaving factories.

"They bend under their burdens," observed the servant. Ahead of them the laden donkey trains and the ox carts crowded together in the rising dust to make way for the imposing figure of Jacob

on his mule. Among the animals, lines of barefoot porters bent
beneath barley sacks or palmwood boxes. The hire of the human
bearers, Jacob knew, was less than that of the draft animals. "When
will you deliver them from their burdens?" asked the servant curiously.

Something intruded into Jacob's memory. Words heard in the
alleys and half-forgotten—that the gods would not deliver Babylon
from its burden. A treasonable saying of the Hebrew Separatists
in the Kebar quarter. Yet Jacob did not believe that the Aramaeans
had visited that unhealthy bank of the canal.

They seemed to be untiring in questing through the suburbs,
looking into every avenue of the shaded estates of the wealthy and
the alleys of the lowest classes. Jacob was aching with the unaccustomed riding when the Aramaeans reached the date plantations
and let their horses gallop in the cool of the evening. They began
to talk together in a language strange to him. Straining his ears as
he jolted uncomfortably after them, Jacob realized with a stir of
excitement that this was their native speech, fluent though their
Aramaic had been. And this decided the question in his mind: the
two were spies from a far land that could not be Egypt. He decided that he would accompany them to their quarters and then
give his information to the nearest post of Rimut's police. For the
first time he noticed how easily they rode, with their soft-booted
feet braced in leather loops, bending to the swaying of their beasts.

They turned into a grove of date palms that seemed no different
from a thousand others. Within the shadows waited a dozen bridled horses as sleek and restive as the mounts of the pretended
Aramaeans. Four men rose from blankets on the ground; they had
bow cases and arrow quivers attached to their belts, and their hoods
hid their faces. The fifth man, gray-haired, limped forward to catch
the foot loop of the sword-bearer who gave a crisp command. At
once the bowmen rolled up their blankets and tied them behind
the saddles. The two sightseers dismounted, and the sword-bearer
handed his weapon to the old groom. "You see we have good
horses," he observed to Jacob, "but I do not think you will be able
to buy them."

Sudden fear chilled Jacob Egibi. Alone and helpless, he understood that he faced armed enemies who must be Medes or Persians. Perhaps they had made their way to the walls of Babylon as horse traders, but they seemed to make no attempt now to deceive him. Under the circumstances, Jacob estimated that he had no more than one chance in ten of departing alive from the covert. Aware of that, he faced the disguised leader boldly, breathing heavily from his unaccustomed ride. "I see that you do possess remarkably fine animals," he replied evenly, "and a spare mount for each man."

The disguised servant laughed pleasantly. The others unmistakably looked to him as a leader and kept silence before him. Jacob conjectured that his rank was high. "Babylonian, your mother did not give birth to a fool," he observed. "I am much indebted to you today, for you have shown me the way that I can open into your city." He flung up his arms, laughing as if at a jest. "Ask what you will for your family or clan when I come to Babylon. I shall grant it."

With that he swung to the back of a fresh horse, and the others fell in behind him, pacing out of the grove. They vanished in the twilight of the grove and Jacob heard their hoofbeats on the road, galloping to the east.

While he rested his mule and caught his breath, Jacob puzzled over the words of the officer, who must be a Persian. ". . . the way that I can open into your city." They had done no more than ride around most of the ten-mile circuit of the great walls that had no entrance except the brazen guarded gates.

The next morning Jacob did not seek Rimut the Surveyor in Esagila. Going to his own countinghouse, he called in his agents to seek out Ealil the prostitute and Nusku the brickmaker and to investigate their actions during the previous day. After reporting to him, they brought in the young couple, and Jacob questioned Ealil himself. Except that she did not mention the gold coins bestowed on her, she told her story truthfully—repeating over again the reading of the tablet that mocked Cyrus.

An incredible suspicion arose in Jacob Egibi. Dismissing everyone, he sat in meditation at his table. Then calling for the Amorite staff bearer and his parasol bearer, he went out into the sun, making his way quietly afoot through Zabara Street and out the eastern gate to the thronged bank of the Kebar. He put off his slippers and entered the prayer chamber where the elders waited as usual.

They were kinsmen of Jacob's mother, elders of the tribes, who held to the Law of Moses as the prophets bade them against all other laws, and to the one Temple of Yahweh that even the oldest of them had never beheld. To them Jacob whispered the incredible tidings that his own eyes had beheld Cyrus, King of the Medes and the Persians, on the Adad Street bridge. Nay more, Cyrus had set foot within Babylon, within Esagila, even before the mockery tablet of Nabu-naid.

"At his departure Cyrus said to me: 'Ask what you will for your family or clan when I come again to Babylon, and I shall grant it.'"

The whispers were barely heard in the darkened chamber by the waters of Babylon. Jacob believed that the unknown Achaemenian who could not read—so the prostitute Ealil testified—held to his spoken word. And of all treasures, he asked the silent elders, what were the greatest? The vessels of gold, of the temple, carried off by Nebuchadnezzar, destroyer of Jerusalem.

They meditated together, and they bore their tidings to Isaiah.

Rimut's spy in the Kebar quarter duly reported that the Jews were conspiring again, that they were spreading rumors of the coming of Cyrus the Persian and talking again of recovering the golden vessels of their temple that had been in Jerusalem.

Rimut himself evaluated the intelligence in this manner: that it was nothing new. The Jewish prophets had spread wild stories of the coming of the Medes in other years, and nothing of the kind had happened. Nothing of the kind could happen. Yet it might be that the more desperate Hebrews—who professed to think of returning to Jerusalem—might attempt to steal the sacred vessels from the vaults of the palace. If so, an example should be made by the public flaying of their leaders, among whom the double-dealing Jacob Egibi now seemed to be numbered. Had not Nebuchadnezzar himself made an example of the leaders of a revolt aforetime in Jerusalem itself? The ever-victorious Nebuchadnezzar had burned the temple of the rebel king, Zedekiah, had slain his children before the eyes of that Hebrew king, and then had burned out the eyes of Zedekiah!

So Rimut the Surveyor informed Nabu-naid the King.

WHAT NABU-NAID HELD SECRET

Nabu-naid took some pains to appear to be mad that summer. After the New Year festival and during that last summer of his reign, he hardly left his chambers in the palace. He was growing old; he wore a false beard, tightly curled, and a false knot of dark hair at the back of his neck on the rare occasions when he needed to consult with his scientists or receive foreign envoys. By tradition the earlier Assyrian monarchs were dark and fearsome, and the new Chaldean dynasty mimicked them by invoking fear. Fear of the gods, and of the king and of the servants of the king, kept the people submissive. This was important during hard years of epidemics and shortage of food. And this summer was a hard one.

Zeria, the resourceful Master of the Temples, took the omens and proclaimed that the anger of Marduk weighed upon the land. (This proclamation served the double purpose of awing the lower classes and turning them against the priesthood of Marduk, who accused Nabu-naid surreptitiously of offending the tutelary deity of Babylon by neglect; in fact, within the walls of the citadel of Esagila the priesthood fought to recover its influence from the court; the Tower and the Ekur Temple stood, as it were, in arms against the royal palace.) No one except the powerful priesthood of Marduk blamed Nabu-naid, who was believed to be mad and, accordingly, apart from human affairs while intimate with the unseen deities.

His conduct had not been, otherwise, understandable. He had forsaken Babylon for long years to journey ceaselessly through the Westlands, beyond the Two Rivers; there he had busied himself rebuilding the most ancient shrines, digging up buried inscriptions, and deciphering them. For no apparent reason, Nabu-naid had rebuilt a city site in the far western desert, Tema, with gleaming palaces and temples that needed to be supplied by caravans from

Babylon itself. (By absenting himself in this manner from Esagila, the astute old man had diminished the importance of Marduk and his priests, his antagonists.)

Actually, in building up the western trade routes to the sea, Nabu-naid had attempted to compensate Babylon for the conquests of the dynamic Cyrus. The Persians were now masters of the northern routes, across the upper rivers to the Anatolian coast. Thus they held the rich grainlands of the north and the vestiges of the Assyrian empire. They claimed, as successors to the Medes, vast territories vital to Babylon, even the Phoenician trading ports and Palestine. In the same way, to the south the reviving Elamites laid claim to the Sealands at the mouths of the Two Rivers, the delta important for its fisheries if not for its access to the sea.

Babylon had armies as great in numbers as those of the vanished Assyrians. Belshazzar saw to that. But the new Chaldean armed hosts lacked the skill with war engines of those intelligent brutes, the Assyrians. Their chariots, imposing and costly enough, could be used only on the level plain. Only by alliance with the fierce Medes had the Chaldean forces been able to break into and destroy Nineveh. Now that Cyrus had possessed himself of the Medic horsemen, the planners of Esagila prepared for the conflict with the rising Achaemenian which they believed to be inevitable. The Babylonian dominion lay entrenched, as it were, between the twin cities of the Persian, Parsagard and Agbatana, and the Mediterranean Sea. It lay across the east-west trade routes and those routes the planners of Esagila meant to retain. They held fast to their alliance with the Pharaohs, who waited as usual to discover—now that Croesus had been disposed of—who would become master of the historic plain of the Two Rivers. So the Egyptians had watched the advent of Hittites and Hurrians, of Assyrians and Medes, and the eventual disintegration of those strong northern peoples. The Egyptians supplied every aid short of war to Babylon, well aware that while the city of Marduk stood firm on the Euphrates, no barbarian invaders could reach the Nile.

Besides the secret mutual-defense pact with Egypt, the planners of Esagila had perfected their strategy for the defeat of Cyrus. It rested upon the fortifications of Nebuchadnezzar. First of all, the barrier of the Median wall stretched between the Two Rivers at Sippar. It was too strong to be stormed by horsemen. Behind it waited the field armies of Belshazzar. Behind the armies lay Babylon itself, transformed into an impregnable citadel. Against these fortifications the barbaric Persians and Medes would waste themselves, as Scythians and Hurrians had done before them. The Babylonians did not make the mistake—as Croesus had blundered—of sending an army against Cyrus in his mountains. The headstrong Belshazzar would have done that, but he had been restrained.

So Babylon waited, her strength fully mobilized. Then for nearly six years Cyrus had failed to appear as expected. He had wandered at will in the eastern limbo of the world. The cost of manning the fortifications weighed heavily on the land. As soon as Cyrus materialized again on the frontier, Nabu-naid had erected his victory tablet for all to see, thus challenging the unpredictable Persian to action, while assuring his Babylonians of the subjection of their foe.

BELSHAZZAR GOES FORTH AGAINST CYRUS

As the summer ended and harvesting began, Cyrus appeared out of the north. From his hills he followed the Diyala River down. His Persians rode over the Babylonian lands, reaping the harvests of standing grain. The inhabitants fled before them to the frontier town of Opis by the bank of the Tigris. The Persian followed slowly, seemingly more intent on gathering in the grain than pillaging the villages.

Word of his coming reached Belshazzar behind the Median wall. It was a spear prick to the angry exasperation of the militant prince of Babylon. For five years Belshazzar had virtually ruled the land. Since Nabu-naid had replaced him at the New Year feast, he had been pent up in the northern front, forbidden to lead his forces beyond the wall. Being an experienced soldier, he disliked keeping his regiments idle in garrison duty behind the secure barrier of the wall. Being a lover of splendor, he hated his quarters in the trading town of Sippar. And he distrusted his father.

As reports from his outposts reached Belshazzar, he believed that the Medes and the Persians were gathering in supplies for the coming winter. They seemed unprepared for battle, and Belshazzar longed to strike at them swiftly during their harvesting operation. Still, he might have kept to his encampment if it had not been for the taunt of the meal grinders.

It happened after a spell of wine drinking. One of the girls with him fastened up her veil to step out on the balcony where the air was cooler. She was a slim, languid girl, as much annoyed as he at their exile from the Babylon palace. Beneath their balcony stretched the courtyard, astir with animals tied up for slaughter, rasping with millstones ground around by old women, Hebrew slaves. Their voices clacked and echoed over the grating of the stones, until one of them cried out in the Akkadian speech: "Come down, and sit in the dust, O virgin daughter of Babylon, sit on the ground: *there* is no throne, O daughter of the Chaldeans. . . ."

The taunt was spoken to the air, yet aimed at the fair girl beside Belshazzar. The millstones rasped louder over low laughter and the voice rose again: "Take the millstones, and grind meal: uncover thy locks. . . ."

At this the girl went back into the hot room, and Belshazzar followed to escape the spite of the old slaves and to drink again. It occurred to him that the enemy forces also acted as if they had no fear of him. What they needed was a bitter lesson of the strength of Belshazzar——

Soon afterward he marched his spearmen and chariots north from the wall. He took them up the Tigris, searching for the host of the invaders.

A wind from the north blew against the Babylonians. It stirred up the dust, bending the tall poplars and the dry willow growth. Through the dust haze the red sun shone until smoke from burning villages—where enemy riders put torch to thatched roofs—darkened the sun. The riders carried fire into the fields of grain, and the wind whipped the fire into flames licking across the plain. The horses of the Babylonian chariots became restive; the columns of marching spearmen left the roads to seek shelter from the conflagration by streams and green fields.

Then, as if borne on the wind, the Persian horsemen came speeding. Their arrows pierced the dust clouds; their dark ranks charged out of the smoke. Their lances thrust before the heads of the racing horses; the metal-sheathed riders bent behind shields and they carried their charge through the lightly armed spearmen of Babylon. When Belshazzar's chariots gathered together against the horsemen, they met flights of arrows that slew the half-naked drivers and set the steeds plunging. At times when the chariots charged, the riders of the swift Nisayans turned and galloped before them, shouting with laughter at this racing of clumsy vehicles against free-running horses. They sent their arrows speeding behind them.

When night came, the fires died with the wind; the Babylonian captains formed their regiments to withdraw to safety in the hours of darkness. But the enemy did not withdraw from this strange battle; in the twilight they assailed the marching columns, compelling them to face about to hold off the charging bands. The Babylonian captains lighted torches to serve as rallying beacons for their spearmen. Flights of arrows came from the shadows toward the lights. Darkness covered the Persian horsemen who kept up the pursuit of the wearied soldiery. Unable to encamp, the Babylonians pressed toward their nearest refuge, the walls of Opis. Darkness did not hide the surviving chariots, clattering over the rough ground.

Exhausted and wracked by thirst, the soldiers of Belshazzar began to slip from the crowded roadways to seek the darker hollows where streams flowed. Belshazzar, with his lords and mounted guardsmen, fled toward the wall between the rivers. He had not gained his victory over Cyrus, he said, because wind and fire and darkness had prevented it.

PRISON OF THE GODS

That same evening in Esagila Nabu-naid took his throne seat to hear the announcement of his calendar keepers that this was the first hour of the new moon month of Tishri (October). Nabunaid expressed his customary hope that the month would be auspicious for all the people of Marduk. Then the keepers of the time tablets changed the symbol over the water-dripping clock to a crescent moon and withdrew with their customary prayer for the length of life of the King of Babylon. For more than thirteen centuries these astronomers had kept their accurate record of the movement of the sun against the stars. Now it remained for the keepers of the Babylonian chronicle to write in the events of the moon of Tishri.

Both the calendar and the chronicle had been recorded in this manner since the reign of the first Sargon. Through flood years and drought, revolution and invasion, the tablets had preserved their tale of time, and it was inconceivable that the record could ever be abandoned. This careful preservation of the thought and ways of the past had become a fixation, and any change was opposed as bringing evil with it. Marduk, the priests repeated, preserved his city of Babylon for eternity. Nabu-naid himself asserted his claim to the throne because, he said, Marduk had appeared to him in a dream to announce that he was the well-loved, legitimate successor to the favored Nebuchadnezzar.

As usual when he had dismissed the calendar keepers, two diviners from the temple stepped before his dais, stretching out their long-sleeved arms. The priest spoke who bore the sign of a spade, symbol of Marduk, on his headband. He gave his prophecy, as so often happened, in the form of a riddle. "One will come in this month who is pleasing to Marduk, our great lord. This one will be as a shepherd leading his flock, and he will set free those in servitude." The spokesman paused as if in meditation. "Auspicious will his coming be for Babylon, beloved city of Marduk."

Nabu-naid dismissed the destiny seers with concealed irritation. Their prophecy had not mentioned the name of Nabu-naid as usual. It seemed to be intended to mystify him. Although the temple owned innumerable herds of sheep, it hardly concerned itself with shepherds or others "in servitude." Nabu-naid rewarded the priests with the customary mana of gold, and as soon as he could leave the throne hall he sought his daughter Shamura. On that evening of the new moon he found her, as he expected, at work in the

underground vault chamber that served as prison for the foreign
gods.

They stood on the pedestals he had made for them, casting their
shadows against the whitewashed walls. During his eccentric journeying, Nabu-naid had hauled them from their temples afar to
Babylon—Shamash of Sippar, bearing the rayed crown of the sun;
Assur, the giant warrior of the vanished Assyrians; Shushinak, the
ugly earth deity of Shushan, being chief of the captive images.
Some, of course, had been imprisoned since the reign of Nebuchadnezzar. At the far end gleamed the gold candelabra, the altar
table, and the tabernacle brought from the Temple of Jerusalem.

His chroniclers had written into the record: "Until the end of
the summer months the gods of Akkad and of the Westlands, all
who are above and below the earth, were entering into Babylon."

When Nabu-naid entered the prison of the captive gods, he felt
a familiar touch of fear. When he closed the bronze-bound door
behind him, the flame of the single lamp dipped and his shadow
swayed above him. He fancied that the giant images moved, turning their eyes of gleaming jewels toward him. Shamura, his daughter, glanced at him, where she held the lamp high to read the
lettering on the breast of Shamash, sun god of Sippar. It was archaic
Sumerian script, but Shamura could read it. By now she had copied
down all the writings carved by dead hands on the black stone
figures rendered smooth by age. Shamura had no fear of the captive
powers in the guarded vault. A woman, Nabu-naid knew, could
penetrate secrets forbidden to males. He observed that she was
burning frankincense on a tripod stand of odd shape—perhaps making symbolic prayer to one of the powers. When he told her of the
riddle of the servants of Marduk, she tossed her head scornfully.

"It is hardly a riddle and most certainly not a prophecy. Zeria
can no longer restrain these connivers of the Ekur. They dare not,
of course," she added meditatively, "defy you and they mock you
only with words of double meaning. As for this shepherd who is
to come, he might be anyone. The priests are shrewd enough; they
can quite easily single out some lord of their faction and proclaim
this is the leader foretold, the man pleasing to Marduk. It is easily

done, and the populace always believes in a prophecy if it seems to be fulfilled. How did you answer them?"

"I gave them no answer."

"Just as well. They were probably better prepared for your anger than your silence. But because they scorned you before listeners, you must act to belittle them. You must act quickly."

Waiting hopefully for her decision, Nabu-naid admired his daughter's simplicity of thought. Shamura was not troubled by his misgivings, nor was she handicapped by pity for others. Because she kept to her chamber on the roof garden, the courtiers seldom beheld Shamura. She had changed her name to that of the legendary queen of Babylon, Shamura, or Semiramis.

Tilting her lean head, darkened by its Egyptian-style tressed wig, Shamura bethought her and nodded vindicatively. "Escort the star-bearing image of Ishtar into the audience hall; go before her as her favored servant; let proclamation be made—and heard in the streets beyond Esagila—that *she* will take Babylon under her safeguard. *She* will have said as much, in a dream, to you. Do this tomorrow. Thereupon the priests of Marduk will gnaw their fingers and cast spittle at each other. They dare not belittle the Lady of Uruk."

Nabu-naid closed his eyes and sighed in relief. Ishtar, the warrior goddess, divinity of fertility, was popular with men and secretly served by the majority of women. There was no effect quite as striking as the appearance of a god in time of stress.

"'The man who hath not a god as he walks the streets,'" he quoted gratefully, "'falls to the demon who follows him.'" And he added, "Your wit is the shield that preserves my poor life."

Shamura did not respond to this fatuity. She bent her head, and the dark tresses hid her eyes. "Do exactly as I say," she bade him sharply. "Let it be seen that you put all your hope and reliance in the Lady of Uruk. Don't try to make a speech." Her light fingers stroked his cheek. "And don't think too much about it. Go to your couch and sleep and tell your dream when they come to robe you in the morning."

As he turned away, she called after him, "Whatever happens, you *must* seek aid from Ishtar."

Obediently Nabu-naid left his daughter at her lamp. As he did so he felt again the presence of the dark gods. He heard Shamura's voice reciting the inscription carved on Shamash ". . . he whose body is abandoned above the earth—he who is not given burial— she who dies in childbed—she whose baby that she suckled is dead —he who hath drowned himself——"

He recognized the invocation to ghosts of the unfortunates. For Shamura, he knew, believed herself called into the service of the Great Goddess, of whom Ishtar was merely one manifestation.

Nabu-naid's uneasiness grew upon him as he ascended to the corridor where Shamura's eunuch guard awaited her return. The creature wriggled up from his stone bench to stretch down his arms before the King of Babylon. Did his lowered head smile at Nabu-naid's plump, inglorious figure? Did Shamura herself seek to protect him, as she declared, or did his daughter conspire by secret arts to raise herself above her father?

Instead of seeking his sleeping chamber, Nabu-naid turned impulsively toward the gate. He hurried past the marble frieze of winged genii that seemed to run beside him, and he almost ran out into the vast courtyard where the spear-bearing guards raised their lanterns in surprise at sight of him unattended. Nabu-naid raised his head to search the night sky for an omen. The low-lying star of Ishtar glowed with a greater brilliance than Nabu's star. No other sign appeared, and Nabu-naid felt the night chill in his flesh. He heard a light movement behind him and turned quickly. A spearman stood like a brazen image, holding high his lantern. Yet within the circle of light the courtyard wall of stone had changed in appearance.

Words glowed upon the stone surface as if traced with phosphorus. Four words in Aramaic, or Hebrew script. Nabu-naid read them easily enough. "The days of thy kingdom are numbered."

The luminous words had not been visible when he entered the courtyard. And as he stared, their outlines flickered and faded. Nabu-naid glanced up at the guard's bearded face. The immobile giant was an Amorite, untaught as an animal and almost certainly unaware of the meaning of the letters. Beyond him a shadow swayed and vanished. Nabu-naid recognized the shape of a woman hurrying away with a water jar on her head.

When Nabu-naid sought his sleeping chamber at last, he sent away the drowsy robing slaves and the harpists who usually soothed his restless mind. The four letters of fire stirred up his repressed fears and he could not sleep. His thoughts flickered among the portents of the last hours, straining toward some divinity that might shield him if Shamura actually sought to deceive him.

When weariness made him drowsy, he became aware of a voice and of words echoing faintly: "Thou art wearied in the multitude of thy counsels . . . let now the astrologers, the stargazers, the monthly prognosticators, stand up and save thee from these things that shall come upon thee." Nabu-naid raised his head to listen and fancied that the voice came from the courtyard below his dark chamber. "None shall save thee!"

It did not occur to Nabu-naid that his worst enemies were his own thoughts.

Dawn lighted the alabaster windows, and in his weariness the King of Babylon desired only to escape from the fears of darkness. When his servitors appeared with their gold basin of water, he said nothing of a dream of Ishtar. He cried out that he would go at once from the palace to Sippar to join his son and the army.

He told Rimut and the counselors that he would grant the armed forces the benefit of his presence. He told himself that if then Belshazzar overcame the invaders, he—Nabu-naid—would gain the credit for the victory. But he felt relief and drowsed comfortably in his covered chariot, drawn by white mules, when the summit of the great Tower disappeared in the plain behind him.

Of all that befell at Sippar on the road to the north, Nabu-naid remembered best the drifting smoke that hid the sun. Under the pall of smoke, terror reigned, and the people filling the streets pressed toward the Temple of Shamash, their sanctuary. They did not make way for the king's cavalcade. Recognizing Nabu-naid in the gilded chariot, holding the staff and ring of authority, they screamed at him. Voices implored aid and shouted abuse. Their terror was greater than their fear of the king, their lord.

"Restore the god of our fathers! Thou who hast taken Shamash from his seat! Behold the sun is hidden, and our shrine is empty!"

Nabu-naid felt that he was held by an evil dream and could not wake. Even women raised their voices from the balconies in defiance: "Thou who hast set foreigners over us—and toll-takers to keep the water of canals from our fields—stealing the divine symbols from our temple! Drive back the fire that wastes our fields!"

Animals and carts loaded with belongings choked the streets of Sippar as the wailing families attempted to flee. There was no proper authority visible. Officials and owners, having the best conveyances, had escaped from the frightened throng of common folk.

Nabu-naid took heart again when he saw the mounted guard of Belshazzar, the helmeted lancers, making their way toward him. Yet he beheld them using their whips and swords to clear the way for his son's chariot. As the chariots came together, Nabu-naid cried anxiously, "Why are you not at the wall?"

Belshazzar's strong body was encased in gold-inlaid metal; he held a shield on his arm. He stared at his father gripping the royal staff and ring. "Because the Persians are there," he said.

Nabu-naid did not understand. Such matters of warfare he had left to others. "Has there been a battle?"

"I would not call it that." Belshazzar's thoughts turned back to the frontier under the smoke pall. "A wolf appeared and these cattle ran."

He flung his arm out at the clamorous crowd held back by the lances of his riders. With contempt he told his father how his armed hosts had fled and forsaken their captains, and the Persians had followed the fugitives through the gates of the Median wall. Belshazzar wasted no more thought on the mob within the wall of Sippar. Nor were his exhausted and panic-stricken soldiers of any further use to him. So said he.

"Behind Imgur Bel and Nimitti Bel my strength will be renewed," he declared. "There I shall prevail over the Persian pagans." His eyes searched his father's drawn face. "And you?"

Nabu-naid ordered his driver to turn and follow the chariot of the lord Belshazzar. He had arrived at the front only in time to be present at the defeat of the field army.

"HE WHO PLEASES MARDUK"

That evening the fires died out in the fields and the sky cleared. At sunrise the messengers of Cyrus rode into Sippar, calling out to the people within their dwellings: "Come forth, collect your herds, draw water for the animals, and give your families to eat. The disturbance is ended, the peace of the Achaemenian prevails. By command of Cyrus the King."

Behind the messengers rode the flute and cymbal players. Behind them, Cyrus entered Sippar with the sun bright in the sky. Thus he made his entry theatrical, to draw the eyes of the frightened folk who hoped only for a quick death when the pagan soldiers sacked the city. Cyrus rode to the temple of Shamash. When he beheld the sanctuary empty, he exclaimed in surprise and asked what had become of the god of Sippar.

The *rab'ali*, the mayor, had come up with the oldest men to make offering of earth and water in submission. He explained that the Babylonians had carried Shamash away from his city on an ox wain, and great ills had befallen because of that: the rains failed and the earth became a dry crust; one half the harvest of millet and barley had been taken away by the Babylonians; and now the last harvests had burned. His people, said the mayor, who hoped to stir pity in his conquerors, were no more than the living dead, seeking their graves.

"It is the law—henceforth—that the strong shall not injure the weak. I, Cyrus, who enforce the law, understand that you have been injured. Who else will testify?"

That morning Cyrus wore his full regalia of pearl-roped tiara of the Medes and purple fringed robe of the Assyrian kings. He had only a jeweled dagger, a token weapon, hanging to his girdle, and no symbols of power in his hands. On either side stood his sword-bearer and bow-bearer. Behind him waited lords of the host, Law-bearers and interpreters. With his graying beard, sun-darkened cheeks, and deep gray eyes, he made an authoritative figure, and meant it to be so. He bent his quick wit and blandishing to giving the populace of this important junction city confidence in him.

When the men of Sippar realized that he was actually listening to their words and did not—apparently—intend to sacrifice their leaders to his unknown god, many more crowded into the temple. They were willing enough to testify to the exactions of Babylon. And the imposing Cyrus was willing to hear them out.

"Now my judgment is this," he declared at the end. "A so-called king, no true descendant of the enlightened Nebuchadnezzar, has named himself high priest. Yet he has set his son to rule over you with an army that eats up the good of the land like locusts. Shamash, your protector, he has taken away; your ritual of prayer, accordingly, he has ended. In nothing but name is he a ruler. Now the evil caused by him shall be remedied. So say I, Cyrus the Great King."

Even while the elders of Sippar vociferated their joy at this judgment and their submission to the Achaemenian, they doubted that he would hold to his pledge. New monarchs had a way of proclaiming justice for all and prosperity to come. And in the years since Nebuchadnezzar, many monarchs had occupied the throne at Esagila. In their desperation the men of Sippar felt relief merely because they were still alive and because the soldiery of the victorious Persian did not carry off the food remaining within the walls. In fact, the soldiers drove back some of the fugitive cattle and the laden carts. They made their encampment outside the walls.

The next day the camp was gone. Sippar and the wall between the rivers beheld no more of the war.

Cyrus was riding to Babylon.

Out of the mountains appeared his followers, led by his son Cambyses, no longer plagued by demons of unrest.

Gubaru brought in the Elamite host, marching fast in their kilts, bearing their plaited leather shields and cases of javelins. From the headwaters of the Tigris the Armenians came down, shining in brazen helmets and iron-bound shields. With Cyrus rode the horsemen of the east, Hyrcanians, Parthians, Sogdians, and Bactrians. The yellow-maned Medes in their fish scales of iron filled the broad highway by the bank of the Euphrates, shrunken by the autumn drought. The Unchanging Thousand had grown to five thousand armored riders who carried lances and bows on chargers draped in iron ring mail. When all joined together, the *Hazarapat*, the Army Commander, reported the number of the host as six hundreds of hundreds, their courage equal to any ordeal, their skill superior to any obstacle.

Hearing that, the aged Gubaru closed his eyes and raised his thin hands. "Can your horsemen ride through ramparts of kiln-dried brick twenty cubits in thickness; can they send their arrows with any force to the summit of walls sixty cubits in height? I tell you that the Babylonians have raised up the barriers of Imgur Bel and Nimitti Bel against just such an army as this. Courage will not give you wings to fly over those ramparts, and skill will not enable you to dig beneath them, for the foundations descend into the earth. I know that because in my youth I helped the engineers of Nebuchadnezzar plan those walls. They can never be stormed."

"Then how will you enter them, Father?" Cyrus asked at once.

The leaders sat together on carpets at the river's bank. Gubaru had a great fear and foreboding. He perceived that Cyrus the Achaemenian had changed since his journey to the Fire of Bactria. Cyrus no longer consulted with his satraps and commanders; his impatience had grown, and he seemed to seek the guidance of some mystical being, perhaps his fravashi, rather than the wisdom of his fellows. Now he made immense demands on his followers and hastened them on as if little time remained for tasks to be accomplished. He had taken the great risk of venturing in the guise of a trader to the gates of Babylon and had been recognized by his enemies.

Gubaru, too shrewd to argue with the Achaemenian conqueror, took refuge in cunning. "Why should your father tell you what your eyes have beheld—the unchanging strength of the walls of Babylon? I say, turn back! The Babylonians do not fear an attack; yet they have a dread of their gods. Invoke it! Let it be known that you serve their Marduk, chief of the gods. The priesthood of Esagila is restless under Nabu-naid's scheming. Proclaim that you have come to restore the worship of Marduk the great lord. That will divide their minds, and in time——"

"It's no use," Cyrus cried out, "saying in time or after a time. The hour is now, and I must use it." He turned to Cambyses, his son, and asked him to speak.

Cambyses answered without hesitation and thereby showed that he had a plan already formed. He applied the logic of the Greeks to the problem. Granting that the city of Marduk could not be attacked, he argued, it could not in equal measure be besieged. The walls were too vast to encircle, the territory too ill-nourished to feed their army. Therefore they could harry the great Plain and burn the earth bare and hasten on to the rich spoils of the Pharaohs of the Nile, leaving starvation to work for them within Babylon.

A shadow crossed Cyrus's weary face. "My son, you are a good commander," he said quietly, "but a poor ruler. I have given the inhabitants of this land my pledge of an Achaemenian peace. Shall I break the pledge? Shall I burn and harry what is now mine? This great Plain is now ours, my son. Only the city stands armed against us."

"Then come to my city of Shushan," put in Gubaru quickly. "Make your winter quarters there. Rest your forces and leave Babylon to stew in its own juices. If the city hoards its food while the countryside hungers, there will be revolt before the next New Year. Strike then, if you will."

"The Harvest Festival is now—in two days. Then all in Babylon may abide in dwellings of safety in my protecting shadow. That is best to do."

Those who heard him fell silent, believing that a demon of madness had affected his mind. Cyrus became aware of the silence, looked at them, and laughed. "A mad prophet said that once—Zarathustra. Shall the Great King of the Medes and Persians—and Babylon—fail to accomplish what Zarathustra has done?"

Gubaru sighed. "Babylon is quite unlike the valley of Bactria."

But Cyrus appeared to be encouraged by his thoughts. "I found the way into that valley, in snow and storm. It's a much simpler matter to enter these bulky walls of Babylon. A Hebrew citizen and a prostitute and brickmaker showed me the way in."

"By battle."

"Without a battle—or skirmish."

"How, then?" Gubaru tried to hide his foreboding.

Again Cyrus laughed merrily. "If you stand within Esagila's citadel, have you not entered the walls of Babylon?"

Again they were silent, and Cyrus returned to his meditation. "That is simple enough to do. The great trouble lies in what is to be done afterward. And by whom." He looked long at the handsome, white-haired Gubaru. "Why, now I see it clearly. You shall make the entry, you, my father, who know the way of the city so well."

Since Cyrus seemed to jest, the aged Elamite smiled. "That was during the energy of my youth. After threescore and ten years, Cyrus, I am too frail to lead an assault party."

"Still you have a most impressive aspect and the necessary wisdom." Cyrus rose, stretching his arms. "Be sure that the way will be prepared for you."

Thereupon he called in his officers, scientists, and messengers to begin work. Even in the hours of darkness, he began preparations. Heralds were given an announcement to make along the Siddar-Babylon highway, at the villages and canal locks: "Marduk, the great lord, hath searched for one pleasing to his heart and hath chosen Cyrus the Great King. He hath called him by name. By his side Marduk walks. His hand Marduk holds. Let all who hear await their coming."

After the heralds departed at a gallop from the encampment, two companies of Hyrcanian guards followed at slower pace. Then Gubaru marched south with his Elamites, escorted by flutists and cymbalists. Cyrus himself, however, went with the engineers to inspect the nearest canals leading from the Euphrates to the plantations. They made the circuit of an old reservoir overgrown with rushes rising from the swamp in the hollow bed. Hebrews who labored on the canals explained that the great reservoir had been made in ancient days, perhaps by the first Sargon, perhaps by the queen of a great name, Semiramis. They pointed out that the clay dug from it had been piled on the rim and stones laid on the clay embankment. The reservoir was meant to store water from the flooded river against a time of drought, but it had fallen into disrepair.

After discussing this with the Hebrew slaves, Cyrus released them from their work, to depart on the road to Babylon. After surveying the weed-grown reservoir, he ordered the carts to be brought from the army encampment and summoned his foot soldiers to work at removing the stones from the embankment. The stones were dumped into the Euphrates, low in its bed.

At the same time the canal to the reservoir was dug out again. As the hours passed, the river water began to flow into the great hollow place. This work went on until the reservoir and all connecting canals became flooded. And the river below them began to sink in its bed.

THE INVISIBLE GATE

At sunset the next day the scribes on duty at the palace of Esagila wrote on their clay tablets that the harvest festival was proclaimed by Nabu-naid the King on the thirteenth day of the month of Tishri. Nabu-naid, wearing a robe adorned with chalcedony and agates, signed the decree and departed to make his prayers.

The scribes on their balcony also recorded the fact that the water level had lowered in the channel of the Euphrates. They marked down the happenings in a peculiar manner of their own, legible to themselves but not to others. By so doing, the caste of palace scribes increased their importance and added bribes to their salaries because it was necessary to call on them to read any record.

At the hour of lamplighting, which really began the festival, the gates were closed, barring intruders. Belshazzar drove around the summit of Imgur Bel in his chariot. His army waited in a state of readiness within the barracks along the walls. By the parapet the engines also waited, the casters of javelins and stones, the oil in caldrons above the heating fires. At any alarm, picked detachments of spear-bearers would collect in swift chariots to speed up the ramps to the scene of the alarm. Watchers in the lofty towers reported nothing disturbing out on the plain. Spies of Rimut related that the Persians still kept their encampment by the old reservoir of Semiramis, indulging in dancing to celebrate some pagan festival of their own.

On the observation tower of the palace Chaldean astronomers took their places, after the appearance of Ishtar's star, to chart the night pattern of the heavens above them. At the end of his inspection, Belshazzar drove down the river ramp, glanced curiously at the sluggish water of the moat, and hastened to the hall where girls waited with harps to pour out the strong wine he craved. Around the inner rampart of Esagila the guard changed and the relief envied the man of the retired watch who hastened to stretch out by platters of spiced meats and jars of beer. Under the lights of the temple portico, confectioners spread their trays of sacred cakes. Music struck up throughout Esagila, illumined for the night.

Babylon divided into its human strata; the noble families seeking their gardens, the merchants and artisans crowding into the lighted streets. Beggars of the Kebar, however, descended the steps to the river landings. There, at the low stone flood wall, they waited in darkness. The Hebrews among them gathered for prayer in their usual silence. By now the water was very low in the river bed, and stones appeared.

Because the illumination was all in the elevated structures and because the people there were gathered at the feasting, the first intruders were not seen. They walked through the knee-deep water, through the archway over the river.

When they came abreast of the landing stages, the vagrants of the Kebar swung open the wooden barrier gates, whispering to them and stretching down eager arms. The strangers made no sound as they climbed up in pliant leather boots; they could barely be seen in their dark felt weather capes that hid their swords, hand axes, and javelins. These Hyrcanians and Parthians followed their officers up to the Esagila entries. There the sentries stretched forth the shafts of their spears to bar the advancing groups from the sacred palace enclosure. Then the guards were seized and struck down, and the intruders marched in, separating to advance toward the lamp niches of the sentry posts. Some of them began to climb the outer stairway of the great Tower.

Above the vast courtyard the Tower stood dark against the stars. No man was on its summit during the night of the feast.

Watchers on the twin towers of the Ishtar Gate were looking toward the north in that hour of the night. Beyond the moat a torchlight procession made its way toward Babylon. Riders in festive garments escorted a carrying chair occupied by a figure of gold, or wearing cloth of gold—the staring sentries could not tell if it were a nobleman or god—followed by musicians. When the breeze strengthened, their song came clear, echoed by the clash of cymbals. The sentries reported this apparition to their officer, who carried the tidings to Belshazzar in the palace festival hall.

There the scarlet-embroidered curtains had been hung beneath the images that the Babylonian artists had made of the conquered deities, the images of gold, silver, brass, and stone and wood. The images looked down through the drifting incense, on the dais where Belshazzar lay on the king's couch, for Nabu-naid had not appeared. There Belshazzar heard the message from the sentries and gave no second thought to it, for that night many bands paraded with torches—and this one would hardly enter the barred Ishtar Gate.

That night the whim seized on Belshazzar, the lord of war, to drink wine from the vessels of gold and silver that the mighty lord of war, Nebuchadnezzar, had taken from the Temple of Jerusalem. After he commanded them to be brought, he gave them to the wives and prostitutes who served the lords of his court, who filled the hall—it seemed as if they numbered a thousand.

The women thronged to drink from the vessels and the great bowl of gold; laughing, they placed wax candles in the golden candelabra with seven branches. They placed this against the wall by Belshazzar. It was seen by elder Jews who labored and drew rations as gardeners of the palace. They looked from the border of cedars in the garden, through the embrasures, down on the flickering lights of the hall.

In that same hour they saw the fingers of a man's hand come from behind the curtain, over by the branched candle staff. The hand wrote words upon the white limestone cement of the wall.

Belshazzar noticed the moving hand. He turned himself to stare at the words, and his face changed. The watching captives heard him demand the meaning of the writing. His companions found they could not read the strange script, and the women could not read any script. Thereupon the impatient Belshazzar called for Chaldeans, astrologers and learned men and diviners of destiny to interpret the meaning of the words.

Thus the astronomers were summoned from their charting of the stars, and the elite scribes from their recording, and interpreters of omens from their sleep—for the night was nigh its ending. Belshazzar was angered and heedless with wine; he offered first to bestow on the reader of the message a scarlet robe of ceremony; then he promised a gold chain of rank; lastly he cried that he would make the man the third ruler of the kingdom, after himself, the second, the prince. The Chaldean men of wisdom could tell him no more than that the script was Hebrew.

It was a woman, a wife of Belshazzar, who ventured to suggest sending for a Hebrew to read the words. So after a short space the watchers beheld a young Jew led to the dais. By then the revelers had ceased their clamor in the hall, and there was silence when Belshazzar demanded to know the meaning of the writing beside his head. Did it concern him?

The young Jewish laborer replied that it did. "God hath numbered thy kingdom, and finished it."

The captive explained further: "Thou art weighed in the balances, and art found wanting."

He said more. "Thy kingdom is divided, and given to the Medes and Persians."

Still there was the silence, while the feasters looked to Belshazzar, who had been driven from the north wall by those same Medes and Persians. Under their staring, Belshazzar roused himself and ordered a robe and chain to be given to the reader of the writing.

Within that hour the watching gardeners beheld the slaying of the king's son. It took place when the sentries at the hall entrance rushed in to report that unknown enemies filled the courtyard. This Belshazzar would not believe. Yet the writing on the wall had angered him and he caught up the nearest weapon to run from the hall without waiting for his officers. They scrambled through the women to follow him.

So Belshazzar and his companions hurried half-armed into the murk of the courtyard. They were beaten down and slain by the swords of the Hyrcanians coming up to the entrance. Beholding this the women screamed; the slaves of the hall fled blindly, crying that foes had sprung from the darkness to slay all the lords. Outcry filled the corridors. It brought Rimut the Surveyor out of the shadows to peer into the courtyard and slip away to his house. It reached the wakeful Nabu-naid in his sleeping chamber, and he cried out at his servitors, who could only babble at the king: "*They* came walking upon the water. Nay, the fire of torches follows them, lighting some god gleaming as with gold."

Nabu-naid ran to the head of the river ramp. He saw torches waving beneath him and a multitude of riders pacing in upon the water of the river bed, entering beneath the archway from which the flood had subsided. No guards kept their posts at this archway where only the water entered.

When Nabu-naid heard that Belshazzar was dead, he fled in fear, first toward the vault where Shamura kept tryst and then blindly toward the palace stable and the covered chariot. A gate opened at the king's command and his chariot took the road to Uruk, the city of Ishtar.

For uncounted years the daily life of Babylon had gone on under the voice of authority. When the flight of Nabu-naid was known and the slaying of Belshazzar reported, the chief ministers barred themselves in their palaces on Marduk Street to await what would happen next. There was no one to give orders to the commanders of the garrison that slept or watched on the outer walls. In many quarters of the city, people slept through the disturbance, unaware that the authority of yesterday had ceased to exist.

When Gubaru was carried up from the river in his chair, his Elamites marched across the courtyard into the palace. They met no resistance. Gubaru entered the hall of festival and seated himself on the empty couch of Belshazzar. He was a little tired after the long night march. He ordered the corridors to be cleared of servitors and the treasury to be seized. When his captains descended to the vault of the captive gods, they were awed by the lofty statues. They asked the woman standing by the solitary lamp if she kept vigil there.

Shamura, daughter of Nabu-naid, responded: "Nay, the vigil that I kept is ended."

She raised the dagger from her girdle and when the Elamites ran at her to seize her, she drove the knife into her body and sank down before them; her blood ran out over the tiled floor beneath the images.

At daybreak Gubaru gave out his first proclamation: "A new day is at hand. Let each person perform his task as before; let no gate be closed and no weapon carried in the streets. The war is ended in Babylon, and the new peace has begun. By command of Cyrus the Great King."

Thereupon the porters went down to the river landings where the water was rising again. The rafts and skiffs brought in their grain and fish as usual; the beasts carried their burdens into the streets. When the Exchange opened above the docks, bankers gathered in the portico, collecting the news and crying for sale shares in the temple corporations—because they fancied the victorious Persians would confiscate all the temple treasures, being pagans. Jacob Egibi, however, had a different fancy and bought up shares in the corporation of Marduk.

Out on the walls the garrison still barred the city gates; the walls of Imgur Bel and Nimitti Bel stood, as it were, against the citadel with the temple and palace now closely held by the forces of Gubaru. Yet the multitudes teeming in the streets beheld the miracle of the city entered without slaughter; as the hours passed without violence or imprisonment, the throngs began to mock the soldiers of the late king, massed on the lofty walls by the moat, asking what they were guarding and when they would come down to their dinners. Before the day ended, the army officers allowed the city gates to be opened. They had no orders from Nabu-naid, and they had no desire to begin a battle on their own account. At sunset the Temple of Ekur sent a delegation of sanctuary priests to Gubaru to discover what he required of them. He informed the delegation that he was no more than the harbinger of the true king, Cyrus the Achaemenian, who had taken the distressed people of Babylon under his protection and peace. Gubaru added that Cyrus did this by will of Marduk, chief of the gods, because Marduk was distressed in heart by the sufferings of his worshipers and the neglect of his ritual.

The priests consulted together swiftly and asked what gifts of gold and silver and precious things the new king, Cyrus the Achaemenian, would deem fitting from his servants, the poverty-ridden priests of Ekur.

"Cyrus said to me," Gubaru made answer, "that he will come to bring gifts to all people of Babylon, not to demand them."

Then the delegation united in praise of Cyrus, and they stretched down their arms before Gubaru, his spokesman. "Verily," they asserted, "now is the prophecy fulfilled that we had in our hearts— that one would come from afar, a Shepherd for our congregation, to remove the yoke of servitude from the worshipers of Marduk, the great lord."

But out on the Kebar the Hebrews flung up their arms and cried: "Babylon is fallen—the great city, the whore of the nations, is fallen!"

JUDGMENT OF CYRUS

On the twenty-ninth day of the moon of Tishri, the scribes wrote in their chronicle that Cyrus the King entered the gate and so began the first day of his reign. (They no longer dated the chronicle by the years of Nabu-naid, who had been captured in Uruk and sent away to Agbatana.)

Cyrus made certain that his appearance would be an impressive spectacle. He rode through the Ishtar Gate over palm branches laid down before him, through the throngs that waved scarfs and green branches; behind him appeared the Five Thousand guards, with swords sheathed and lances slung. Along the horizon rose the pavilions of the Persian encampment. He also took pains to make clear that his authority would be different from that of the Babylonian kings before him. As he had told Gubaru, his most difficult problem would be how to act after he had taken Nabu-naid's place.

Although he wore the regal robes that became him well, he carried neither ring nor staff, symbols of authority. With thousands of eyes upon him, and Gubaru at his side to advise him, he reined in at the palace steps and remained in his saddle—to be easily seen —while he summoned the high priests of Marduk's sanctuary and all the scribes on duty. Then he spoke where all could hear, giving his first proclamation, to be rendered into Babylonian and Elamite.

"I am Cyrus," he told the listening throngs, "king of the four quarters of the earth—Great King of Anshan, son of Cambyses.

"My dynasty," he assured the people, "is beloved of Bel and Nabu; my rule is dear to their hearts."

By this he identified himself with the mighty Nebuchadnezzar.

"I have entered Babylon, the ancient city, peacefully, with the cheering and rejoicing of the inhabitants. I shall set up my rule in the palace of their princes."

The implication was that, although Cyrus was monarch of the distant Medes and Persians, he intended to make Babylon his capital city. Cyrus then stretched out his hand to the attentive priests.

"Marduk, the great lord, has been seeking a righteous prince after his own heart, and he called me, Cyrus by name, to lordship over the world. To his city of Babylon he made me go, taking me by the hand. He inclined the hearts of the people toward me, for I was mindful of his worship. Marduk went at my side; without skirmish or battle he allowed me to enter Babylon. He spared his city, Babylon, a calamity. Nabu-naid, the king who did not fear him, he delivered into my hand."

When the priests murmured assent, Cyrus flung out his arm to the throngs behind them. "Throughout the whole of Sumer and Akkad I allowed no enemy to raise his head. I have given careful thought to the internal state of Babylon and to its many shrines. So shall I remove the yoke of servitude from the necks of the inhabitants; I shall repair the ruined dwellings and rebuild the shrines. Now I command this to be done."

Although the Achaemenian had used customary phrases, by Gubaru's coaching, he made an unusual pledge at the end, and the sophisticated Babylonians waited to see what their conqueror would do about it. They did not have long to wait. Cyrus had observed a good deal during his visit in disguise, and he did not see fit to explain that he had been in the courtyard of Esagila before. He singled out Nabu-naid's tablet of mockery. "That is a lie," he declared and ordered his own tablet of command to be set in its place. (And those who had heard that the Persian could not read began to wonder.) When he noticed the palace scribes marking the records in their cryptic style, he dismissed them from their duties and ordered all writing to be done in legible Akkadian, Elamite, and Persian. When he found dealers branding slaves for the market, he commanded that the slave dealers be branded as doers of evil. He made use of a simple yardstick in passing judgment; if an action were good in itself and useful to others, it should be aided; an action that caused evil was to be abolished. This rule seemed naïve at first to the Babylonians, but Cyrus enforced it ruthlessly.

He found that the temple managers had a scale of values in which an ox, slave, plow, and one cypress beam were all given the worth of two shekels of silver. Cyrus gave greater value to the ox and slave. In fact, he seemed to think in terms of what was useful in farming. Iron plows were held by the temples as a monopoly. Cyrus ordered them to be distributed to the workers on the plantations to increase the yield from the land. With a word he abolished the tax on water for irrigation, saying that the flow of water could be restricted no more than the beneficial light of the sun.

"How will you end the death of the earth?" Cyrus demanded. "How will you renew the life of the earth unless water flows free and seed fertilizes in the earth? How will the animal herds nourish you unless they are nourished by plentiful grass?"

The Babylonians pledged obedience to every command and then proceeded surreptitiously to carry on their affairs as before. And Cyrus's anger, always swift to rise, raged against these devotees of ancient customs.

He stormed at the temple envoys. "What are these Seven Demons of evil that you say follow after each citizen of this walled-in breeding ground of sin? I will name them, and do you remember them: filth of human bodies, disease of bodies, sickness of minds, avarice of the strong, cowardice of the weak, and suspicion and fear of others!"

Bowing before his anger, the priests exclaimed at the truth of his words and departed to decide among themselves that this Persian conqueror possessed little more intelligence than the late unlamented Scythian war lords. They ascertained, as they had suspected from the first, that he served no known god and therefore had no celestial guardian. "If a man stand not with the gods," they repeated, "how shall his own strength save him?" As for the Seven Demons, they existed as before, waiting to seize upon humans who failed to carry out the rituals of ancient days.

For the first few days of his reign Cyrus held the fascinated attention of the citizens by his circus performances in the streets. Unlike the moody, withdrawn Nebuchadnezzar or the secretive Nabu-naid, their new Achaemenian king appeared without ceremony, riding into alleys as well as the Processional Way. He argued fiercely with beggars as well as his proper ministers, and he threw out judgments like spittle without recording them in writing and passing the tablets to officers to file away. He was more entertaining than a performing elephant, even if more dangerous when angered. The anger of Cyrus, destructive as a streak of lightning, added the zest of dread to the curiosity of the spectators. He also stopped to tell entertaining stories. On his first ride of inspection upon the great walls, he encountered a chariot drawn as usual by wild asses trained to the yoke. He said to the Babylonian driver, "Listen! Once a man said to the wild ass, 'Let me harness thee and I will feed thee.' The ass thought well of the man's offer; but when it was yoked to a cart, it lamented and said: 'Keep thy feeding and bear thine own yoke, and suffer me to do the same.'"

The spectators remembered this story when Cyrus decided the fate of the Babylonian army. He offered all ranks, officers, spearbearers, chariot fighters alike, the choice of remaining in the regiments under his command or of putting down their weapons and going to their homes. Hearing this, the regiments elected to remain in their duty. They fared well because they drew rich rations for themselves and their families dwelling in the city, and they had easy duties to perform. At first Cyrus was satisfied; then he was not so well pleased at seeing the spearmen and chariots parade daily along the walls. He said Babylon no longer had need of a garrison, and he commanded the regiments to depart on foreign service to the frontiers where they could be useful. At that, two thirds of the garrison elected to leave the ranks and seek their homes in the streets below. Within a week, for the first time since the peace of Nebuchadnezzar, the summits of Imgur Bel and Nimitti Bel were bare of troops.

As free citizens, the ex-soldiers could draw weekly rations of millet, dates, and a little oil of sesame and meat. Cyrus discovered that in ancient times the Mar Banu—the nobility—had the obligation to supply a quota of fighting men yearly to the armed services; yet by degrees this had altered to the payment of a sum of hard money by the nobles to the treasury, and this in turn had changed to a mere accounting on the books; since the bookkeepers could be bribed, the contribution of the nobles had dwindled to fees paid the treasury clerks after each New Year. It seemed to Cyrus that the Babylonians kept only the ancient customs that added to their ease of life.

This made it difficult for him to carry out his promise that he would leave the rule and the customs of the great city unchanged.

Two foreigners, Rimut, the Surveyor, and Zeria, the Temple Master, had virtually administered the state under the absenteeism of Nabu-naid and the indifference of Belshazzar. When the twain brought propitiatory gifts of great price to the feet of the new king, Cyrus touched the gifts and returned them, while he kept Rimut and Zeria at their posts, with Law-bearers of Shushan and Parsagard to observe all transactions and report to him. "These Observers of Justice," he warned the ministers, "do not keep written tablets, but they have excellent eyes and memories. Take care, henceforth, to remember that you are subject to the laws you administer."

Alone with his son and Gubaru, Cyrus gave vent to his feeling of frustration in Babylon. "At Sardis the people were like untamed horses, pulling different ways; here they are like oxen bearing a yoke, yet only pulling when they are goaded."

He wanted to ride away from the lofty palace and the "heaven-touching" Tower. After hearing of the suicide of the princess, Shamura, he would not set foot within the Hanging Gardens, where flowering vines hid the ugliness of the streets below. It seemed to him that the Great Goddess must have power in such a shrine of her votaries.

"You count each day," Gubaru objected, "and you begrudge the passing of each day. Give the dark heads of Babylon time to change their thoughts. A potter," he added hastily, seeing Cyrus's impatience, "can mold a jar of wet clay with his hands swiftly, yet he cannot alter a jar that is once finished and the glaze burned into it by the fire of a furnace."

"He can, if he breaks it."

Thereupon the Achaemenian applied himself to the task of changing Babylon without destroying the city. Hittites and Kassites from the mountains had attempted to do that before him, only to have the city rebuild herself on the ancient plan. Cyrus did not alter a stone in the buildings, but he made great changes in the inhabitants. "Tell them," he instructed Gubaru, "that the new year, in truth, will bring a new day to them."

"I GATHERED TOGETHER THE PEOPLES."

When spring brought the moon of Nisan, Cyrus ordered the festival of the New Year to be held as in all other years. To open it he himself appeared on the Processional Way, followed by a guard of Elamite spearmen. He walked along the wide, cleansed street to the Esagila gate, where he left the spearmen and entered alone before the waiting priesthood of Marduk. Then they led him to the steps of the Ekur Temple; they removed the symbolic barrier at the head of the steps to lead Cyrus into the sanctuary.

When the Achaemenian stood before the wreathed statue of Babylon's god, he laid down the rod of authority that he carried—to signify that he gave up his power to the master of Babylon—only to have the high priest restore the scepter to him after he had placed his hands upon the hands of Marduk—to signify that he served the god in loving accord.

And the priests intoned their prayer for the reign of Cyrus, King of the Lands. Thus they gave to the Achaemenian the title of the ancient kings of Babylon from the first Sargon to Nebuchadnezzar.

When the crowds gathered along the Processional Way, no guards lined the curbing of the street. Messengers appeared from the palace with tidings for all the classes of spectators, by command of Cyrus:

The city, declared the messengers, would have a king of its own henceforth, who would be Cambyses, son of the Great King, King of the Lands.

The land would not be divided; as in the time of the first Sargon and Nebuchadnezzar, its frontiers would extend from sea to sea—that is, from the far Great Sea to the Persian Gulf. This great territory was now a single satrapy of Babylon—of *Babyrush*, as the Persians pronounced it. And it joined itself to Shushan, for Gubaru, lord of Shushan, was satrap of Babyrush entire.

"All those who ruled within the borders," Cyrus proclaimed, "from the Upper Sea to the Lower Sea, and the kings of the Westlands who dwell in tents—all of these brought large tribute to my feet in Babylon."

All the cities afar, even Tema in the desert, Harran in its highlands, and Sippar, would be restored and their fields renewed.

And the gods of those distant places would be freed from their captivity in Esagila and escorted back to their empty shrines. Even Shamash might be restored to the Temple of Sippar, and Shushinak to the shrine of Shushan. "All the gods of Sumer and Akkad which Nabu-naid—to the anger of the lord of the gods—had carried to Babylon, I, Cyrus, will bring back to their dwelling places to abide there forever that joy may be again in their hearts."

And with the captive gods, the captive peoples would go—the Amorites of the great plains, the Elamites of the hills, the Manneans skilled in arts, the boatmen of the Sealands, the Phoenicians of the sunset coast. Those peoples, whether prisoners of war under former kings of Babylon, enslaved, or held in forced labor, would be released with their families and belongings. "I, Cyrus, will

(*Above*) "Saka," or European Scythians leading a stallion in the Procession of the Tribute Bearers, Persepolis (ca. 520-330 B.C.). *Courtesy Oriental Institute, Chicago.*

(*Below*) Greek portrayal of Persians in a panther hunt. Of Hellenistic date, from the so-called Sarcophagus of Alexander, found in Sidon, now in Istanbul.

Entry to audience hall of Darius, Persepolis. The unusually slender and lofty columns, the subordination of all sculptured ornament to the architecture are typically Persian. In background the palace of Darius. *Courtesy Oriental Institute, Chicago.*

gather together all those peoples and restore them to their homes."

So in the year 538 Cyrus began his attempt to relieve the congestion of humanity within the walls of the capital city. By so doing he meant to increase the population of the provinces with agricultural workers and fishermen.

It seemed to his half-barbaric mind that the great evil of Babylon was that it had become a breeding place of slavery. Since he held details clear in his memory, he was careful to order the class of ex-soldiers out of the metropolis, to work in the dried-up fields of Opis and Sippar. And he remembered that the Hebrew canal laborers had aided him in shifting the waters of Babylon, while their kinsmen of the foul Kebar quarter had assisted his storming party to go up from the river to Esagila.

In his private record, kept on a single cylinder of clay, something of this was written in brief words: "My soldiers went about peacefully, widespread through the extent of Babylon. In all Sumer and Akkad I let no man be afraid. I devoted myself to the internal conditions of Babylon and of all the other cities. I freed the dwellers from the yoke that was ill placed upon them."

In the Kebar the elders of the prayer chamber sought out Jacob Egibi, who had been the first Jew to foretell the coming of Cyrus. Jacob, who had avoided the presence of the conqueror in fear, consented to go with them to make their plea before Cyrus. Other bankers and heads of business accompanied them.

They argued that Jacob should be spokesman because he had met with the Achaemenian before the fall of Babylon. Again Jacob consented, but he made no mention of that meeting on the bridge. For Cyrus had said nothing about it. Instead, Jacob spoke as a stranger offering to make a gift of his private fortune to the Great King. "For I have laid away the sum of thirty-nine talents and fifty-nine manas of silver. This sum I give to the hand of my lord, the king."

It was a point of pride with Jacob Egibi to offer his wealth, and a nice point of diplomacy to offer a gift that would open the way to a request.

Cyrus looked at him and at the delegation of the elders and

smiled. "In that case," he responded, "it would be more fitting if I gave thee another single mana instead—to make the sum of thy wealth an even forty talents."

Jacob mustered his courage to answer, as he was bound to do. "Rather let the Great King grant one small favor, to bestow upon my people a treasure beyond estimation."

"Then you speak not for yourself, or your family, but for your tribe?"

The words were those of the offer of Cyrus in the palm grove the year before. In his peculiar way the Achaemenian had brought the banker of Babylon to speak openly to him. Jacob responded quickly: "For my tribe, yes."

"For those of us," the elders cried eagerly, "of the Law of Moses that came to Joshua and to the prophets. Our Temple is that of Jerusalem, and it lies empty."

They explained that the vessels of the temple had been taken by Nebuchadnezzar many years before and held captive in Babylon, with the gods of stone and wood and silver and gold. They, the captives of Judah, possessed no such image of a god—such as Cyrus had restored to the shrines of Akkad. They had only the vessels, taken by the prince, Belshazzar, to adorn his feast. Now they besought the Great King to restore the sacred vessels to their keeping.

"Let it be done," Cyrus commanded.

The elders exclaimed and cried out together. Let the Great King grant an end to their captivity—to all Jews in Babylon— to seek their land of Judah across the western desert and their temple. For Jehovah had departed from that ruined temple at its destruction.

Cyrus heard them out and said: "It is ordered that all the peoples who are captive in Babylon shall return to their homes. Are the Jews different from the others? My word covers you. Set out when you will. Rebuild your temple."

When they bowed before him and took their leave, he singled out Jacob.

"And you, man of affairs. Will you aid in restoring this temple without an image?"

For a moment Jacob Egibi faced the king in silence. He was bound to answer, and he said, "Lord and master, thy servant will give of his talents of silver to aid in the building."

The half of Jacob that was Babylonian held him to the city; he and most of his fellows had rooted their lives upon the Euphrates, where their children had been born. He did not mean to journey from Babylon to a Judah that was no more than a name by now.

That evening the Jews gathered in prayer along the Kebar and the bank of the Euphrates. The voice of Isaiah was heard and his words repeated joyfully among them:

"Thus saith the Lord to his anointed, to Cyrus, whose right hand I have holden, to subdue nations before him; and I will loose the loins of kings, to open before him the two leaved gates; and the gates shall not be shut;

"I will go before thee, and make the crooked places straight: I will break in pieces the gates of brass, and cut in sunder the bars of iron:

"And I will give thee the treasures of darkness, and hidden riches of secret places, that thou mayest know that I, the Lord, which call thee by thy name, am the God of Israel. . . .

"Thus saith the Lord . . . that saith of Cyrus, He is my shepherd, and shall perform all my pleasure: even saying to Jerusalem, Thou shalt be built; and to the temple, Thy foundation shall be laid."

DEPARTURE OF THE SINGING MEN

From the waters of Babylon came the laborers, the diggers of the canals; from the lofty gardens came the gardeners; from the factories of brick and asphalt came the blackened furnace tenders, and from the sewers emerged the scrapers of filth. These Jews of the Captivity brought their women and offspring, and some brought asses and sheep. The chiefs and fathers of the tribes of Judah and Benjamin made ready the burnt offering of the moon after Tishri.

They also kept the Feast of Tabernacles without concealment.

The chiefs numbered their people. Mithradat, the royal treasurer, who had arrived from Agbatana, numbered the vessels of silver and gold that were restored from the treasury of Esagila to the elders of the tribes. Sheshbazzar, a prince of Judah, gathered his people and their belongings for the migration across the western deserts.

Jacob Egibi and other Jewish bankers of the Exchange and the families who had prospered in Babylon did not join the migration. They had learned that the hills of Judah had become bare; splendor had departed from the City of David. For more than two generations these Jews of Babylon had built their homes and established their trades; often their children spoke no language except the Babylonian. Then, too, the elders—strict keepers of the Mosaic Law—remained, choosing to worship at their shrines on the Euphrates as their fathers had done.

Those of wealth who remained gave a store of silver to the Jerusalem-bound throng, and this for the most part was made up of the laborers. When they began their march across the Adad Street bridge, they carried a goodly stock of stores with them on pack animals, because carts were not suited to the desert march. By number they had of horses seven hundred, thirty and six, of camels four hundred, thirty and five, and of mules two hundred, forty and five. Their laden asses numbered six thousand, seven hundred and twenty, by count of the inspectors at the western gate. "And there were among them two hundred singing men and singing women."

From the terrace of Esagila, Cyrus and Gubaru watched the exodus of the Jews and listened to their singing. Gubaru had observed the processions returning to other temples with their images in boat vehicles or chariots. He had seen Ishtar escorted through her gate to take the road to Uruk.

"Yet these Hebrews possess no image," he mused. "And therefore, surely their shrine is empty, except perhaps for some altar to which they pray."

Gubaru was growing older, Cyrus thought. He still believed that a divine being could inhabit an image, or at least could bestow on the image some peculiar power of his own. Gubaru had made quite a ceremony of escorting the very old and ugly statue of Shushinak back to his original home in Shushan—whence Assur-bani-pal had wrested him. No doubt his Elamites—and Gubaru still cherished them above other people—were duly gratified. Yet they had managed well enough in Shushinak's absence, owing to the energy and devotion of the entirely human Gubaru.

"I have never understood what powers the different gods possess," Cyrus admitted. "The Magians could not describe their Ahura-Mazda, who they say is master of the gods. He seems to be invisible as the Jehovah of the Jewish people. And they say he is in all the quarters of the earth."

"No priests of Ahura are registered here."

Cyrus assented and for a moment pondered a new thought. Might there be a single master of the gods residing somewhere beyond the orbit of the earth, remote and unknowable? Cyrus could not imagine whether such a divinity would prove to be beneficial or evil. Who would ever name him? And would the Magians appear in Babylon? He merely said, "The flowing water of the river should be channeled into the moat and the canal called the Kebar. Nebuchadnezzar planned better for the fortification of his city than for its health."

With each moon of that year the aspect of Babylon changed. After the departure of the army and the Hebrews, the Amorites moved out to their homes beyond the river. The Aramaeans drove their herds away to the west. The Sealand folk departed on their palm-tree rafts.

At the same time the scribes who were keepers of the Babylonian chronicle wrote that caravans appeared from beyond the Crystal Mount, and the *rabs* of the Phoenician cities, Tyre and Sidon, brought gifts to Cyrus the Great King. Throngs, coming and going, filled the east-west highways. The great Tower had not altered, but the city beneath became a thoroughfare of moving nations. Since the bronze-bound gates were left open, the ramparts of Imgur Bel and Nimitti Bel began to be deserted.

No one perceived that a greater change was at hand. The scribes wrote that it was the time of "great disturbance." The images and the peoples that departed Babylon did not return. The names of Ishtar and Nabu were less often spoken.

Unseen by the human beings an age was ending. The empires of the ancient Semitic East had vanished, not to return. A new era of the Aryan Greeks and Persians had begun.

SIX

Summons of the Magian

MEN do not go to sleep upon an evening in antiquity and wake up in the first modern age. Nor do prophets who predict a change often manage to foretell what the change will be. The inhabitants of Babyrush slept soundly enough under the rule of Cyrus and woke only with the conviction that they had a new and even unpredictable king in their old established world, of which Babylon was the center.

That, however, was no longer the case. Now that the Achaemenian peace extended from Bactria to Miletus on the shore of the "sea of the sunset," caravans began to make the transcontinental journey to the seaports. Miletus thrived and her scientists journeyed forth to explore or to gain wealth by teaching. Her errant son, Pythagoras, finished his experiments in Egypt and sailed west to teach in the new medical center at Crotona on the shore of an Italy-to-be. On the west coast of that same Italy, the Etruscans, earlier migrants from Anatolia, had been established for a long time; now they carried their wares of skilled metalwork out to sea. In their hill towns, notably at Tarquinia, the Etruscan artists enjoyed a renaissance; they decorated even the walls of rock tombs with paintings revealing a new mastery. Heredity had bequeathed to these artists a strong sense of decoration imbued with the delicacy of Crete, the restraint of Egypt, and the naturalness of Syria. The artists, however, ceased to paint human figures in outline; they improvised portraits of people and infused the portraits with animation.

Across the sea from the Etruscan colonies stretched the trading ports of the Carthaginians—descendants of Phoenicians, who had entered upon a new way of life in North Africa. The ships of Carthage vied with the Etruscan merchant craft and excelled them in voyaging out of the western gate of the sea. The Carthaginians alone dared to seek new shores upon the uncharted ocean.

An age of discovery had begun, unheralded. Adventurous people like the Phocaeans—displaced by the coming of the Persians to Ionia—realized that there existed more seas than the Mediterranean, which they called the Middle Sea. The barriers of Greek myth, the Pillars of Hercules in the west, and the Mount of Colchis reached by the nebulous Argonauts in the east did not prevent their vessels from faring farther to unknown waters.

At Athens, Pisistratus was aware of the new discoveries. That enlightened tyrant had completed the stone aqueduct which gave flowing water for the first time to his city, and he had collected the victory chants of the Homeric poets into a single written book, the *Iliad*. This in turn gave his people a forceful tradition of their ancestors, those noble-born voyagers who had proved to be better swordsmen than the Anatolian Greeks of Troy—although the same gods had aided and abetted both sides. Athenians who listened to a reading of the *Iliad* began to wonder if a well-forged iron sword might not accomplish more in the end than the intervention of Artemis. Could not a human hero defy the Fates?

Pisistratus invoked tradition and catered to the new vogue for exploration—on the heels of the far-wandering Phocaeans and Carians of Ionia—by colonizing the great peninsula of the eastern sea, the Euxine. Athenian sea traffic to this remote Chersonese might hope to control the strategic strait of the Dardanelles, which the Greeks still called the Hellespont, the Sea of the Hellenes. On that same strait the advancing Persians had set their frontier posts. For the time being there ensued no clash of conflict between them because the Persians were interested only in occupying the land, while the Athenians and Spartans kept to their sea travel.

Oddly enough, in so doing, Pisistratus was imitating Cyrus. He was sending out the younger and more energetic families to farm adjacent coasts and colonize distant shores. This policy of decentralization of the Athenians, of course, had a purpose. It kept the restless youth out of politics and accordingly made Pisistratus's tenure of office more secure. Still more oddly, however, the dichotomy of the Greek tyrant served to enhance the grandeur and extent of his city of Athens, while the Diaspora of Cyrus served to reduce Babylon to the rank of other capital cities. Then and thereafter the Greeks worked for the advantage of their city states, while Cyrus the Achaemenian labored to create an empire.

In spite of the adulation of the inhabitants, Cyrus had no joy in Babylon. Yet he could not leave it. His shake-out of the social structure antagonized the powerful Mar Banu, who found themselves deprived of most of their slave labor and privileges. Under Nabu-naid's indifference the nobility had lived comfortably in their estates. The new king expected them to be useful to others, a concept very difficult for the old families to carry out. As the months passed, the magnates of Babylon felt a nostalgic regret for the harmless mysticism of Nabu-naid, the military renown of the late prince, Belshazzar, the spectacular public works of Nebuchadnezzar, and the glory of Babylon as mistress of the world.

This antagonism within the walls found a voice in complaints of the favor shown to foreigners—barbaric masters who wore trousers and invoked laws never known to Sargon. "There is no justice since Sargon."

Aware of this hidden hostility, Cyrus asked Rimut to do something about it.

"We will make a song," the experienced Rimut decided. "Nothing affects the Babylonians as much as a street song."

Their counterpropaganda song chanted the misdeeds of Nabunaid's reign. "Nabu-naid wandered about and did no right thing. He blocked the way of the merchant, he took plow-land from the peasant. He took the joy-shout from the harvesting. He shut up the water in the canals and closed the outlets to the fields. He let the river water run unchecked. Alas for the right-doing citizens!

They did not walk in the open places with pleasure. Their faces changed. They beheld no joy around them."

The song explained the cause of Nabu-naid's misconduct. "A demon seized upon him. He turned his back on his true subjects, and built a city of his own in the desert. He sent away the army of Akkad. He shut his ears to the lamenting of his own people."

Cyrus wondered a little whether this song of Rimut's did not hold some mockery of himself. However, new verses were added and sung in the streets in the cool of the evening. "Nabu-naid boasted foolishly of victory over Cyrus. He said untruthfully that Cyrus could never read the wedge writing on his tablet. Perhaps Cyrus could not read but the gods sent him vision. He made seed sprout again in barren ground. At his first New Year he restored joy to the inhabitants of Babylon. He pacified their hearts and gladdened their lives. He tore down ruined walls and rebuilt the sanctuaries of the gods. He renewed the wasted lives of the people. Now, for reward, may Nabu-naid be thrown into prison in the underworld. May Marduk look kindly upon the kingdom of Cyrus."

While the propaganda song did not alter the resentment of the nationalists, it delighted the crowds in the streets—the multitudes that had known the confiscation of water and the grinding of taxes that increased each year. The common folk always believed that any change would be for the better.

Zeria, on his part, suggested that Cyrus invoke the aid of the astronomers who kept the record of the heavens. These scientists who worked with silent instruments in their tower office stirred the admiration of the Achaemenian. They had charted the behavior of the stars to within a sixtieth of an hour—the Babylonians used sixty as the controlling number. They had discovered the *Saros*, the great cycle of years after which the succession of the eclipses returned to its starting point; they charted the passage of time through its eternity. At any moment of a clear day they could also determine the exact time by a bronze needle set upright in the center of a marked bowl. Where the tip of the needle's shadow fell, the hour and minute could be marked. These watchers of the stars made light of the mystery of numbers. Numbers, they explained, progressed in two directions. You counted up as well as down, and the pin point of your counting began at *bar*—"nothing" (zero). And these intelligent Chaldeans agreed, with no surprise, to find a favorable horoscope for their Persian monarch.

Cyrus, after taking thought, suggested that they find it for his son, not for himself. The sophisticated Babylonians probably had no great expectations from him but they might have hopes of Cambyses who took pride in his title of King of Babylon.

"The king's son stands under the sign of the crescent moon," the astronomers reported, after making their examination. "The sign of the Archer conjoins. Therefore, it is clear that in the reign of the Great King's son—may the years of his life lengthen—the kingdom will increase, and its glory will increase by war."

The single-minded Cambyses was the one who took this prophecy to heart. Cyrus was content to let Cambyses take his place at the sacrifices and festivals. Gubaru struggled with the enforcement of the new laws, which became a very complex matter because the Babylonians would not accept a simple truth. The old Persian axiom "that the strong shall not oppress the weak" had been in the city's law code since the time of Hammurabi, but in the interval had been reduced by so many qualifications that the Persian Law-bearers could not identify the strong from the weak. Cyrus's simple idea of gifts brought to the king did not serve to reduce the customary taxes.

"The way of Parsagard," Gubaru assured him, "is not the way of Babylon. A farmer can give of his produce, but a merchant pays in money and expects to be paid. You gave your pledge that the customs of this city of Marduk and Ishtar, his wife, would not be changed. Then why do you attempt to do it? Accept the taxes and entertain the Mar Banu in some splendid affair at the palace with the tax money."

Cyrus complied in a way of his own. Remembering the longing of Mandane to be restored to the Hanging Gardens, he sent for the widow of Astyages. With her chamberlain, eunuchs, and treasurers, the aged Mandane returned to Babylon and occupied with satisfaction the quarters vacated by the death of Shamura.

"Now it brings joy to my eyes to contemplate my glorious birthplace again in my death years," she confided to Cyrus. Her throne seat was placed among the cedars of the artificial grove, and around her, frankincense burned to relieve the odors of the streets. "Now, my son, you have conquered all the world except the realm of the Nile with exceedingly rich treasures and clear mirrors that would rejoice my eyes. No doubt in summoning me hither you have taken thought for a fitting tomb overlaid with alabaster, with cramps of gold, not iron, to receive my poor remains when Nergal summons me to the underworld."

Beside Mandane in the lofty garden Cyrus had a strange impression of grandeur and death. He looked out at the shimmering peak of the Tower and down at the pattern of streets, not wandering but straight to the walls on the four sides. He looked far out at the plantation green of the Plain stretching to the gray horizon of the deserts. Beneath him toiled multitudes of sickly beings fashioning rare articles and machines with a skill learned in centuries of years. Even while he admired Babylon, he hated it.

Cyrus later gave out to the scribes of the Chronicle that Mandane, daughter of Nebuchadnezzar, was his mother. This was written into the record, and it bestowed on Cambyses a claim to the throne, but it was a lie.

Then Cyrus summoned his lame friend, Mithradat, and handed over all finances to him; he gave problems of government into the hands of Gubaru, and he left Cambyses to act as ruler. Calling the Five Thousand from their luxurious barracks, he started across the river to explore the western desert of his new satrapy.

The Persians forged across the Plain toward the sunset. They carried their water in jars borne by camel trains, for they were on the face of the true desert, on gray empty earth under a cloudless sky. Their Aramaean guides told Cyrus that no great king had ventured here before him—no lord of Assur, or Hatti, or Pharaoh of the Nile. They left behind them the half-finished brick walls of Tema where Nabu-naid had isolated himself; already the walls were partly buried in sand, and the Babylonian settlers had been driven out by raiding tribes. Cyrus suspected that they needed little excuse to flee back to Babylon.

They entered the Red Land of heat-burned earth where beehive villages stood over the wells, and the people prayed to black pinnacles of rock. From well to well Nabataean caravans journeyed north with the incense, gold, and raw copper of *Arabaya*. These were bound for Damascus or the Phoenician ports, and they gave a pulse of life to the barren earth that endured no growth of a city upon it.

In the protecting shadow of a ravine, Nabataean trading folk dwelt in pavilions beneath the tombs they had cut into the rock walls. Here Cyrus summoned the chieftains of the Red Land, both Aramaean and Ishmaelite, and declared that now they dwelt under his rule and law. His law forbade the warring of tribe against tribe and brother against brother within the tribe. The speech of his rule would be Aramaic, and the purpose of his rule would be to join the habitations of the Two Rivers to the sea of the sunset by caravan traffic. This vast satrapy would have the name of Arabaya.

To this council of the nomad chiefs came uninvited strangers. Phoenician envoys appeared in light chariots with camels bearing their supplies. In their skullcaps and flowing purple wool, the Phoenicians flung themselves down at Cyrus's feet, and their slaves laid down gifts of rare excellence—glass vessels with the colors of the rainbow, thin bronze bowls and copper jars adorned with mythical griffins and beasts having the heads of women, called sphinxes. To appeal to Cyrus, they offered a winged symbol of lapis lazuli set in gold, resembling the wings of the Achaemenians although it was ancient Egyptian work. They offered him seven girls of fragile beauty, each of a different type, for they had been sought out among the young daughters of Egypt and Ethiopia, the islands of Crete and Delos, and also the Greeks. These handmaidens in turn bore small treasures of silver mirrors, incense burners, and alabaster lamps to aid them in pleasuring the ever-victorious Great King.

The Phoenicians hoped that sight of the lovely maidens would stir desire in the Achaemenian to conquer their homelands in the west. Cyrus understood as much; he made a present of a different jewel to each of the girls—looking longest upon the daughter of

Crete whose white flesh fairly shone from the darkness of her unbound hair—and returned them to their slave masters, saying,
"Indeed, I fear their beauty. It is said wisely that beauty comes
from loyalty. Surely it is not fitting for a king such as I am to be
afraid."

And he puzzled the Phoenician envoys deeply with another
proverb: "A throne was set up for a liar; yet when his lies overtook
him, they spat in his face."

The astute Phoenicians exclaimed at his wisdom and the mag-
nificence of his throne, while they sought his meaning, until Cyrus said, "I prefer to speak the truth."

For a week while he feasted them, the ambassadors of Sidon
and Tyre probed at what was in his mind in making the journey to
the west. They were entirely familiar with the ways over the Red
Land, they explained, because it had been their home in remote
times; they had ventured with their caravans out to the sea and
across the sea—for the highways go out to sea. Now they made use
of ships instead of pack animals, and the black ships of Tyre were
superior to Egyptian river barges or Greek rowing galleys. Moreover, no mariners except their own knew the long ways of the sea
or used the stars as guides.

At the end of the week they came to spoken agreement with
Cyrus—for the Phoenicians, unlike the Babylonians, wrote nothing
down, although they possessed the finest papyrus. Phoenicia, as
well as Palestine, would be included in the satrapy of Babylon,
subject to the orders of the governor of that city—at present
Cambyses—but ruling itself with customs unchanged, paying
tribute only from the increase of trade with Babylon. Yet the
Phoenician shipping might be called into the service of the Great
King.

Cyrus did not sense any need for that as yet. But his compact
with the maritime cities prepared the way for an invasion of Egypt
—Cambyses's desire—and of the Greek islands.

At parting with the Phoenicians, Cyrus told them another proverb, and by now they paid the closest attention to his stories.
"The greatest evils are two: that the plowman who draws food
from the earth should starve, and that the man of strength should

take the possessions of the weak without labor of his own." And he added, "I have set my face against those evils."

Thus word of the strange Achaemenian peace reached the sea-coasts. Because the ancient peoples of the coast began to hope for much from his rule, there was an end of the alliance against him. Both Amasis on the Nile and Pisistratus at the Acropolis of Athens ceased to be concerned at the advent of the Persians.

Cyrus did not journey on to the sea. He turned back when his army beheld the vision over the Red Land. Ahead of them in the glare of the sun the white walls of a towered citadel took shape above the shimmering plain. A lake stretched beneath the walls, fringed with cool tree growth. Amazed, the Persians cried, "Kang-diz! The stronghold of the gods! It is here, before us."

The Aramaeans, accustomed to such mirages, explained that the water and the palace did not exist and would disappear if they rode on. However, the Persians were weary of the unchanging heat of the lowlands, and the apparition seemed to be a warning to them. Cyrus granted their instant request to turn back. Secretly he longed to be journeying to the east, not to the west. In all his life he had not been able to come upon any trace of the homeland of the Aryans, which could not lie on the shores of this western sea. The longing to discover *Aryan-vej* had grown with the years, and now he had passed his sixtieth year.

Two circumstances fed this longing during the return march. Pressing need took him from Babylon to Agbatana, whence he had withdrawn the dependable Mithradat. And when the kingdom couriers caught up with him there, they brought an appeal for help from one Zerubbabel, who was unknown to him. The scribes told him that this Zeru-babil—or Seed of Babylon, as the name should be in Akkadian—had become the leader of the Jewish exiles, now returned to Jerusalem. He wrote in Aramaic that the villages of the land had been wasted long since by Nebuchadnezzar and never repaired; that the fields were barren, the sheep few, and the enmity of the Samaritans great toward the Jews from Babylon. The natives of Judah questioned the right of Zerubbabel's people to build anew the Temple of Jehovah on its height. To do that they had dire need of aid in silver money from the Great King.

After pondering the appeal, Cyrus dictated his answer: "As for the house of God which is at Jerusalem, let the house be built, the place where they offer the fire sacrifice continually; its height shall be ninety feet and its breadth ninety feet, with three courses of great stones and one of timber. And let its cost be given from the king's house." He remembered the sacred vessels that Zerubbabel's people had carried with them. "Also let the gold and silver utensils of the house of God, which Nebuchadnezzar took from the house of God and brought to Babylon, be restored and brought again to the temple which is in Jerusalem, each to its place. And you shall put them in the house of God."

Then he dictated an order to Mithradat at Babylon to pay the silver talents to Zerubbabel at Jerusalem. He reflected that the refugees who had set out across the desert seemed to be impoverished now, but at least they had managed to return to their homeland. It was vital that they should rebuild their temple. Cyrus could not absent himself in the west again. Agbatana had become the center of his reign, and a host of problems pressed upon him there —to mark the frontiers of restless Armenia, to open roadways to Cappadocia beyond, to send emergency supplies to Vishtaspa as he had promised, to furnish some kind of schooling for the Iberians of the Hollow Land——

Wearied by the problems, he sought out Croesus, as he had been accustomed to do at Sardis. He found the Lydian quartered in a single chamber opening on the palace garden. Reclining on a couch in the sun, Croesus was studying an alabaster jar, admiring the delicate figures joined hand to hand upon it as he turned it in the strong light. "Whoever made this," he exclaimed, "meant it to stand in the sun. A rare artist—to master the secret of light."

Absorbed in his vase, Croesus appeared to be entirely content.

"Those oracles, at Delphi, for instance," Cyrus asked. "Did you trust their answers to your problems? At Sardis?"

Without putting down the vase, Croesus laughed. "Too much, Achaemenian lord." Then he frowned in thought. "Yet the oracle foretold that my son would speak. Now at last we can talk, he and I."

Cyrus glanced around the room, bare except for some objects which, like the alabaster vase, were beautiful rather than useful. "Are you comfortable here?" he asked.

Croesus considered the question. "Perhaps not, yet I enjoy it. I sit daily in the sun. At Sardis the sun beat upon us; here in the mountains, it revives us. And look what it does for the vase!"

Leaving his captive, Cyrus reflected that he would never understand the Lydian. Wherever he might be and whatever happened around him, Croesus managed to enjoy himself. He distrusted the oracles, while he believed in them. He took comfort in what the Greeks called philosophy.

When Cyrus was able at last to set out for Parsagard, he took the familiar road by Shushan. There he hardly recognized the palace over the river. The rough walls were resplendent with tiling; marble gleamed on the floors. In the temple the ugly image of Shushinak stood within a gold-plated sanctuary. Date palms from Babylon lined the garden walls. Gubaru must have squeezed many talents of silver out of the revenues at Esagila to adorn his own palace in this fashion! Angered, Cyrus thought of recalling the aged Elamite and replacing him by Mithradat, who took nothing out of the treasury. Then he laughed. "A bird will feather its own nest."

Gubaru had toiled for nearly two generations to rebuild Shushan and its land. The country was a happy one; the peasants had the new iron plows that Cyrus had wrested from the monopoly of Marduk's temple; the villagers traveled far to behold the wonder of their golden temple. And Gubaru could seek his tomb in peace.

It did not occur to Cyrus that the wise Elamite had accomplished this by means of the Achaemenian himself. With heightened anticipation, Cyrus took the mountain road to his valley. When he reached the river, he reined in to listen to the familiar rush of the rapids and he breathed deeply of the cold air, thinking that he glimpsed the laughing Anahita in the spray of the falling water. In truth when he entered this protected spot the weariness of thirty years came upon him like slumber. In spite of his resolve to explore the farther east, he did not leave his valley for six years.

THE CHRONICLE IS SILENT

The inhabitants of the new Persian empire did not realize that these were years of unexpected peace until they had passed. From Tyre to Maracanda, statesmen looked for the Achaemenian to set out on fresh conquests; merchants watched for rebellion to break out against the rule of one man over the vast area of their traffic; peasants in the fields expected raiders to appear as usual or—more evil, to their thinking—an officer with spearmen to requisition their harvests in the king's name. Nothing of the kind, however, happened. During the last six years of Cyrus's reign, the Babylonian Chronicle merely recorded the passage of time, and the Hebrews, on their part, described the disputes that delayed the building of Jehovah's Temple. "Every man goes only to his own house."

There were several reasons for this unwonted tranquillity. Nomad raiders from the north sought the rich looting of the Achaemenian's dominion—expecting to break in with the first good grazing and to leave with the last harvests—only to be met by trained horsemen as dangerous as themselves. As for the civil wars of brother against brother and princes impatient for the deaths of reigning fathers, the command of Cyrus lay against such customary conflict. Then, too, no thrones remained to fight for, except his own. The guardians of each country were named by the Achaemenian, and their rank was not hereditary. In restive Babylon, after the retirement of aged Gubaru, Cambyses the heir ruled with an iron hand, backed by soldiers who hoped for much from him. This Chaldean Babylon had been actually a mercantile imperialism, and with trade expanding under Cyrus no nationalist leader cared to risk a revolt.

The Babel-like diversity of tongues had been ended by making Aramaic the common tongue, even in Jerusalem. At sophisticated Sardis, Croesus was no longer mourned for. There the champions of Greek liberation found it difficult to answer the question, from what were the Ionian Greeks to be liberated? The more western cities like Sparta and Athens still sought their heritage on the

Ionian coast. The shrewdest political observers, the priests of Apollo at Delphi, still cast their prophecies for the Persian. (The Medes were gradually forgotten.) But the underlying reason for this tranquillity was something unknown to the chroniclers, although suspected by the people at large. It was the tolerance of the king.

This was a new concept in a ruler, and Assyrians and Babylonians had no word for it. They had made a proverb for the presence of a ruler: "Sharper than a two-edged knife is the speech of a king. Behold, before you is something hard; in the presence of a king do not think to delay—his anger is swifter than lightning. Take thou heed to thyself; if a thing is commanded thee, it is a burning fire; hasten, do it, put sackcloth on thy hands, for the word of a king is wrath of a heart."

In thirty years Cyrus the Achaemenian had managed to overcome this fear. Both Medes and Persians named him Father, and in the mouths of the peasants he was "the people's king." His tolerance alone would not have marked him so; it was joined to power greater than Nebuchadnezzar's. The conjunction of humanity with the ability to punish utterly had an odd force that altered age-old happenings.

A tale is told of the Mardian tribe, dwelling in the bare highlands of the future Persepolis. Their chieftain and elders came before Cyrus with a plea. Their land, said the spokesmen, was poor and they labored greatly in cultivating it. Therefore the Mardians desired to be given a land of rich fertility, such as their king had conquered elsewhere. The Mardians were prepared to migrate to this territory of greater ease and less labor. Let Cyrus but say the word.

He considered their request and said, "Well, then do it."

When they thanked him, he added, "Remember this, however. Elsewhere in that fertile spot you will, soon or late, have to obey some master. In your highland you are free men and nobody's slaves."

After considering his words, the Mardians announced that they had decided to remain in their homes.

A Maspian chieftain, now commander of a thousand, confessed to Cyrus that he felt rewarded by his service. Formerly at his home the Maspian had needed to grow the food for his family and to eat it out of the pots. Now, said he, as officer of a garrison he did not lift a hand to feast when he willed, with wine to drink and servants to fetch sugared fruits, while he reclined on a sweet-smelling cedar couch. After hearing him out, the Achaemenian took him through some question and answer of their school days.

Cyrus: "You take good care of your charger, I notice."

Maspian (gratified): "Yes—as I should!"

Cyrus: "You exercise him well before feeding."

Maspian: "Yes, certainly."

Cyrus: "Why?"

Maspian: "To keep him fit, else he would sicken."

Cyrus: "If you take such care of a horse, why should you feed yourself before doing a day's labor? Tell me next time what work you have done before feasting."

One thing he could never accomplish; he could not coax his people to embark on the sea. An Achaemenian chieftain explained: "There are three kinds of men: the living, the dead, and those who wander on the seas."

Although Cyrus had made no change in the pastoral customs of the Persians themselves, he had long since abandoned the old councils of the Three Tribes and even that of the assembled Ten Tribes. These Persians now made up only a portion of the Iranian peoples under his rule, and a fragment of the varied peoples. They could have been housed entire within one quarter of Babylon. He saw no good and much possible evil in giving the scattering of Persians supremacy over the others—as over their own Caspians. His authority stemmed from the throne alone; a Persian satrap had no power over a Hyrcanian Hazarapat. To aid this amalgam of divided peoples, he had assumed the traditional titles of Babylon, Agbatana, and Sardis—yet had named no one city as his capital. Parsagard, remote in its valley, remained the residence of the Achaemenian clan—managed by his younger son, Bardiya, aided by the grandchildren. Amytis still secluded herself in Zadracarta on the Hyrcanian Sea, and there her daughter became the wife of Darius, son of Vishtaspa and Hutaosa, a brilliant army officer, by all report.

Cyrus's counselors were the satraps and—independent of them—

the envoys of the subject peoples. Since he kept no regular army in the field, he did not have to deal with a commander in chief who might become a danger.

This rudimentary world state, however, was held together solely by the personality of Cyrus. He had become its supreme judge, protector, and provider. The burden of such authority was greater than that of the treasure of Croesus, about which he had jested in a carefree earlier day. The danger of rule by one indispensible man Cyrus probably did not foresee; in any case, he could do nothing about that. At the end of his years he was simply trying to carry out the pledge of his enthronement by the three Persian tribes, although his subjects had multiplied four hundredfold. At least they had food enough; a shepherd must, first of all, feed his flock.

Because throngs of them waited at his portico, beseeching the presence of the Great King, Cyrus could not journey farther away than the Salt Desert of the Germanians and the Crystal Mount.

Even facing the multitudes he felt himself to be alone. Emba no longer held the rein of his charger; Kassandan was dead, and he had made a tomb for her in the cliff by Anahita's cave. For all her nagging, Kassandan had held the children in her heart. Of his two wives, Amytis had veiled her thoughts from him; the Elamite—he heard from his observers—had become a Zarathustrian and had married his daughter to the son of Vishtaspa, a zealous follower of the mysterious prophet. Her reason for doing so he could not guess, but he knew that she had a reason. His grandchildren feared him because court dignitaries surrounded him, and the foreigners who sought him bowed down to his feet. At his coming, the chamberlains intoned: "Silence! Bow down before the Royal Glory!"

Cyrus no longer had the will to sit with the throng at his tables. Around the residence—that had once housed his family—four colonnades had been built, lofty as the great audience hall that measured thirty-one paces by twenty-two; ninety and eight columns stood on their plain black bases upon the white of the marble floor. Cyrus took his food alone on a dais, raised like that of Astyages, above the courtiers and servitors. Across from him he beheld his own image cut into the stone of the wall facing. In silent procession officers and servants, each with his weapon or implement, followed the king; above him spread the Achaemenian wings. This image remained there, to signify to all comers that they were in the royal chamber. In the same way, the white columns rising from black bases—pleasing enough to the eye—symbolized the triumph of good over evil. The new dignity of the festival chamber spared Cyrus one evil; no wandering poets ventured in to sing the glories of his ancestor Achaemenes while he ate.

Beyond the colonnades the scrubby gardens had been altered to masses of rose bloom and dark cypress borders above the stone-flagged water channels; but now the quiet gardens were rendezvous for courtiers, all wearing insignia of their rank and watchful of others who sought the presence of the king. Even on the height of the fire altars, Zarathustrians trooped up to make their prayers to Ahura-Mazda, the Master.

Something in their murmuring reminded Cyrus of a chanting of the Hebrews by the Kebar—"covet not thy neighbor's ox nor his ass . . . nor anything that is his." The Hebrews said that was one of Ten Commandments revealed to a prophet of theirs on the height of a mountain called Sinai. Since the Hebrews of the west could hardly have talked about such matters with the Zarathustrians of the east, the revelations must have been somewhat similar. Would a day ever come when the two congregations prayed together, making offerings to their fires on the heights?

Would the Milesian philosophers probing into the vastness of the universe ever keep watch with the Chaldean astronomers who charted the course of the stars? Searchers after the same truths usually arrived at different convictions, Cyrus decided. He had brought some of the learned Chaldeans and their instruments with him to Parsagard. They promptly set up their clocks to keep track of time by the drip of water, while his Caspian servants had no notion of time, beyond sunrise that began their day's labor and sunset that ended it.

Cyrus, master of them all, felt that his life was drawing to its end, and he mused upon the time to come when he would be surely alone. He sent for his architects—some of the planners of Esagila were among them now—and bade them make a design for his tomb.

"May the gods forbid!" they exclaimed in different tongues. "May the years of our Lord the King be without end!"

"I wish something small," Cyrus observed, "of simple stone."

When he wanted a thing done, it was his habit to call on the ablest men and not tell them how to do it. After the passing of a moon, the royal architects brought him a design beautifully colored on spotless vellum. It was a lofty tower guarded by winged genii, having a chamber for attendant priests and a fire altar on the summit. "The bronze door of the tomb chamber," they explained, "if let fall, locks itself into place forever."

After one glance, Cyrus put the plan aside. Ten years ago he would have loosed the shaft of his anger upon the architects. Now he understood them. A technician worked by the methods he had learned. One who knew how to build an arch or a vault would build an arch or a vault to support a ceiling. It was always necessary to confine them to the simple things desired. "I do not wish to be sealed up," he said. "Come, all of you, and we will go to the spot and talk together about this abiding place of mine that is to be on it."

Then the Achaemenian led them out of the audience hall. He took a path that led away from the entrance stair, south and west toward the sunset. Within bowshot of the river bank, he listened for the laughter of the flowing water and heard it. Looking around, he beheld the summits of the valley and was satisfied. "Here," he told the architects, "we will raise a foundation of white limestone on seven steps. On the top of these steps we will set a room of the same stone; inside, the room will be seven cubits long and four cubits broad. The roof will slope down as if the room were a house. It will slope on both sides from the ridge." For a moment he considered this small house, such as his ancestors had built in their woodlands. "Two doors will lead into it—an outer door of the stone I have described to you and an inner door of the same stone; both will open, but you must close the outer door in that narrow space before you can open the inner door." He considered the building and could think of nothing to add to it. "Now is the form of my tomb clear to you? Have you any questions to ask?"

"The ornament—what will it be?" asked one.

"The gold—where will it be set in?" another inquired.

"What ornament is better than the good white stone itself?" Cyrus asked in his turn. "Yet it should be firm and cramped with iron." He smiled, considering that. "Let the gold be applied to the edges of the iron where they show," he concluded. "It will preserve the iron from rust."

Then the Babylonian technician inquired what the wording of the inscription would be—because a long inscription of all the proper titles and invocations would be better cut into the stone facing before the blocks were set in place.

Cyrus thought about the inscription. Perhaps it should have an invocation. It occurred to him that many men would come to the river to look upon this tomb, and doubtless the writing should explain what it was. "Well," he decided, "let the inscription say: 'O man, I am Cyrus the Achaemenian, the Great King.' And that is all."

The architects praised his wisdom but inwardly felt cheated at being called upon to design a tomb that was no more than a stone cell resembling a peasant's house. No royal tomb, to their knowledge, had been shaped like that.

"—AND WHATEVER OTHER GODS THERE ARE."

Watching the drip of their water clock, the Chaldeans dropped a bronze ball into a bronze basin, and its chime announced to the palace the second and the moment and the hour of the beginning of the New Year in the month of Nisan. This was the year 529 before Christ.

As usual, Cyrus went out at the stroke of dawn from his residence palace, past the doorway of the guardian genius, the image of his own fravashi. He ascended the long flights of steps to the fire altars where the priests waited with their balsam rods. The throng that waited by the steps below the marble terrace were Zarathustrians for the most part. Cyrus noticed several pilgrims from the White Congregation among them, and it exasperated him that these visitors from the east never entered his audience hall to do reverence to himself as their king. They did that readily enough at their Fire of Bactria. He heard their chanting to Ahura-Mazda, the invisible and ever present. They gave voice to the name of no other deity. Probably when that day's sun reached the rock of the high place of the Hebrews, prayer was made to Jehovah alone. And in the temples of Egypt to Ammon——

When Cyrus lifted his arms, those around him fell silent. The priests listened, to discover what invocation the king made. It was well known that Cyrus believed in no particular god. He had been ready enough to take the hands of the idol of Babylon. Yet here he stood at the fire altar of Ahura-Mazda.

Quite aware of that, Cyrus wondered what he might utter that would be the truth. Shrine priests always attached importance to spoken words, regardless of what was in the heart of the speaker. And what did spoken words avail unless they came from the heart?

Cyrus pondered and voiced his prayer: "To Ahura-Mazda—and whatever other gods there are."

His phrase was heard and repeated. It caused much debate as to the identity of the divinities that the king had failed—wittingly or unwittingly—to name.

That year brought heavy problems to Cyrus in Parsagard. In Babylon the forthright Cambyses had raised a great armed force to overawe the restive factions; having created such a powerful army, his son begged for permission to march by Jerusalem into Egypt, claiming that the conquest of the Nile Valley would end the border disputes with Babyrush. On the other hand, the aged Amasis, who no doubt desired to make a peace that would add to his fame, sent an imposing embassy to request—the word used by the proud Egyptians—a treaty of alliance and mutual defense with Cyrus. So might a stall-fed ox request an alliance with a lion. . . .

In the Middle Sea, Phoenician warships attacked Greek merchant convoys, claiming that they were acting to safeguard their own merchantmen against pirates. On that sea, apparently, an enemy became a pirate. In their hearts the crafty Phoenicians meant to destroy the ships of their rivals. . . .

The satrap of Sogd, writing from Maracanda, reported that raiders were crossing the border river. The guard posts were few on this river, and the satrap requested a payment from the royal treasury to provide for new posts and more adequate garrisons. And Cyrus saw no good whatever in building fortifications against tribesmen who merely rode around them. Even the wall of Nebuchadnezzar had not kept Babylon safe. . . .

On a mild summer evening he dismissed all petitioners to snatch a half hour of rest before supper. He left the throne and its guardsmen and went to the rear colonnade where he could walk undisturbed. He meditated upon the last report by his observer at Sardis. It concerned the Mysians, an Aeolian—hence Aryan—people dwelling along the shore of the Dardanelles around the ruins of Troy. In fact the Mysians claimed part of the glory of defending Troy in the siege described to Cyrus by Croesus. Now they were exacting a tax from Greek vessels passing through the strait with cargoes of grain, hides, and slaves from the Euxine. The satrap at Sardis approved this action because it increased the revenues of Sardis. But it vexed Cyrus because the Mysians quite naturally held up Greek vessels that did not pay the tax. And Cyrus could not understand why the shore-dwelling Mysians had any claim on the waters between the seas. In any case, they were risking bitter disputes for a small amount of money.

Pacing between the columns, Cyrus decided that it would do no good to order Sardis to let navigation be free in the strait. Of course the order would be carried out, officially, and the Mysians would contrive to collect their dues in some other manner. The best solution would be to create a new Mysian satrapy and make its guardian responsible, on the spot, for all doings in the strait.

He had decided that much when he was aware of the other man standing between the columns. The stranger had a familiar face, and his gray robe showed the dried mud stains of long travel. He must have been waiting for quite a while, and no chamberlain stood beside him to announce him. As Cyrus faced him, he stretched out his hand. "Great King," he implored, "protect the valley of Zarathustra."

By his voice, Cyrus recognized the Magian, the slave of the tower at Agbatana and the spokesman at the grave of the prophet Zarathustra. "Magian," he said curiously, "at last you have seen fit to enter my gate."

The pilgrim smiled. "Your gate is too well guarded; your Master of Ceremonies demanded to know from what official I came with a petition for the king's mercy. So I slipped in by the back door."

"Still, I welcome you to my house. I do not recall that you welcomed me when I entered your valley by the back door." When the Magian assented, Cyrus asked, "What need has your valley now? It seemed well enough."

"Fire and sword will lay it waste. The nomads of the north are invading the lands. We have no means of defense. Cyrus, you pledged your protection to Bactria."

The Magian spoke as if he were reminding Cyrus of some trifle forgotten. This pilgrim seemed to know nothing of war. Cyrus remembered the report from the frontier of Maracanda and started to explain that this was a matter for the satrap of Sogd to deal with. The northeast frontier was a month of riding—of a courier's riding at speed. He had not been able to return to Bactria for many years. If the nomads were moving in force, he could dispatch the Hazarapat to summon the levies of Parthia and Chorasmia to drive them back. He started to explain this to the man who had journeyed all that way, thinking only of his personal pledge. For a moment he considered this, and he said, "Magian, you have traveled far. Come to supper with me now and, after that, rest. Man, I am Cyrus and I will keep the promise made to you."

BATTLE ON THE STEPPES

When Cyrus announced his decision to journey to the River of the Sands to drive away the nomad raiders, his counselors advised against it. And then they begged him to summon Cambyses and the army of Babylon to go with him. Instead, Cyrus ordered his son to come up to Parsagard to act for him in his absence. He reminded his advisers of the law of the Persians and the Medes that king and heir should not leave the country at the same time. He added that the departure would be on the morrow's dawn.

That night he heard the voice of his fravashi on the right hand of his couch, saying that it was well to make the journey toward his homeland; he heard the laughter of winsome Anahita quite clearly in the rush of the river. He longed to behold the face of the goddess and to feel her body for this once within his arms. Then he told himself that he was becoming a lecherous old man, to dream of draining the body of a girl who eluded him.

They left the valley in the warmth of a midsummer day, with the fire of poppies in the grass beneath them. They rode at courier speed on the Nisayans, up the Royal Road by Rhagae and the Crystal Mount with its plume of flying snow. One thousand of the Five Thousand followed the king, without chamberlains, scribes, chair bearers, or fly swatters. Thus it befell that no record was kept of the journey, except for the tidings at the end.

At the roadside villages women ran out with baskets of pomegranates, melons, and apples for the king, and Cyrus judged that the crops were good that summer. To each woman he gave a gold coin minted at Sardis, and he promised that he would abide at the villages on his return from punishing the Dahae—the Enemies. At the ravine of the Hyrcanian Sea the Hyrcanian warrior levies rode to meet him, led by Darius, son of Vishtaspa. A silent man who thought for himself—a good leader, Cyrus decided. Beyond the red Choara pass the Parthians thronged to join him. In fact the young swordsmen of the eastern lands were eager to achieve fame by following the Great King to a war. And Cyrus regretted that he had been absent so long from the smiling Eastlands. It seemed as if the darker west held him enchained by its disputes and plotting.

Faring on at such speed, he did not take the time to test-maneuver the new regiments or replace their officers. Across the wide River of the Sea the Chorasmians joined him, and he did not wait for the infantry from Maracanda to come in. In any case the foot soldiers could not keep up with the horsemen. There would be time to visit the gardens of Maracanda on his return.

By then they had reached the devastated area. The thatch-clay villages lay in ashes, and the harvests had been carried off or burned by the nomads. Cyrus lengthened the marches of his army and presently came on bodies still unburied in the wreckage. These were the peasants and older people and the smaller children; the others had been carried off. The tribesmen had killed them with edged weapons in order to save their arrows. The invaders were Sarmatians from the northern steppes and they had withdrawn after the manner of nomads at the approach of the civilized army.

At the frontier the stronghold of Cyra had been burned. The reed-grown bank of the River of the Sands was empty of human life, although swarming with carrion birds seeking the unburied bodies. Cyrus ordered a bridge of boats to be thrown across the river and the pursuit to continue on. He had no wish to turn back, with such armed strength, without giving the tribesmen bitter retribution for the invasion.

His army pressed on over a dry plain where gray tamarisks danced in the wind, like the ghosts of trees. The trail of the nomads was marked by the remains of fires and the thin cadavers of prisoners who had been too weak to keep up with the riders. The army increased its pace and came in sight of nomad patrols slipping away along the skyline. It threaded through hills that stood grotesquely above the red dust, being burned black by the heat of the sun. Scouts explained that the dust had been stirred up by the retreating hordes—no more than an hour's fast ride in advance of the army. Cyrus ordered the last camp to be left standing under guard of the sick or dismounted warriors.

Taking all the able-bodied warriors with him, he pressed the pursuit. The Persians rode through the black hills. The ground beneath them fell away into a narrow valley, like a corridor between the heights.

There on either side waited the nomads who no longer fled away. As the Persian column entered the valley the masses of nomads drove down at its flanks. Ahead of them other masses appeared.

"Massagetae!" the scouts warned Cyrus.

The retreating Sarmatians had led them on to this valley where the Massagetae waited, and the Persians were caught in a nomad ambush. The racing horses stirred up dust clouds that choked the soldiers, and through the dust hissed flights of arrows. The ululation of the tribesmen rose like the howling of wolves at each charge. The chosen riders of the Thousand began to close in around Cyrus to shield him.

Cyrus realized then that they were outnumbered and could not form for an attack to sweep the foemen from the narrow valley. He passed back an order for the rear regiments to retire and the others to follow. He bade the commander of the Thousand to hold off the tribesmen and to withdraw by companies.

They did this through the gamut of the black hills, where Sarmatians and Massagetae surged in on them from the ravines. The disciplined Thousand held its ranks while horses and riders fell. Cyrus then ordered his regiments to ride on through the encampment to open ground beyond. He reasoned that the excited nomads pursuing the column would break from their bands to pillage the camp and kill its defenders.

That happened as he had expected. Sarmatians and Massagetae alike turned from the pursuit to the Persian camp and swirled through the tents like wolf packs over a carcass.

On the plain beyond, the Persians gathered together at the calls of their commanders. They formed again in their hundreds and thousands. Cyrus dared not give them time to breathe the horses. Riding out in front where he could be seen—the white plumes of his headband marking him—he called to the regiments to follow after him. To follow the officers where he led.

It was an old trick of his. They had been at the edge of disaster in the sunken valley; here on clear ground they could gallop easily and, in following him, they would be certain of sweeping through the disordered enemy as they had done so often before. He felt no weariness and he shouted aloud when he heard the hoofbeats of the Nisayans galloping. He heard the shout of the Persians.

Cyrus was struck by an arrow at the edge of the camp. As the charge swept into the tents, a lance wounded him. His guards fought around him, making a ring to hold off the foemen. They carried him from the battle.

The surviving Persians closed their ranks to retire with Cyrus to the river. There they found shelter for him in the mud walls of a hut. On the third day Cyrus the Achaemenian died by the river.

Since no scribes accompanied the army, the truth of what happened beyond the river was never written down. The Chronicle of Babylon merely stated in its dry manner that Cyrus, King of the Lands, was killed in battle with the Dahae—the Enemies—in the northeastern steppes. When the Greek poets came to consider it, they added romantic interest by telling how Cyrus was lured into the steppes by a queen of the Sarmatians, Tymiris by name. The poets related that Tymiris avenged herself by challenging Cyrus to battle, and that, when he was slain, the queen of the Sarmatians raised his head in her hands to behold the blood falling from it into the earth. Some truth there may have been in this, but the whole truth will never be known.

The news sped to Maracanda and down to Bactria and along the Royal Road for two thousand miles to Miletus and the isles of the sea. All the way the people mourned for the man who had ruled them for twenty years. Survivors of the army sealed the body of Cyrus in wax and bore it back on a horse litter. The Fire of Bactria was extinguished on its height, and the fire altars of Parsagard became dark.

By the north gate of the valley of Parsagard Cambyses waited. At the coming of the horse litter, he dismounted to take the reins of the leading Nisayans and guide them down the track into the valley. There assembled the chieftains of the ancient tribes and the satraps of the world empire.

The small tomb on the seven steps by the river bank was finished by then. So no one questioned what was to be done with the body of the king. But many of the Achaemenians felt that the dark stone chamber was ill fitted to become the room of Cyrus, the first Great King of their race. They persuaded Cambyses and the Law-bearers to prepare a sarcophagus of pure gold such as the Egyptian Pharaohs occupied. In this they placed Cyrus, wearing a tiara of jewels and cloth of beaten gold, upon a couch with legs of wrought gold. In doing so the chieftains and priests had to light a torch and hold it, because the inner door could not be opened until the outer door of the tomb was closed. In the narrow space by the couch, on a table also of wrought gold, the mourners placed Cyrus's sword—which he had seldom worn—and his chiton of Babylonian linen and riding trousers dyed purple with Tyrian dye, together with a belt of jewels and soft leather boots. The cell walls were hung with tapestries woven in Sardis.

It seemed to them all that Cyrus had meant to have a visitor in his chamber. Such a visitor could only be the heir to the mighty kingdoms of the Persian empire. The first visitor, then, was Cambyses. When he had entered the tomb and put on the garments of Cyrus, he came forth and the Achaemenians escorted him to the twin altars on the height where he gave the king's pledge to protect his people and partook of the meal of a mess of figs, terebinth, and sour milk. This meal signified that Cambyses the Great King was in truth a man no different from a peasant. After that, Cambyses gave his first order, to kindle the fires again on the altars.

In their grieving for Cyrus, the varied people, even in Babylon and Bactria, did not question the right of Cambyses to come to the throne from which the world was ruled.

At the end of the coronation a strange incident took place. It was not according to the customs of the Persians and the Medes. A Magian was found keeping watch at the lowest step of the tomb. He had been a pilgrim but he explained that his pilgrimage was ended here. He had a spade with him and he said he would like to make a garden around the tomb of Cyrus—that he could do no better work than that.

They allowed this aged Magian to channel water from the nearest runlet, and after the garden was made, they built a small hut by the river to shelter him and granted him rations of one sheep with flour and fruit and wine each week.

To the visitors who could not read, the Magian explained, when they marveled at the unusual tomb: "O Man, whoever thou art, know that this is Cyrus who founded the Persian empire and ruled the world. Grudge him not his monument."

Afterword

CYRUS the Great died needlessly. The punitive expedition against the Sarmatians and Massagetae could have been led across the far frontier river by Cambyses or another army commander. But by leaving his son at the reign center of Parsagard, Cyrus had made certain that Cambyses would assume the rule of the still-formative world state without opposition. Cambyses (Kanbujiya) merely added the title King of the Lands to his previous title of King of Babylon. He possessed the firm allegiance of the Iranians, and he gave his younger brother Bardiya the rule over the northern core of Media, Armenia, and Cardusia (Kurdistan), with residence at the vital junction city of Agbatana. He also married, by Persian custom, two of his younger sisters.

With Cyrus, however, died "the people's king." He had brought into being the novel concept of a ruler responsible to all his subjects—what Clément Huart* terms "a new idea in the East, with principles of government unknown before him." He was not able to finish the organization of his new state. That remained for Darius (Darayous, the son of Vishtaspa) to accomplish in a somewhat different manner. Yet the ideals of Cyrus inevitably influenced what came after him, including the later Macedonians and Romans.

Sayings of the common folk often give enlightening portraits of

* Titles of works mentioned here are given on page 300.

their masters. The Iranians said: "Cyrus was a father, Cambyses a master, and Darius a penny pincher."

This new loyalty of varied peoples to one man on the throne manifested itself in the great undertaking of Cambyses, which was the conquest of Egypt. (Why Cyrus did not attempt this remains obscure. Perhaps the nomadic strain in him held him back from venturing into the torrid desert bridge to Africa; he did not seem at ease on the warm Lydian coast among Greeks and Anatolians. He appeared to be drawn instead to the great hinterland of the Aryans, and in any case he never journeyed far from the nebulous but critical northern frontier, beyond which waited the barbaric Scythian folk. It was not the least of his achievements to put a stop to the incursions of these northern nomads, endemic invaders of the ancient empires.)

Cambyses devoted himself to the subjection of the last of them, Saitic Egypt. The land of the Pharaohs, far from being moribund, was enjoying a trade revival under the aged Amasis, with Greek settlers thronging into the port of Naucratis and Phoenician fleets plying the western shores as far as Carthage. And almost as far as that, Cambyses carried the Persian domain. His invasion had most of the characteristics of his father's ventures—the quite novel Achaemenian ride in, with friendly advisers at the king's side and neighboring peoples aiding the march, and enemy commanders going over to the Achaemenians. Although Cambyses could not quite duplicate Cyrus's feat of conquering Babylon "without battle or skirmish."

Observe the manner of his march in, just as the death of Amasis left Egypt in the hands of the weaker Psamtik. The philosophic Croesus goes along to advise Cambyses; Arab chieftains furnish camel transport for the arduous desert stretch beyond Gaza, "outpost of Africa and gate of Asia." Polycrates, tyrant of the island of Samos, ally of Amasis, smuggles out men and ships to help Cambyses along the coast; Phoenicians, also technical allies of the Pharaohs, do likewise. Cambyses's expedition encounters the Egyptian army at Pelusium. As usual now—and for two centuries to come—there are Greek mercenaries hired by both sides. But the commander, Phanes, of the Egyptian-hired hoplites, quarrels about pay and goes over to Cambyses with the best kind of information about the defenses of Egypt. The Persians thereupon win the battle of Pelusium and so demonstrate what the destiny of Egypt is to be.

When they appear at the Nile, the Egyptian naval commander treacherously surrenders Saïs to them. Psamtik flees upriver to Memphis, to be captured in that great city early in 525. Whereupon the Greek colony port of Naucratis opens its gates, and Cambyses bestows so many privileges upon the merchants of Naucratis that the Greek-Libyan ports of Cyrene and Barca in the west send in their submission also. Cambyses thus becomes master of most of the Greek centers in Asia and North Africa, and of the Phoenician fleets as well. For the first time the Persians control shipping in the eastern Mediterranean, with the trade thereof.

With Lower Egypt in his hands, Cambyses imitated the example of Cyrus at Babylon by giving due reverence to the ancient gods of Egypt. Inscriptions show him wearing the royal uraeus serpent and describe him as "Cambyses, possessor of all life, all surety, and good fortune, with health and gladness."

The rebel admiral, who was rewarded with the post of head physician, left a memorandum explaining that he became the governor of the palace of "the great lord of all the foreign lands, the great king of Egypt." Like Babylon, Egypt held itself to be the center of the world and inhabitants of other lands to be foreigners. The Achaemenian empire now stretched over two continents.

Then—as Cyrus had anticipated at Babylon—Cambyses ran into the difficulties of administering a quite alien land in the guise of a Pharaoh. (And at his advent, Alexander of Macedon was to imitate their method after two centuries.) Observers had sometimes described the extraordinary actions of Cyrus as mad; here in Egypt they stated that his son actually went mad. The tales of the younger Achaemenian's insane ferocity—as in his supposed slaying of the sacred bull of Apis—can be discounted. He had a tensity in him and a brittle temper. At first he treated the captive monarch Psamtik (Psammetichus III) leniently; then at tidings of a conspiracy against the Persians, Psamtik was killed. Cambyses dispatched an army along the North African coast to capture Carthage —then rising to her great maritime supremacy. His Phoenician mariners balked at attacking their kinsmen in Carthage. Without a fleet to supply it along the desolate coast, the expedition eventually turned back. (The tale that it marched away to vanish in the deserts without survivors is merely a purple patch.) This failure had its effect on Cambyses. Until then the Persian armies had been successful in every campaign; the last expedition of Cyrus had managed to drive the nomad invaders back across the frontier.

At the same time, and perhaps because of the check at Carthage, the Achaemenian ran into temple trouble. His zealous admiral-physician-in-chief had induced him to make great gifts and give honor to the temples at Saïs; elsewhere the hierarchy of the temples —mainstay and burden of Egyptian communal life—did not receive such royal gifts from the Persian. In fact Cambyses made a sweeping cut in the revenues of the priesthoods except in Memphis and Saïs. The priests were ordered to get in their own firewood and boat timber and to raise their own geese. (The chicken, an Iranian fowl, had not reached Egypt as yet.) As for cattle, Cambyses commanded the tribute to be reduced to half that of the reign of the Pharaoh Amasis. In reaction, the majority of the priesthoods indulged in propaganda against the "mad Persian," and tales were told of his destruction of shrines. Yet evidence shows that Egyptian life was little disturbed, and the peasantry seemed to lack less under Cambyses than under Amasis.

Although impatient of the problems of government in this land of ancient privilege, Cambyses thrust his authority far up the Nile, past Thebes and the first cataract into Ethiopia. This exotic country aroused the curiosity of the Persians, with its elephants and ivory and gold. They said that the prisoners in Ethiopia wore fetters of gold. In their march they befriended a Jewish settlement at Elephantine, a circumstance that had important consequences; centuries later, documents written in Aramaic, found in the ruins of this colony, shed light on the rule of the Achaemenians, yielding, for one thing, the solitary copy of the autobiography of Darius who followed Cambyses.

The son of Cyrus, although not mad, had been absent too long from the center of his empire. When at last he appointed a satrap for Egypt and left the Nile, after five years, it was too late. He had never been seen in the Eastlands, or Anatolia for that matter.

His viceroys thousands of miles distant were in trouble; cliques in the provincial centers, rather than the subjected peoples, simmered in revolt. Babylon was restive, uncertain of the tidings that came out of Egypt. A dozen leaders of revolt persuaded Bardiya to declare himself Great King. When Bardiya did so in his mountain stronghold, he was acknowledged in Babylon. The keepers of the Chronicle dated the New Year of 522 as the first of the reign of Bardiya (usually called Smerdis by the Greek writers). Bardiya gained popular support by doing away with tribute for three years, but did not win the loyalty of the Iranian feudal nobles.

Cambyses was near Mount Carmel on his way home when he heard of his brother's revolt. It is said that he died there of an injury when mounting his horse, or that he committed suicide. Whatever the truth may be, Cambyses died, and after seven months Bardiya was slain by a counter-rebel in the mountains of Medea. There were no other heirs of Cyrus to take the throne.

With that year ends the dawn obscurity of the Achaemenian empire. A year later, with the rise and mastery of Darius, son of Vishtaspa and husband of a daughter of Cyrus, the empire comes into the full light of history. In the year 521 began the building of Persepolis and the abandonment of Parsagard. Under Darius the faith of Zarathustra became the religion of all Iranians; the laws of the Medes and Persians were codified into the law of the first western world state that extended "from India even unto Ethiopia." So it was written in the Book of Esther in the time of Ahasuerus, who was Xerxes, son of Darius.

It is odd that this Persian empire should be known to us best by the battles of Marathon and Salamis during campaigns in a small province of Europe. They were hardly mentioned in the records of the immense empire of Asia.

CYRUS AND DARIUS

With the emergence of that dominion, "the civilized world came nearer to a single control than ever before or since." It took place within fifty years, during the lifetimes of Cyrus, Cambyses, and Darius. It brought about a change so great that we of the twentieth century have difficulty in imagining the transition. Two millenniums of the most ancient Semitic East came to an end; three small empires, the Medic, the Lydian, and the Neo-Babylonian, or Chaldean disappeared from the pages of history; Egypt ceased to be sovereign in her isolation; in Judah the kingdom of the House of David gave way to the divided Jewish people. India was indeed brought into contact with Ethiopia, and with the eastern shores of the Mediterranean for the first time. The taciturn Babylonian Chronicle was moved to record it as the period of "the great disturbance." The other phrase of that time—"the ending of the death of the earth"—implies more than we can easily imagine. For one thing, the advent of the Achaemenians may have preserved the civilization that became our heritage in the West.

We think of Darius as the founder of the empire. His is the name on the Behistun rock inscription and on the first monuments of Persepolis, and of course he was familiarly known to the Greeks who faced him as a formidable antagonist. But the Achaemenian empire did not emerge full-blown, like the notorious Athena from the forehead of Zeus in complete armor with a war shout. It came into being at the hand of Cyrus. Edouard Meyer, a careful student, defines the relationship between Cyrus and Darius: "The fundamental features of the imperial organization must have been due to Cyrus himself. Darius followed in his steps and completed the vast structure. His role, indeed, was peculiarly that of supplementing and perfecting the work of his great predecessor."

The obscurity that surrounds Cyrus is deepened by three circumstances so unusual that they have baffled students until recently. First, the remains of Parsagard—or Pasargadae, as it is commonly named—in remote hills escaped the search of archaeologists until this century, while Persepolis, fronting the main Isfahan-Shiraz highway, was explored by European travelers as early as the seventeenth century. Second, the empire building of Cyrus to the east went almost unrecorded. Herodotus mentions his irrigation work on the Amu Darya, as well as his death beyond the Syr Darya. But the methodical Darius listed all the eastern satrapies from Parthia to Sogdia (before he had visited them himself). These, however, must have been the conquests of his predecessor. Third, Darius was a dedicated Zoroastrian, giving reverence in every public utterance to "Ahura-Mazda, and the other gods who are." Cyrus did nothing of the kind in his few inscriptions that have survived. In fact, his well-known Cylinder is devoted to his propaganda tribute to Marduk during the Babylonian campaign—an early instance of Paris being worth a Mass. This wide difference in religion between the two great Achaemenians, whose lives overlapped, has puzzled scholars deeply. Yet the simplest explanation may well be the truth. Cyrus probably did not come into contact with the disciples of Zoroaster—who were then in the Eastlands—until middle age. He may have been pagan in belief, attached to the older Aryan divinities. Darius seems to have grown up in the Zoroastrian faith. Yet surely the elder Achaemenian must have encountered converts of that faith. Hence, the Magian of our tale.

RELIGION OF THE ACHAEMENIANS

During and after their time, religion motivated the actions of the Iranians.

A proclamation of the son of Vishtaspa states his case: "Darius the king says thus: In the protection of Ahura-Mazda, this is my character: What is right I love, and what is not right I hate. Never has it happened [under me] that any serf made trouble for a lord, or any lord for a serf. I am not one who is angry, and whoever is angry I restrain in my heart. And whoever has injured another, I punish him according to that injury. Nor do I trust in the word of a man who speaks against the truth."

The advent of this missionary faith was apocalyptic. The concept of a single god to be worshiped universally may not have been entirely new. But that this deity should be beneficent to men and not merely fearsome was undreamed of in the ancient Semitic East. The old fear of a last judgment yielded to hope of a soul's immortality. The abrupt cessation of wars in the Achaemenian Peace appeared to be a visible sign of this spiritual change. Zoroastrianism, in its simpler early form, affected the concepts of Judaism and became the harbinger of the mystery faiths of Roman days, and of Christianity itself.

MYSTERY OF THE IRANIAN CONQUESTS

Religion apart, how did the obscure tribal group of Persians secluded in the highlands of southern Iran rise to mastery over the civilized world in little more than a generation? They had been almost unknown until then. Yet their sweep to conquest was as swift as that of the Mongols of Genghis Khan, although quite different in nature.

With so little evidence to go on, historians for the most part have been content to note the fact as accomplished and pass on to the well-recorded administration of Darius. Edouard Meyer finds a cause of "this astonishing success" in the superior archery of the Iranians, both mounted and afoot. They certainly held almost a monopoly of the Nisayan breed of horses, hitherto eagerly sought by both Assyrians and Medes. However, both the Kurds and Parthians possessed more powerful "long" bows at the time, and the steppe nomads were as formidable on horseback.

Perhaps Cyrus led forth his Persians at one of the rare intervals when such military success could be achieved. There had been an ebb and flow of human tides over the great plains where stood the centers of civilization. The more barbaric Hittites, Hurrians, Kassites, and Assyrians had emerged from the northern highlands, to retreat again or to become vitiated. The Aryan Medes had made their conquests after Cyaxares had remodeled his army on the pattern of the Assyrians—the Germans of the ancient East. Under Astyages the expansion of the Medes had come to a pause in the enjoyment of plundered luxuries. Apparently Cyaxares had made the mistake of drafting his cavalry from the politically weak but physically formidable Persian tribes. When Cyrus seized the throne at Agbatana, he had the mechanism of a trained army and he infused it with his own energy.

It is often said—*faut de mieux*—that Cyrus was a supremely able soldier. He was hardly that. He depended on the advice of his generals, such as Harpagus (as Greek and Roman writers name him). And either he or his generals used strategy deftly to upset an enemy. Herodotus, who traveled over the Royal Road to their battlefields a century afterward, still heard the tale of how their camels frightened the Lydian horses and how they climbed into the citadel of Sardis after watching a defender climb down the cliff after his helmet. It is true that Herodotus relished anecdotes, but the remarkable capture of Babylon by draining off the river is attested by the writings of the Hebrews and the records of the Babylonians, as well as the tales of the Father of History. That is almost the only occasion when Cyrus emerges from the obscurity of legend into full visibility.

Then, too, he was capable of acting with breathtaking speed, often appearing unexpectedly from his mountain fastness, through which the Medes and Persians traveled high-altitude roads of their own. (Those highways still exist. This writer has traveled the upland valleys through the length of the mountains now called the Zagros, from the Persian Gulf to Lake Van, the earlier homeland of the Persians.)

While Cyrus was not a supremely able battle commander, he had Hannibal's gift of leadership. Like the great Carthaginian he somehow managed to win over most of the peoples he encountered—making them fight for him rather than against him. The tolerance of the early Persian rule gained allies in a manner unknown to the Assyrians or Babylonians. The Persians made diplomacy their best weapon and at times used no other. Because they broke out of their pastoral seclusion so unexpectedly, we assume that they were barbaric. Although still half-nomadic, they possessed a culture. George Cameron reminds us they were "terribly efficient." Cyrus engineered roads as he journeyed and usually kept himself well-informed of events elsewhere by courier post. We read often enough how Xerxes led his host out of Asia to invade Greece in 480 B.C. We fail to notice just as often how the Persian engineers flung a bridge of boats across the treacherous currents of the Dardanelles and attempted to cut the neck of the Mount Athos peninsula with

a ship canal—still visible today. (Later on, they did complete such
a canal from the Nile to the Red Sea.)

In the sixth century Greek culture was represented chiefly by the
mercenary soldiers serving in Asia and Africa.

WHEN GREEK MET PERSIAN

We still view the European Greeks of that day as the armored
hoplites on their victorious battlefields. Our fathers were schooled
in the hero tales of such Greek history—of Leonidas and the three
hundred (who were actually 5000 at the beginning of the battle)
at the pass of Thermopylae, of the runner bearing the word of
victory from the plain of Marathon, and of Themistocles rallying
the Greek ships to the decisive conflict at Salamis. (Themistocles,
son of Neocles, fled from the bickering of his countrymen at the
end of his life to seek asylum on the Persian coast.)

Out of these repeated stories has grown the illusion of "our"
ancestors standing heroically against the "enemies" from Asia, the
false concept of Occident in arms against a vaguely luxurious
Orient, of Europeans preserving our heritage against invading Asi-
atics. Herodotus, of course, helped create the illusion; he was devoted to the cause of his countrymen. Generations will pass before
the picture that he drew, and that Aeschylus staged, is changed
back to reality. School children today still imagine Xerxes
(Khshayarsha) as a despot leading his satraps and heterogeneous
hordes and armadas of ships from the shores of Asia in an attempt
to enslave our forefathers.

Yet a careful reading of Herodotus yields particulars that show
this same Xerxes to be a man of understanding and high ideals,
in the Iranian tradition. He spares the two Spartan envoys who
come to report the torture death of the Persian envoys sent to
Sparta—who were thrown into a dry well, to find there the "earth
and water" they requested as a sign of submission. He refuses the
gift of the wealth of the Lydian Pythius, saying that he would like,
instead, to give Pythius the 7000 staters that would round out his
wealth at four million (the anecdote used in this book for Cyrus).

With rare generosity, he orders the bridge of boats across the Dardanelles to be opened to allow three grain ships of the Greeks from the Black Sea to pass through to feed his enemies. Reaching hallowed Mount Olympus, he is struck by the beauty of the coast and puts out to sea in a trireme to see it better (although Herodotus thinks he may have wanted to spy out the land). Such interest in the beauty of scenery is characteristic of the Achaemenians, not of the hardheaded Achaeans. The Greek stand on their homeland was courageous enough; but they revealed no idealism in waging war. Sir William Ramsay reminds us that their grasping methods of trade estranged the inhabitants of the Black Sea coast, from which cities like Athens drew their basic provisions of grain and tuna fish. Nor did they ever manage to win over the native Anatolians to Greek rule. Greek culture rested on the base of slave labor. As late as the coming of Alexander these Ionians—"the sons of Yavan" —looked upon his army of hoplites as a hostile invading force. As for the islands of "the sea of the sunset," the Athenians at the height of their power could enforce their thalassocracy over the Aegean islands only for a brief and troubled interval.

Meanwhile, except for these expeditions into Thrace and Greece, the Achaemenians maintained their peace through the vast hinterlands. Their state was based upon peasant labor, not slave labor.

OUR ANCESTORS, EAST AND WEST

"The vast Iranian panorama in which our ancestors arose and flourished seems as remote to the majority as the moon." So Dr. J. H. Iliffe wrote of the Achaemenians in the Oxford publication, *The Legacy of Persia*. "For us its early history is restricted to those occasions when it formed part of that of Israel or Greece. Our sympathies are enlisted on behalf of the Jewish exiles, the drama of Marathon and Thermopylae, the March of the Ten Thousand, or Alexander's meteoric career; incidental in our minds to these events are the extent of the realm of Ahasuerus [Hebrew form of the Greek "Xerxes"], the background to the decree of Cyrus, King of Persia [the decree for the building of the Temple in Jerusalem: Ezra 1.1], the initiative shown by Darius on his accession, or the rise of Zoroastrianism. In part the reason is no doubt that Persia has lacked a chronicler of its own. No Herodotus or Xenophon has arisen (or survived) from amongst the Persians themselves; the advocates are all on the side of the Greeks. . . . To present the Persian side is to assume the role of 'advocatus diaboli.'"

Assuming the role of devil's advocate, we can find characteristics of these ancestors of ours in the east that are quite familiar to us. Because they happened to migrate to the Iranian plateau instead of the peninsula of Greece, they did not thereby become "oriental." Dr. Iliffe reminds us of the following:

The Achaemenian king was far from being a despot, responsible only to himself. He resembled the western "King in Council" and his actions were limited by custom and tradition.

These early Persians were devoted to dogs, an animal singled out for honor by Zoroaster.

They celebrated birthdays by family festivals. They upheld the tradition of hospitality to the stranger within their gates.

They believed that ethics affected human life: that man was engaged in a struggle against Evil, which they recognized as an active force.

In government they evolved the first provincial system, the mainstay of such later empires in the West as the Roman.

The Persian network of post roads (an improvement on the Medic) became the model for the famous Roman road system.

Before the Romans, they made a success of the policy of *divide et impera*. But their division of peoples into national groups beneath a governor also gave the divided folk direct access for appeal to the Great King. They gave isolated groups, like the priesthood at Jerusalem, a special status.

Although the Anatolian coinage was first in the field, the Persians established the first world currency, officially guaranteed, and made it work. Characteristically, under Darius the "Daric" coins were stamped with the figure of the king using a bow.

They established one official language, the Aramaic of their chancellery. Although more prevalent in the western regions, it became known as far east as India—with consequences that still remain to be fully determined. At the same time the Indo-European speech of the Persians extended widely.

On the sea, unfamiliar to them at first, they launched official exploration—such as the voyage of Scylax of Caryanda c.500 B.C. toward India. Under Darius (521–486) the lore of astronomy was harnessed to the science of navigation. In Egypt, where medical studies had advanced far, he founded the first known medical school.

Many of the ideals they set before mankind failed to be realized. But the concept that government could be good for the people instead of the rulers never quite died out. Nor did the concept that the civilized world could have one rule.

Perhaps the buildings erected by the first Achaemenians show more than anything else their kinship with the western Aryans, especially with the Greeks.

SECRET OF PARSAGARD

This home of the Achaemenian kings from 559 to 520 B.C. could tell us much about them. But in more than twenty-five centuries the wear of the elements and the hands of human enemies have left very little to be seen—chiefly a single standing column, the strange houselike tomb of Cyrus, vestiges of wall friezes, terraces and limestone floorings, water channels and pillared porticoes.

Visiting it, however, you feel the majesty of the deserted valley in its setting of bare hills. Like Palmyra, the equally deserted caravan city, the ruins are eloquent of the life that occupied them because no later buildings intrude on them. Parsagard affects you as a fragmentary Acropolis apart from any Athens. In the last two generations, archaeologists, both Iranian and foreign, have delved into the ground for traces of the Achaemenian buildings and have found little because the structures were few and quite different from the massive Assyro-Babylonian elsewhere. They differed also from the palaces and harems crowded above the stairway on the rock plateau of Persepolis some fifty miles distant. The searching

archaeologists have verified the strangeness of the residence town
of Cyrus. It lacked an encircling wall, citadel, temples, and palaces
in the ordinary sense—with the guardhouses, treasuries, and vast
courtyards of the more ancient cities, from Hattushash of the Hittites to Susa (Shushan).

Its wide halls with veranda fronts, only a half-dozen steps above
the ground, opened directly into the woodland garden, or *paradise*
of the Achaemenians. This retreat had one imposing entrance gate
and a single shrine of twin fire altars on the highest point above
the river. It had no figure of a monstrous god, "the dark genius
of Assur," nor the anthropomorphic gods of Hellas which inhabit
so many European museums today. Figures at first appearing to be
demons turned out to be guardian spirits—fravashis.

All figure work was incised, blending in decoration with the
walls which were of white limestone rather than the mud brick
of Sumer and Akkad. The columns were slenderer and more lofty
than in Greek temples. The simplicity of decoration reveals restraint; the simple black and white color scheme is unique. Although much is borrowed—from Assyrian winged beasts and Egyptian flower symbols, for example—the whole is blended into a new
art. That art could hardly be a wish fulfillment of nomads newly
rich and hungry for embellishment. "It exhibits," Professor A. T.
Olmstead maintains, "a fully developed national culture." He cites
its characteristics as remembered from earlier wooden architecture
of the north—the gabled roof and columned porch. Now those
are essential characteristics of Greek architecture of a later day than
Parsagard. The Persians of Cyrus gave us the first art that can be
called "Aryan." The Greek achievement came later.

The art of Parsagard in the years 559–520 is as mature as the art
of Athens three generations later.

It is, perhaps, more utilitarian. The buildings all serve a purpose;
the sculpture serves to decorate the architecture. No statues stand
apart from the structures. Designs are repeated. The Persians liked
to present objects in pairs and in fours—a doubled pair being better
in their eyes than a single pair. And the incised figures move
rhythmically, breaking away from the immobility of the earlier
Egyptian and Babylonian designs. At this stage—and in the earlier

work at Persepolis under Darius—the animal and human figures are touched with stylization.

It is a royal art, sponsored by the king and confined in architecture—although not in minor objects—to his residences.

It is a religious art. Yet, like the Romanesque in Europe in a later day, it manages to express religious faith rather than to present objects of worship. It is touched by spiritual grace, without the heavy figuration of more ancient paganism. A squat, robed Marduk—or a naked, muscular Jupiter—would have been a monstrosity among the delicate wings, the flower symbols, the light-stepping feet and uplifted faces of Parsagard.

If Parsagard suggests the Romanesque, the culminative art of Persepolis after the reign of Darius resembles the Gothic. This is the beginning of deterioration, the "Empire Style" of the Achaemenians. The scale then grows larger; the figures become natural—although still marching in procession. The famous frieze of the tribute bearers might have been modeled from life. The later kings appear in full state, robed, enthroned, backed by courtiers and faced by petitioners. Above the king hover the Achaemenian wings, now attached to the orb of the sun above which appears a small crowned head of Ahura-Mazda.

The mystery of a mature art appearing in the historical wilderness of the Iranian mountains, of course, called for an explanation. And a satisfactory explanation was found long ago: such an art, experts said, did not exist. The Persians then merely borrowed from Assyrians and Elamites rather crudely, and if their work had some beauty, it was due to Greek artists imported by the despots of Persepolis. That satisfied everyone except some meditative orientalists until well after the turn of the twentieth century when Ernst Herzfeld went to work in Iran and archaeologists of the modern school began to dig deeper into the ground.

The theory of the borrowed arts seemed to be proved by what remained above ground in Shushan and Persepolis. At Susa, however, the first Darius had rebuilt the palace in splendor, using mainly the enameled tilework that was Elamite rather than Persian. And the most visible remnants at Persepolis were the entrance guardians, the human-headed winged bulls of Assyrian ancestry.

But Herzfeld soon uncovered much more that was purely Persian. Little masterpieces of silver and bronze and carved seals turned up throughout Iran. And it was discovered that Greek artists did not work for the successors of Cyrus until after the expeditions of Darius and Xerxes, early in the fifth century, at which time Persian art was in its deterioration.

Darius himself has testified to the variety of artisans he called to the building of his palace at Shushan. A foundation inscription relates: "I erected this palace at Susa [Shushan]. From afar its ornamentation was brought . . . the bricks that were molded, the Babylonian folk did that. The cedar timber from a mountain called Lebanon was brought. The Assyrian people brought it, from the Carian and Ionian folk. The gold used here was brought from Sardis and Bactria. The stone—both carnelian and lapis lazuli—was brought from Sogd. The turquoise, it came from Chorasmia, and the silver and copper from Egypt. The ornamentation upon the walls, it was fetched from Ionia. And the stonecutters were the Ionians, the goldsmiths were the Medes and Egyptians, and they also adorned the walls. . . . Here at Susa, I, Darius, ordered a splendid task, and very splendidly did it turn out."

The sculptured reliefs upon the walls of Persepolis, as well as Shushan and Parsagard, were by no means dull stonework. Color touched them with life. Only faint traces remain of the turquoise blue and lapis lazuli blue, of emerald green and the gilding of metal trappings. Yellow and purple gave brightness and the illusion of depth to the backgrounds.

Olmstead admits the borrowings from the more ancient culture centers, but adds (1948): "Nevertheless, the whole is blended into a new art whose origins must be sought in as yet unexcavated sites."

THE MYSTERY OF THE ORIGINS

A search for the prototypes of Parsagard inevitably led to exploration of the migration route of the Iranian tribes and of their nature. "A tribe," Henri Frankfort sums up, "of nomadic or seminomadic horsemen took charge of the civilized world and did not destroy civilization but enhanced it."

Somewhere along their road—still unknown—from northeast of the Caspian Sea, down around its shores to the highlands of Anshan, the Persians came into contact with the arts of other peoples, and in some manner formed the mold of their own. It now appears that they were very conservative about such things; once they established a pattern they held to it. As they held to their attitude toward life. Speaking of the motley artisans and varied materials listed by Darius in his rebuilding of the Shushan palace, Frankfort says: "It is an astonishing fact that this motley crowd produced a monument which is both original and coherent; a style of architecture and a style of sculpture possessing unity and individuality to an extent never achieved, for instance, in Phoenicia. The pervading spirit, the very design of the buildings and reliefs, never changed from the reign of Darius I until the defeat of Darius III [331] by Alexander. And that spirit—and the design, too—was Persian."

The road of the Persians began in the steppes of the northern nomads. Inevitably their early artistry was confined to the tools of the horse wanderers—like the axes, horse gear, carpets, and body ornaments. That ornamentation was in the Scythian, or "animal" style. Herzfeld has traced similarity in Persian designs—notably the recumbent stag—with native design as far distant as the River Yenisei. Recent excavation of Scythian tombs at Pasirik yielded carpets woven in Persian manner near the headwaters of the Ob. The early Greek traders sought such Scythian-Persian pile carpets. Very early indeed the Scythians above the Black Sea (in Cyrus's Sea of Grass) craved one product of the Greek artisans—battle helmets. They probably wore some of these when they rode against Cyrus.

Herzfeld finds the origin of Achaemenian pillared architecture in the timbered houses of the Iranian ancestors in the north rather than in imitation of the Egyptian columned temples. Unquestionably the southbound Persians were in close contact for some centuries with the Medes, kindred Aryans. But the archaeologists have found almost nothing as yet of Medic artistry surviving in their mountain fastness. Several rock tombs, guarded by nomadic figures in half relief, have been found. Possibly the Medes lacked the creative imagination of the Persians.

(This writer fell under the spell of derelict Parsagard almost thirty years ago and has traveled over the probable route of the Iranian migration since then, through the mountains of Kurdistan up to and around the shores of the Caspian. Along that route most traces of the civilization of twenty-five centuries ago have vanished above ground. They remain scattered among unknown graves and city sites buried under tumuli of earth.)

Here and there, however, the earth has yielded up precious secrets. Some thirty years ago the bronzes of Luristan came to light in graves dug up by tribesmen. These were nomadic in type, being weapons, horse bits, and small articles easily transported. They mystified western scientists, being a mature art close to the Scythian animal style, yet showing Babylonian influence. Why had skilled metalworkers remote in the mountains made such things—as early as 1200 B.C.—for nomadic clients?

Then in 1947 came the finding of the "treasure of Ziwiye." This was a collection of gold and precious things evidently buried for safekeeping and never dug up again near a village named Sakkiz— a name certainly descended from *Sakai* or Scyth. Here, too, archaeologists were faced by the mystery of skilled craftmanship in Assyrian designs, using the motifs of the Scythian animal style and Persian as well. The treasure of Ziwiye presented us with a cross section of things which seemed to have no connection. Was it a haphazard gathering of different valuables or the handiwork of unknown masters? Frankfort believes that here and in the Luristan finds we have the work of highly skilled metalists made to order for still-nomadic masters, who would be the conquering Aryans, whether Scythian or Iranian. But in that case civilization of a fairly high order must have existed just south of the Caspian in the unexplored mountains during the deeply obscure centuries from perhaps 1200 to 700. And our Persians, about the time of their legendary Achaemenes, must have filtered through a "Caspian" culture entirely unrecorded by history.

Ten years later, in 1958, this missing link came to light. A great golden bowl emerged from the ruins of a walled city state at

Hasanlu, near the shore of Lake Urmia, southwest of the Caspian. The buried inhabitants proved to be Mannean mountain folk, the date the ninth century B.C. The golden bowl itself was evidently the treasure of the temple, if not of the unknown Mannean king; its decoration formed a blend of seemingly disparate arts, showing a lion-riding goddess with Assyrian symbols, a god emerging from a mountain according to Caspian legend, and lions of the brood of Ziwiye and Persepolis.

Now these Mannean metal workers had learned from Assyrian or other masters, yet had developed an artistry of their own.

So when the Persians arrived in the upland pastures of Anshan-way a little after that, they had no need to borrow the arts from Shushan, or Babylon, or the Nineveh of Assur-bani-pal. Culture existed then in the mountains, and from it the Persians shaped their own.

CYRUS AND ALEXANDER

Without Cyrus there could not have been an Alexander.

In his conquest of the Achaemenian's empire, Alexander possessed certain advantages: he had the mechanism of the strong Macedonian army, the counsel of veteran commanders like Parmenion, not to mention his tutoring by Aristotle. He had the base of the hegemony in Greece established by his father, Philip.

The great Macedonian trusted to his generalship and the fighting ability of his phalanx and elite cavalry; lacking the statecraft of the Achaemenian, he resorted often to bloody conflict and tenacious sieges, as at Tyre and in Indian territory. His celebrated burning of Persepolis was probably accidental. Like Cyrus, he met the grim challenge of the Scythian tribes beyond the Syr Darya but survived it. He thrust the limit of the empire farther east, beyond the Indus. When he came to organize the Macedonian empire, however, he failed where Cyrus had succeeded. The rule of the Achaemenians had lasted for two full centuries until overthrown by the son of Philip. It did not outlast Alexander.

Actually, Alexander sought to carry on that rule by the creation of his Eurasian state with leadership blended of Macedonians and Persians—even resorting to the hurried and wholesale marriage of his officers to Persian women. He found himself more at home among the Aryan Iranians than either in Egypt or Babylon, although he tried to make that ancient city his capital. The kinship of the western and eastern Aryans was evident two centuries after Cyrus had been carried to the tomb at Parsagard. Alexander paid honor to that tomb and punished the looters who broke into it during his absence. He found Magians still keeping watch over it, in the house by the river.

It is said too carelessly that Greek culture entered the East for the first time with the victorious Macedonian. Yet Hellenization of the shores of Asia had been going on for a long time, and the Greeks already possessed such trading ports as Naucratis on the Nile and Tanais at the mouth of the River Don. There had been a human ebb and flow—tending west as well as east—between Greece in Europe and the Anatolian coast ever since Agamemnon led his raiders toward Troy. After the Persian wars of the fifth century, Greek visitors found their way east as far as Shushan; Herodotus and Aeschylus paid tribute to the grandeur as well as the decadence of the people of the Great King. (Herodotus relates that the Persians learned homosexuality from the Greeks.)

What Alexander accomplished was to open the floodgates of humanity. He broke down the barriers between the Mediterranean world and India—bringing Greek influence to the Parthians, founding a Greek state in Bactria, scattering seeds of Hellenic artistry as far as the heights of Gandhara. This cataclysmic merging of peoples, languages, and thought never ceased to have its effect thereafter. Traces of Zoroastrian thought and Aramaic speech appeared in the dominion of Chandragupta, and Achaemenian treasures reached the far junction point of Taxila.

But this was a two-way flooding. Almost nothing is said, usually, about what came out of Persia to the West after Alexander. The concept of the golden road to Samarkand may have begun then, when the riches of far China and Turkistan were carried to Alexandria on the Nile. Tricks of eastern architecture turned up where Rome was a-building; bronze and enamel work invaded the arts of the westerners, as the mystery faiths came with the cult of Mithras to disturb Roman equanimity. When Roman rule sought its last refuge in Byzantium on the Bosporus, its court imitated the ceremonial of the Persian apadana—much more complex than in the day of Cyrus.

The Great King who survived after six centuries was Persian, not Macedonian.

TESTIMONY OF XENOPHON

Xenophon, an Athenian gentleman of leisure, may have been a pupil of Socrates who saved his life in a skirmish. He seems to have been an able politician and undoubtedly was a keen observer. Journeying into Asia with Greek mercenaries in the service of a later Cyrus, he became commander of the hired soldiery by accident and did a good job of leading them back to the Euxine Sea. He wrote up this *Anabasis*, or Journey Back, and it became famous as the tale of the retreat of the Ten Thousand in the year 401, late in the Achaemenian dynasty, although long before Alexander.

While fighting his way through the deserts and mountains that Cyrus had conquered, Xenophon fell under the spell of the legend of the first Achaemenian. Like Herodotus, who had an easier journey, Xenophon picked up stories as he went and he became increasingly curious about the personality, and particularly the upbringing, of the remarkable Cyrus who failed to fit into the pattern of Greek life as known to this soldier-writer.

"The whole of this enormous empire," Xenophon observed, "was governed by the mind and the will of one man, Cyrus. His subjects were cherished and cared for as if they were his children, and they reverenced him like a father."

Thereupon Xenophon, son of Gyllus, wrote another book—much less known than his *Anabasis*—which he called *Cyropaedia*, or The Education of Cyrus. In this he tried to reconstruct the life and upbringing of the Achaemenian who had become something of a hero to him. There were few facts to go on, and the Athenian soldier really drew the portrait of a young Greek in the setting of Asia. (His book is often called the first historical novel of record.) Still, he had been over some of the territory of Cyrus, had encountered much the same people, and he interpolated his Hellenic fantasy with bits of Achaemenian fact. He pictured the Armenians and other mountain folk well; he understood personalities of some women, and he managed to get a clear idea of Cyrus's purpose and driving force. Many of his incidents have been used in this book. For Xenophon the soldier was a much better reporter than Herodotus the historian, as often happens nowadays.

In his Epilogue, Xenophon indulges in a little editorial musing on the deterioration of the Persians he encountered—some six generations after Cyrus—from the standards of the day of the first Achaemenian. This sheds a little light on the rigor of life in Cyrus's day. Be it said, however, that Xenophon can be whimsical.

"In the old days a man was honored who risked his life, especially for the king. But now some Mithradates or Ariobarzanes . . . is loaded with the highest honors if they connive some advantage for the king.

"Nor do they care for their bodies as they did of old, when they would neither spit or blow noses. They used to strengthen themselves by toil and sweat. But this has all gone out of fashion.

"Again, from the first it was the rule to take only a single meal in the day. It's still the rule, but the meal begins at an hour early for breakfast and ends when they choose to go to bed. So likewise they once abstained from meat and drink while on march, while now they make the marches so short that you need not wonder at their abstinence.

"In the old time they went out to hunt often and the chase gave exercise for man and horse alike. When the day came that Artaxerxes [probably Artaxerxes II Mnemon, 404 B.C.] and all his court were the worse for wine, the old custom began to pass away.

"It is still the habit to bring up the boys at the palace gates, but fine riding has disappeared because there's no place where the lads can show their skill. The old idea that the children of Persia would learn justice by hearing the judges decide the cases has been turned upside down. Children now only need to use their eyes to see that the verdict goes to the man with the biggest purse. Children once were taught all about plants in order to know the poisonous ones; but now the children seem to want to find out about poisons to inflict them on others.

"In the time of Cyrus they still clung to Persian self-restraint, and only took from the Medes a manner of dressing and a certain grace of life. Today they cherish the softness of the Mede. They are no longer content with good sheets and rugs on the beds; they must have carpets beneath the bedposts. In winter they must have long sleeves and gloves for the hands. Nor are they content with the shade of trees and rocks; they must have servants beside them with artificial sunshades.

"Formerly no Persian was ever seen on foot; the idea of that was to make perfect riders. Now they lay more coverings on a horse's back than on their own beds.

"In times past a landowner's servants had to go on active service, and the garrison troops afield got regular pay. Now the Persian grandees have invented a new sort of cavalry, to draw pay as stewards and cooks and cake-makers, or bathmen and rubbers."

Xenophon ends his comparison with a penetrating criticism of the morale of the Persian soldiery of his day. He believes that Cyrus trained fighters to close with an enemy and rewarded them accordingly. "The generals of today flatter themselves that untrained men will serve quite as well as trained. Now none of them will take the field without Hellenes to help them. . . . The Persians of today are less religious, less dutiful to their kindred, less just toward other men, and less valiant in war. And if any man doubts me, let him examine their actions for himself."

Author's Note

WHILE the world of the first Achaemenian is not quite as remote from us as Dr. Iliffe's moon, it is still an historical void. This book, accordingly, is not history nor is it a historical novel. To write a novel a man must know the *mise en scène*. He can invent interesting things for his people to do, but he can't very well invent the clothes they put on in the morning, nor the clock that told them the hour of the day, nor what they were accustomed to do that day—unless they happened to be Utopians or Hyperboreans.

This is an attempt to go back in imagination to the world of Cyrus, twenty-five centuries ago. It is not invented but pieced together from known fragments and discoveries of clues to the nature of the people. Cyrus is drawn as he might have been, the son of the small king of Anshan. Legend, of course, very quickly endowed Cyrus with mystery at his birth, saying that his mother was actually Mandane, royal daughter of Astyages: that the child was smuggled out to a herdsman—the old chestnut of ancient storytellers—to be done away with, only to be preserved by the honest peasant and recognized joyfully thereafter. Herodotus draws "Harpagus" into the legend by adding the other chestnut of the officer made to eat the flesh of his slain son, unwittingly, by the wiles of the evil king. There could be no more than a small basis of truth in such a blending of legends.

All the major characters of this book existed. Some others like

Vishtaspa are drawn from pretty firm legends. Names of several
lesser folk such as Amytis and Abradat are taken from Xenophon,
who may have heard about them. Names appear in their most
familiar form, whether that derives from the Latin, Greek, or various cuneiform versions or Hebrew-Aramaic. However, in the case
of Iranians and others close to Cyrus, I have tried to give the names
as they were spoken then, without linguistic endings—Gubaru instead of (Greek) Gobryas. The word Persia itself, of course, comes
through the Greek from the original Parsa, or Parsuash. So, too,
with the geographical names of his homelands—Hyrcanian Sea, for
instance, for the Caspian. Cyrus and his followers were actually
exploring many regions new to them, and they coined descriptive
terms: the Blue Mountains, or the Bitter Waters, and Sea of Grass,
as other voyagers have done from time immemorial. Names of major landmarks such as the Tigris and Euphrates are modern. Dis-
tances are computed in miles but often given native fashion in
time of travel, whether afoot or horseback. The New Year in Persia
or Babylon is, of course, the spring equinox, about March 20. It
still is in Persia.

Remember that we are dealing with pre-history. All the verified
historical data about Cyrus, including the famous Cylinder, could
be translated and published in no more than six pages. In those
pages Cyrus can be followed quite easily when he approaches Sardis
or Babylon, but he disappears almost entirely when he ventures
east of Babylon. Then, too, the legends have suffered a sea change
in twenty-five centuries. The words of Ezra and Isaiah reach us in
the pages of the Old Testament; Zoroastrian prayers survive in the
later Gathas; Herodotus beheld the Persian empire about that time
in its deterioration (as did Ctesias, Diodorus Siculus, and Plutarch
after him). Strabo, however, gives many bits of earlier tradition
with his geographical lore. In the Persian epic of the kings—*Shah-
nameh*—Cyrus fails to appear at all among the myths of creation
and the deeds of Jamshid in the conflict between Iran and Turan.
Ironically, the archaeologists, in uncovering so many traces of Achaemenian times, have shed the fullest light on the real Cyrus. I
shall never forget the hours of discussion with the late Ernst Herz-

feld at work in Persepolis nor the days with George Cameron in the mountains of the Medes.

And I am grateful for the wise and tolerant comments of John Rosenfield on this Afterword.

By chance, during World War II, I was sent to the area between modern Turkey and Afghanistan, which once formed the core of the Achaemenian empire. At that time the archaeological excavations lay open for any visitor to explore, and they led me to many happy hours of leisure study in the museums of Baghdad and Tehran and the excellent libraries thereof. During those three years I began to wonder if the life of Cyrus could not be reconstructed from the manifold findings of the archaeologists.

But in the time of Cyrus, these "sources" had not become disparate and foreign. Then the Aryan poets sang of traditions real to them; the Zarathustrian hymns rose from the dream of redemption; Isaiah voiced his undying hope for the freeing of his captive people; all the other little-known peoples were living and suffering or triumphant when Cyrus was a small king in Anshan. There was neither East nor West then, and the words Europe and Asia had not been coined. The prejudice against everything east of Athens did not exist, before the day when that great detective, Sherlock Holmes, needed to remind his readers: "There is as much sense in Hafiz as in Horace."

WORKS CITED, OR RELIED ON, IN
THE AFTERWORD

Ali-Sama: *Pasargadae*, Shiraz, 1956

Aymard and Auboyer: *L'Orient et la Grèce antique*, Paris, 1955

George Cameron: *History of Early Iran*, University of Chicago, 1936

Ctesias: *La Perse, L'Inde, les sommaires de Photius* (R. Heny), Paris, 1947

Morteza Ehtecham: *L'Iran sous les Achéménides*, Fibourg, 1946

Henri Frankfort: *The Art and Architecture of the Ancient Orient*, Baltimore, 1955

R. Ghirshman: *L'Iran des origines à l'Islam*, Paris, 1951

André Godard: *Le trésor de Ziwiye*, Haarlem, 1950

George Hanfmann and A. Henry Detweiler: *New Explorations at Sardis, Archeology*, Vol. 12 No. 1 (1959)

Herodotus: *The History* (Rawlinson), London, 1910

Ernst Herzfeld: *Archeological History of Iran*, London 1935
Iran in the Ancient East, London, 1941

Clément Huart: *L'Iran antique*, Paris, 1943

J. H. Iliffe: *Persia and the Ancient World* in *The Legacy of Persia*, Oxford, 1953

Edouard Meyer: article, "*Persia, Ancient History*, Encyclopaedia Britannica, 11th edition

A. T. Olmstead: *The History of the Persian Empire*, (Achaemenid Period) University of Chicago, 1948

Sir William Ramsay: *Asiatic Elements in Greek Civilization*, Yale, 1928

Tamara Rice: *The Scythians*, London, 1957

Gisela Richter: *Greeks in Persia*, American Journal of Archeology, Vol. 50 (1946)

Eric Schmidt: *Persepolis I*, Chicago: Oriental Institute Publications, Vol. 68 (1953)

Strabo: The *Geography* (Loeb Classical Library), London-New York, 1917

Xenophon: *Anabasis* (Loeb Classical Library), 1921
Cyropaedia (Loeb Classical Library), 1914

(These works have little to say of Cyrus, founder of the Achaemenian rule; Cameron's study ends with the accession of Cyrus; Olmstead's masterly presentation of the two Achaemenian centuries devotes twenty-four of its 576 pages to the founder.)

Index